Centre for Innovation in Mathematics Teaching
University of Exeter

FURTHER PURE MATHEMATICS

Writers	Sam Boardman
	David Burghes
	Tim Cross

Editors	Victor Bryant
	David Burghes
Assistant Editors	Garrod Musto
	Nigel Price

Heinemann Educational

Heinemann Educational

a division of Heinemann Educational Books Ltd.

Halley Court, Jordan Hill, Oxford OX2 8EJ

OXFORD LONDON EDINBURGH
MADRID ATHENS BOLOGNA PARIS
MELBOURNE SYDNEY AUCKLAND SINGAPORE
TOKYO IBADAN NAIROBI HARARE
GABORONE PORTSMOUTH NH (USA)

ISBN 0 435 51605 1

First Published 1994

© CIMT, 1994

98 97 96

10 9 8 7 6 5 4 3

Typseset by ISCA Press, CIMT, University of Exeter

Printed in Great Britain by The Bath Press, Avon

FURTHER
PURE MATHEMATICS

This is one of the texts which has been written to support the AEB Mathematics syllabus for A and AS level awards first available in Summer 1996.

The development of these texts has been coordinated at the

Centre for Innovation in Mathematics Teaching

at Exeter University in association with Heinemann and AEB.

The overall development of these texts has been directed by David Burghes and coordinated by Nigel Price.

Enquiries regarding this project and further details of the work of the Centre should be addressed to

Margaret Roddick
CIMT
School of Education
University of Exeter
Heavitree Road
EXETER EX1 2LU.

CONTENTS

PREFACE

This century has seen many and varied applications of mathematics including pollution control, conservation of scarce resources, planning and management, computing, transportation and sport. Indeed, mathematics underpins almost every aspect of modern life although in many cases, you may not be aware of how the mathematics has been applied. For example, methods of coding have now been designed for use in situations such as

- London Transport tickets

- bar codes

- pin numbers

- car window glass.

You do not need to understand the mathematics that underpins these developments in order to use these modern aspects of life, but the developing and designing of solutions to problems does require a fluency in mathematics, often to a high level.

This text builds on the foundation of mathematics as laid in the associated text *Pure Mathematics*. It will be assumed that you are familiar with the main concepts in this text although some of the important maths will be repeated. On the whole, you will be concentrating on understanding the topic, with applications being left for future study.

This text has been produced for students and includes examples, activities and exercises. It should be noted that the activities are **not** optional but are an important part of the learning philosophy in which you are expected to take a very active part. The text integrates

- **Exposition**   in which the concept is explained;
- **Examples**   which show how the techniques are used;
- **Activities**   which either introduce new concepts or reinforce techniques;
- **Discussion Points**   which are essentially 'stop and think' points, where discussion with other students and teachers will be helpful;

  Discussion points are written in a special typeface as illustrated here.

- **Exercises**   at the end of most sections in order to provide further practice;
- **Miscellaneous Exercises**   at the end of most chapters , providing opportunities for reinforcement of the main points of the chapter.

Note that answers to the exercises are given at the back of the book. You are expected to have a calculator available throughout your study of this text and occasionally to have access to a computer.

Some of the sections, exercises and questions are marked with an asterisk *. This means that they are **not** central to the development of the topics in this text and can be omitted without causing problems.

This text is one of a series of texts written specially for the new AEB Mathematics syllabus for A and AS level coursework. The framework is shown opposite. Essentially each module corresponds to an AS level syllabus and two suitable modules provide the syllabus for an A level award. Optional coursework is available for students taking any of the three applied modules

Mechanics, Statistics and Discrete Mathematics.

Full details of the scheme are available from
  AEB, Stag Hill House, Guildford GU2 5XJ.

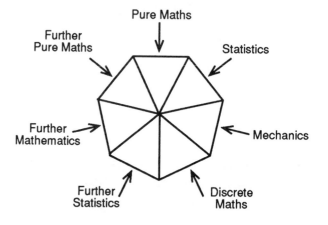

We hope that you enjoy working through the book. We would be very grateful for comments, criticisms and notification of any errors. These should be sent to

Margaret Roddick
CIMT
School of Education
University of Exeter
EXETER EX1 2LU.

ACKNOWLEDGEMENTS

This text has been written for the new AEB Mathematics syllabus and assessment, which will be examined for the first time in Summer 1996. I am grateful for the continued support from AEB through its mathematics officer, Jackie Bawden, and to the staff at Heinemann, particularly Philip Ellaway.

I am grateful to Sam Boardman and Tim Cross for writing their components of the text, to Victor Bryant and Nigel Price for help with editing, and to Garrod Musto, Geoff O'Donnell, Alan Sherlock and David Samworth for checking the calculations. Finally, I am indebted to the staff at CIMT who work with dedication and good humour despite the pressure which I continue to put them under; in particular, to Liz Holland, Margaret Roddick and Ann Tylisczuk for producing camera ready copy.

David Burghes
(Project Director)

1 TRIGONOMETRY

Objectives

After studying this chapter you should

- be able to handle with confidence a wide range of trigonometric identities;
- be able to express linear combinations of sine and cosine in any of the forms $R\sin(\theta \pm \alpha)$ or $R\cos(\theta \pm \alpha)$;
- know how to find general solutions of trigonometric equations;
- be familiar with inverse trigonometric functions and the associated calculus.

1.0 Introduction

In the first *Pure Mathematics* book in this series, you will have encountered many of the elementary results concerning the trigonometric functions. These will, by and large, be taken as read in this chapter. However, in the first few sections there is some degree of overlap between the two books: this will be good revision for you.

1.1 Sum and product formulae

You may recall that

$$\sin(A+B) = \sin A \cos B + \cos A \sin B$$

$$\sin(A-B) = \sin A \cos B - \cos A \sin B$$

Adding these two equations gives

$$\sin(A+B) + \sin(A-B) = 2\sin A \cos B \qquad (1)$$

Let $C = A + B$ and $D = A - B$,

then $C + D = 2A$ and $C - D = 2B$. Hence

$$A = \frac{C+D}{2}, \ B = \frac{C-D}{2}$$

and (1) can be written as

$$\sin C + \sin D = 2\sin\left(\frac{C+D}{2}\right)\cos\left(\frac{C-D}{2}\right)$$

This is more easily remembered as

'sine plus sine = twice sine(half the sum) cos(half the difference)'

Activity 1

In a similar way to above, derive the formulae for

(a) $\sin C - \sin D$ (b) $\cos C + \cos D$ (c) $\cos C - \cos D$

By reversing these formulae, write down further formulae for

(a) $2\sin E \cos F$ (b) $2\cos E \cos F$ (c) $2\sin E \sin F$

Example

Show that $\cos 59° + \sin 59° = \sqrt{2}\cos 14°$.

Solution

Firstly, $\sin 59° = \cos 31°$, since $\sin\theta = \cos(90-\theta)$

So
$$\begin{aligned}
\text{LHS} &= \cos 59° + \cos 31° \\
&= 2\cos\left(\frac{59+31}{2}\right)\cos\left(\frac{59-31}{2}\right) \\
&= 2\cos 45° \times \cos 14° \\
&= 2 \times \frac{\sqrt{2}}{2}\cos 14° \\
&= \sqrt{2}\cos 14° \\
&= \text{RHS}
\end{aligned}$$

Example

Prove that $\sin x + \sin 2x + \sin 3x = \sin 2x(1 + 2\cos x)$.

Solution

$$\begin{aligned}
\text{LHS} &= \sin 2x + (\sin x + \sin 3x) \\
&= \sin 2x + 2\sin\left(\frac{3x+x}{2}\right)\cos\left(\frac{3x-x}{2}\right) \\
&= \sin 2x + 2\sin 2x \cos x \\
&= \sin 2x(1 + 2\cos x)
\end{aligned}$$

Example

Write $\cos 4x \cos x - \sin 6x \sin 3x$ as a product of terms.

Solution

Now $\qquad \cos 4x \cos x \; = \dfrac{1}{2}\{\cos(4x+x)+\cos(4x-x)\}$

$$= \dfrac{1}{2}\cos 5x + \dfrac{1}{2}\cos 3x$$

and $\qquad \sin 6x \sin 3x \; = \dfrac{1}{2}\{\cos(6x-3x)-\cos(6x+3x)\}$

$$= \dfrac{1}{2}\cos 3x - \dfrac{1}{2}\cos 9x$$

Thus, $\qquad \text{LHS} = \dfrac{1}{2}\cos 5x + \dfrac{1}{2}\cos 3x - \dfrac{1}{2}\cos 3x + \dfrac{1}{2}\cos 9x$

$$= \dfrac{1}{2}(\cos 5x + \cos 9x)$$

$$= \dfrac{1}{2}\times 2\cos\left(\dfrac{5x+9x}{2}\right)\cos\left(\dfrac{5x-9x}{2}\right)$$

$$= \cos 7x \cos 2x$$

The sum formulae are given by

$$\sin A + \sin B = 2\sin\left(\dfrac{A+B}{2}\right)\cos\left(\dfrac{A-B}{2}\right)$$

$$\sin A - \sin B = 2\cos\left(\dfrac{A+B}{2}\right)\sin\left(\dfrac{A-B}{2}\right)$$

$$\cos A + \cos B = 2\cos\left(\dfrac{A+B}{2}\right)\cos\left(\dfrac{A-B}{2}\right)$$

$$\cos A - \cos B = -2\sin\left(\dfrac{A+B}{2}\right)\sin\left(\dfrac{A-B}{2}\right)$$

and the product formulae by

$$\sin A \cos B = \dfrac{1}{2}(\sin(A+B)+\sin(A-B))$$

$$\cos A \cos B = \dfrac{1}{2}(\cos(A+B)+\cos(A-B))$$

$$\sin A \sin B = \dfrac{1}{2}(\cos(A-B)-\cos(A+B))$$

Exercise 1A

1. Write the following expressions as products:

   (a) $\cos 5x - \cos 3x$ (b) $\sin 11x - \sin 7x$

   (c) $\cos 2x + \cos 9x$ (d) $\sin 3x + \sin 13x$

   (e) $\cos\dfrac{2\pi}{15} + \cos\dfrac{14\pi}{15} + \cos\dfrac{4\pi}{15} + \cos\dfrac{8\pi}{15}$

   (f) $\sin 40° + \sin 50° + \sin 60°$

   (g) $\cos 114° + \sin 24°$

2. Evaluate in rational/surd form

   $\sin 75° + \sin 15°$

3. Write the following expressions as sums or differences:

   (a) $2\cos 7x \cos 5x$

   (b) $2\cos\left(\dfrac{1}{2}x\right)\cos\left(\dfrac{5x}{2}\right)$

   (c) $2\sin\left(\dfrac{\pi}{4} - 3\theta\right)\cos\left(\dfrac{\pi}{4} + \theta\right)$

   (d) $2\sin 165° \cos 105°$

4. Establish the following identities:

   (a) $\cos\theta - \cos 3\theta = 4\sin^2\theta\cos\theta$

   (b) $\sin 6x + \sin 4x - \sin 2x = 4\cos 3x \sin 2x \cos x$

   (c) $\dfrac{2\sin 4A + \sin 6A + \sin 2A}{2\sin 4A - \sin 6A - \sin 2A} = \cot^2 A$

   (d) $\dfrac{\sin(A+B) + \sin(A-B)}{\cos(A+B) + \cos(A-B)} = \tan A$

   (e) $\dfrac{\cos(\theta+30°) + \cos(\theta+60°)}{\sin(\theta+30°) + \sin(\theta+60°)} = \dfrac{1-\tan\theta}{1+\tan\theta}$

5. Write $\cos 12x + \cos 6x + \cos 4x + \cos 2x$ as a product of terms.

6. Express $\cos 3x\cos x - \cos 7x\cos 5x$ as a product of terms.

1.2   Linear combinations of sin and cos

Expressions of the form $a\cos\theta + b\sin\theta$, for constants a and b, involve two trig functions which, on the surface, makes them difficult to handle. After working through the following activity, however, you should be able to see that such expressions (called **linear combinations** of sin and cos – linear since they involve no squared terms or higher powers) can be written as a single trig function. By re-writing them in this way you can deduce many results from the elementary properties of the sine or cosine function, and solve equations, without having to resort to more complicated techniques.

For this next activity you will find it very useful to have a graph plotting facility. Remember, you will be working in radians.

Activity 2

Sketch the graph of a function of the form

$$y = a\sin x + b\cos x$$

(where a and b are constants) in the range $-\pi \le x \le \pi$.

From the graph, you must identify the amplitude of the function and the x-coordinates of

    (i)   the crossing point on the x-axis nearest to the origin, and

    (ii)   the first maximum of the function

as accurately as you can.

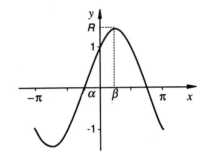

An example has been done for you; for $y = \sin x + \cos x$, you can see that amplitude $R \approx 1.4$

      crossing point nearest to the origin O at $x = \alpha = -\frac{\pi}{4}$

      maximum occurs at $x = \beta = \frac{\pi}{4}$

Try these for yourself :

(a) $y = 3\sin x + 4\cos x$ (b) $y = 12\cos x - 5\sin x$

(c) $y = 9\cos x + 12\sin x$ (d) $y = 15\sin x - 8\cos x$

(e) $y = 2\sin x + 5\cos x$ (f) $y = 3\cos x - 2\sin x$

In each case, make a note of

    R, the amplitude;

    α, the crossing point nearest to O;

    β, the x-coordinate of the maximum.

In each example above, you should have noticed that the curve is itself a sine/cosine 'wave'. These can be obtained from the curves of either $y = \sin x$ or $y = \cos x$ by means of two simple transformations (taken in any order).

  1. A **stretch** parallel to the y-axis by a factor of R, the amplitude, and

  2. A **translation** parallel to the x-axis by either α or β (depending on whether you wish to start with $\sin x$ or $\cos x$ as the original function).

Consider, for example $y = \sin x + \cos x$. This can be written in the form $y = R\sin(x + \alpha)$, since

$$R\sin(x + \alpha) = R\{\sin x \cos \alpha + \cos x \sin \alpha\}$$

$$= R\cos \alpha \sin x + R\sin \alpha \cos x$$

The $R(>0)$ and α should be chosen so that this expression is the same as $\sin x + \cos x$.

Thus

$$R\cos\alpha = 1 \text{ and } R\sin\alpha = 1$$

Dividing these terms gives

$$\tan\alpha = 1 \Rightarrow \alpha = \frac{\pi}{4}$$

Squaring and adding the two terms gives

$$R^2\cos^2\alpha + R^2\sin^2\alpha = 1^2 + 1^2$$

$$R^2(\cos^2\alpha + \sin^2\alpha) = 2$$

Since $\cos^2\alpha + \sin^2\alpha = 1$,

$$R^2 = 2 \Rightarrow R = \sqrt{2}$$

Thus

$$\sin x + \cos x = \sqrt{2}\sin\left(x + \frac{\pi}{4}\right)$$

Activity 3

Express the function $\sin x + \cos x$ in the form

$$\sin x + \cos x = R\cos(x - \alpha)$$

Find suitable values for R and α using the method shown above.

Another way of obtaining the result in Activity 3 is to note that

$$\sin\theta = \cos\left(\frac{\pi}{2} - \theta\right)$$

so that

$$\sin x + \cos x = \sqrt{2}\sin\left(x + \frac{\pi}{4}\right)$$
$$= \sqrt{2}\cos\left(\frac{\pi}{2} - \left(x + \frac{\pi}{4}\right)\right)$$
$$= \sqrt{2}\cos\left(\frac{\pi}{4} - x\right)$$
$$= \sqrt{2}\cos\left(x - \frac{\pi}{4}\right)$$

since $\cos(-\theta) = \cos\theta$.

Example

Write $7\sin x - 4\cos x$ in the form $R\sin(x - \alpha)$

where $R > 0$ and $0 < \alpha < \frac{\pi}{2}$.

Solution

Assuming the form of the result,

$$7\sin x - 4\cos x = R\sin(x - \alpha)$$
$$= R\sin x \cos \alpha - R\cos x \sin \alpha$$

To satisfy the equation, you need

$$R\cos \alpha = 7$$

$$R\sin \alpha = 4$$

Squaring and adding, as before, gives

$$R = \sqrt{7^2 + 4^2} = \sqrt{65}$$

Thus

$$\cos \alpha = \frac{7}{\sqrt{65}}, \quad \sin \alpha = \frac{4}{\sqrt{65}} \quad \left(\text{or } \tan \alpha = \frac{4}{7} \right)$$
$$\Rightarrow \alpha = 0.519 \text{ radians, to 3 sig. figs.}$$

so $\qquad 7\sin x - 4\cos x = \sqrt{65}\sin(x - 0.519)$

Exercise 1B

Write (in each case, $R > 0$ and $0 < \alpha < \frac{\pi}{2}$)

1. $3\sin x + 4\cos x$ in the form $R\sin(x + \alpha)$

2. $4\cos x + 3\sin x$ in the form $R\cos(x - \alpha)$

3. $15\sin x - 8\cos x$ in the form $R\sin(x - \alpha)$

4. $6\cos x - 2\sin x$ in the form $R\cos(x + \alpha)$

5. $20\sin x - 21\cos x$ in the form $R\sin(x - \alpha)$

6. $14\cos x + \sin x$ in the form $R\cos(x - \alpha)$

7. $2\cos 2x - \sin 2x$ in the form $R\cos(2x + \alpha)$

8. $3\cos\frac{1}{2}x + 5\sin\frac{1}{2}x$ in the form $R\sin\left(\frac{1}{2}x + \alpha\right)$

1.3 Linear trigonometric equations

In this section you will be looking at equations of the form

$$a\cos x + b\sin x = c$$

for given constants a, b and c.

Example

Solve $3\cos x + \sin x = 2$ for $0° \le x \le 360°$.

Solution

Method 1

Note that $\cos^2 x$ and $\sin^2 x$ are very simply linked using $\cos^2 x + \sin^2 x = 1$ so a 'rearranging and squaring' approach would seem in order.

Rearranging: $\qquad\qquad 3\cos x = 2 - \sin x$

Squaring: $\qquad\qquad 9\cos^2 x = 4 - 4\sin x + \sin^2 x$

$$\Rightarrow \quad 9\left(1 - \sin^2 x\right) = 4 - 4\sin x + \sin^2 x$$

$$\Rightarrow \quad 0 = 10\sin^2 x - 4\sin x - 5$$

The quadratic formula now gives $\sin x = \dfrac{4 \pm \sqrt{216}}{20}$

and $\qquad \sin x \approx 0.93485$ or -0.534847

giving $\qquad x = 69.2°, 110.8°$ or $212.3°, 327.7°$ (1 d.p.)

Method 2

Write $3\cos x + \sin x$ as $R\cos(x - \alpha)$ (or $R\sin(x - \alpha)$)

$$3\cos x + \sin x = R\cos(x - \alpha)$$

Firstly, $\qquad R = \sqrt{3^2 + 1^2} = \sqrt{10}$

so $\qquad 3\cos x + \sin x = \sqrt{10}\left(\dfrac{3}{\sqrt{10}}\cos x + \dfrac{1}{\sqrt{10}}\sin x\right)$

$$\equiv \sqrt{10}\left(\cos x \cos\alpha + \sin x \sin\alpha\right)$$

Thus $\cos\alpha = \dfrac{3}{\sqrt{10}}\left(\text{or } \sin\alpha = \dfrac{7}{\sqrt{10}} \text{ or } \tan\alpha = \dfrac{1}{3}\right) => \alpha = 18.43°$

The equation $3\cos x + \sin x = 2$ can now be written as

$$\sqrt{10}\cos(x - 18.43°) = 2$$

$$\Rightarrow \qquad \cos(x - 18.43°) = \dfrac{2}{\sqrt{10}}$$

$$\Rightarrow \qquad x - 18.43° = \cos^{-1}\left(\dfrac{2}{\sqrt{10}}\right)$$

$$\Rightarrow \qquad x - 18.43° = 50.77° \text{ or } 309.23°$$

and

$$x = 50.77° + 18.43° \text{ or } 309.23° + 18.43°$$

$$x = 69.2° \text{ or } 327.7° \quad (1 \text{ d.p.})$$

The question now arises as to why one method yields four answers, the other only two. If you check all four answers you will find that the two additional solutions in Method 1 do not fit the equation $3\cos x + \sin x = 2$. They have arisen as extra solutions created by the squaring process. (Think of the difference between the equations $x = 2$ and $x^2 = 4$: the second one has two solutions.) If Method 1 is used, then the final answers always need to be checked in order to discard the extraneous solutions.

Exercise 1C

1. By writing $7\sin x + 6\cos x$ in the form
   $R\sin(x + \alpha)(R > 0, 0° < \alpha < 90°)$ solve the equation
   $7\sin x + 6\cos x = 9$ for values of x between $0°$ and $360°$.

2. Use the 'rearranging and squaring' method to solve

   (a) $4\cos\theta + 3\sin\theta = 2$

   (b) $3\sin\theta - 2\cos\theta = 1$

   for $0° \leq \theta \leq 360°$.

3. Write $\sqrt{3}\cos\theta + \sin\theta$ as $R\cos(\theta - \alpha)$,
   where $R > 0$ and $0 < \alpha < \dfrac{\pi}{2}$ and hence solve
   $\sqrt{3}\cos\theta + \sin\theta = \sqrt{2}$ for $0 \leq \theta \leq 2\pi$.

4. Solve

   (a) $7\cos x - 6\sin x = 4$ for $-180° \leq x \leq 180°$

   (b) $6\sin\theta + 8\cos\theta = 7$ for $0° \leq \theta \leq 180°$

   (c) $4\cos x + 2\sin x = \sqrt{5}$ for $0° \leq x \leq 360°$

   (d) $\sec x + 5\tan x + 12 = 0$ for $0 \leq x \leq 2\pi$

1.4   More demanding equations

In this section you will need to keep in mind all of the identities
that you have encountered so far – including the Addition
Formulae, the Sum and Product Formulae and the Multiple Angle
Identities – in order to solve the given equations.

Example

Solve $\cos 5\theta + \cos \theta = \cos 3\theta$ for $0° \le \theta \le 180°$

Solution

Using $\qquad \cos A + \cos B = 2\cos\left(\dfrac{A+B}{2}\right)\cos\left(\dfrac{A-B}{2}\right)$

$\qquad\qquad$ LHS $= 2\cos 3\theta \cos 2\theta$

Thus $\qquad 2\cos 3\theta \cos 2\theta = \cos 3\theta$

$\qquad \Rightarrow \qquad \cos 3\theta(2\cos 2\theta - 1) = 0$

Then

(a) $\cos 3\theta = 0$

$\qquad \Rightarrow \qquad 3\theta = 90°, 270°, 450°$

$\qquad \Rightarrow \qquad \theta = 30°, 90°, 150°$

or

(b) $2\cos 2\theta - 1 = 0$

$\qquad \Rightarrow \qquad \cos 2\theta = \tfrac{1}{2}$

$\qquad \Rightarrow \qquad 2\theta = 60°, 300°$

$\qquad \Rightarrow \qquad \theta = 30°, 150°$ as already found.

Solutions are $\theta = 30°$ (twice), $90°, 150°$ (twice).

[Remember, for final solutions in range $0° \le \theta \le 180°$, solutions
for 3θ must be in range $0° \le \theta \le 3 \times 180° = 540°$.]

Exercise 1D

1. Solve for $0° \le \theta \le 180°$:

    (a) $\cos\theta + \cos 3\theta = 0$ (b) $\sin 4\theta + \sin 3\theta = 0$

    (c) $\sin\theta + \sin 3\theta = \sin 2\theta$.

2. Find all the values of x satisfying the equation

$\qquad \sin x = 2\sin\left(\dfrac{\pi}{3} - x\right)$ for $0 \le x \le 2\pi$.

3. By writing 3θ as $2\theta + \theta$, show that

$$\cos 3\theta = 4\cos^3\theta - 3\cos\theta$$

and find a similar expresion for $\sin 3\theta$ in terms of powers of $\sin\theta$ only.

Use these results to solve, for $0 \le \theta \le 360°$,

(a) $\cos 3\theta + 2\cos\theta = 0$

(b) $\sin 3\theta = 3\sin 2\theta$

(c) $\cos\theta - \cos 3\theta = \tan^2\theta$

4. Show that $\tan x + \cot x = 2\operatorname{cosec}2x$. Hence solve $\tan x + \cot x = 8\cos 2x$ for $0 \le x \le \pi$.

5. Solve the equation

$$\sin 2x + \sin 3x + \sin 5x = 0 \text{ for } 0° \le x \le 180°$$

6. Find the solution x in the range $0° \le x \le 360°$ for which $\sin 4x + \cos 3x = 0$.

7. (a) Given $t = \tan\tfrac{1}{2}\theta$, write down $\tan\theta$ in terms of t and show that

$$\cos\theta = \frac{1-t^2}{1+t^2}$$

Find also a similar expression for $\sin\theta$ in terms of t.

(b) Show that $2\sin\theta - \tan\theta = \dfrac{2t}{1-t^4}\left(1 - 3t^2\right)$

(c) Hence solve $2\sin\theta - \tan\theta = 6\cot\tfrac{1}{2}\theta$ for values of θ in the range $0° < \theta < 360°$.

1.5 The inverse trigonometric functions

In the strictest sense, for a function f to have an inverse it has to be 1–1 ('one-to-one'). Now the three trigonometric functions sine, cosine and tangent are each periodic. Thus the equation $\sin x = k$, for $|k| \le 1$, has infinitely many solutions x. A sketch of the graph of $y = \sin x$ is shown opposite.

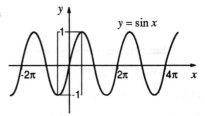

When working on your calculator, if you find $\sin^{-1} 0.5$, say, a single answer is given, despite there being infinitely many to choose from. In order to restrict a 'many-to-one' function of this kind into a 1–1 function, so that the inverse function gives a unique answer, the range of values is restricted. This can be done in a number of ways, but the most sensible way is to choose a range of values x which includes the acute angles. This is shown on the diagram opposite.

Thus for $-1 \le k \le 1$,

$$\sin x = k \implies x = \sin^{-1} k$$

will be assigned a unique value of x in the range $-\dfrac{\pi}{2} \le x \le \dfrac{\pi}{2}$:

these are the principal values of the inverse-sine function.

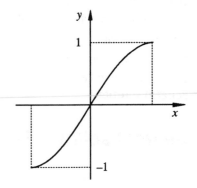

Activity 4

By drawing the graphs $y = \cos x$ and $y = \tan x$, find the ranges of principal values of the inverse-cosine and inverse-tangent functions. (These should include the acute angles of x.)

Note that the inverse functions are denoted here by

$$\sin^{-1} x, \quad \cos^{-1}, \quad \tan^{-1} x$$

These are not the same as

$$(\sin x)^{-1} = \frac{1}{\sin x}, \quad \text{etc.}$$

and to avoid this confusion, some texts denote the inverse functions as

$$arc\sin x, \quad arc\cos x, \quad arc\tan x.$$

1.6   General solutions

Up until now you have been asked for solutions of trigonometric equations within certain ranges. For example:

Solve $\sin 3x = \frac{1}{2}$ for $0° < x < 180°$

or

Find the values of θ for which $\sin 2\theta + \sin^2 \theta = 0$
with $0 \le \theta \le 2\pi$.

At the same time, you will have been aware that even the simplest trig equation can have infinitely many solutions: $\sin \theta = 0$ (θ radians) is true when $\theta = 0, \pi, 2\pi, 3\pi, \ldots$ and **also** for all negative multiples of π as well.

Overall, one could say that the equation $\sin \theta = 0$ has general solution $\theta = n\pi$ where n is an integer. Moreover, there are no values of θ which satisfy this equation that **do not** take this form. Thus, '$\theta = n\pi$' describes **all** the values of θ satisfying '$\sin \theta = 0$' as n is allowed to take any integer value. This is what is meant by a **general solution**.

General solution for the cosine function

For $-900° \le x \le 900°$ (radians can come later), the graph of $y = \cos x$ is shown below.

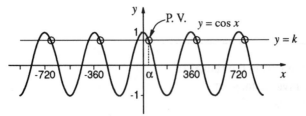

The line $y = k$ (k is chosen as positive here, but as long as $-1 \le k \le 1$, the actual value is immaterial) is also drawn on the sketch.

The **principal value** of x for which $x = \cos^{-1} k$ (representing the point when $y = k$ and $y = \cos x$ intersect) is circled and labelled 'P.V.' Since the cosine function is periodic with period $360°$, all other solutions to the equation $\cos x = k$ corresponding to this principal value are obtained by adding, or subtracting, a multiple of $360°$ to it. The points of intersection of the two graphs representing these solutions are circled also.

Now the cosine curve here is symmetric in the y-axis. So if α is the principal value of x for which $\cos x = k$, then $-\alpha$ is also a solution, and this is not obtained by adding, or subtracting, a multiple of $360°$ to, or from, α. All the remaining solutions of the equation can be obtained by adding or subtracting a multiple of $360°$ to or from $-\alpha$.

The general solution of the equation

$$\cos x = k \quad (-1 \le k \le 1)$$

is then $x = 360n \pm \alpha$

where $\alpha = \cos^{-1} k$

is the principal value of the inverse cosine function and n is an integer.

In radians, using $360° \equiv 2\pi$ radians, the general solution looks like

$$x = 2n\pi \pm \alpha, \; n \text{ an integer.}$$

Activity 5

Use the graphs of $y = \tan x$ and $y = \sin x$ to find the general solutions of the equations (in degrees) of the equations

$$\tan x = k \quad (-\infty < k < \infty)$$

and

$$\sin x = k \quad (-1 \le k \le 1).$$

In each case, let α be the principal value concerned, let n be an integer, and express the general solutions in terms of radians once the results have been found in terms of degrees.

These results are summarised as follows:

In radians	In degrees
If $\sin \theta = \sin \alpha$, then	If $\sin \theta = \sin \alpha$, then
$\theta = n\pi + (-1)^n \alpha$	$\theta = 180n + (-1)^n \alpha$
If $\cos \theta = \cos \alpha$, then	If $\cos \theta = \cos \alpha$, then
$\theta = 2n\pi \pm \alpha$	$\theta = 360n \pm \alpha$
If $\tan \theta = \tan \alpha$, then	If $\tan \theta = \tan \alpha$, then
$\theta = n\pi + \alpha$	$\theta = 180n + \alpha$

[In each case, n is an integer.]

The AEB's *Booklet of Formulae* gives only the set of results for θ, α in radians, but you should be able to convert the results into degrees without any difficulty by remembering that $180° \equiv \pi$ radians, etc.

Example

Find the general solution, in degrees, of the equation

$$\tan 3\theta = \sqrt{3}$$

Solution

$$\tan 3\theta = \sqrt{3}$$

$\Rightarrow \qquad \tan 3\theta = \tan 60°$

$\Rightarrow \qquad 3\theta = 180n + 60 \quad$ quoting the above result

$\Rightarrow \qquad \theta = (60n + 20)°$

[...; $n = -1 \Rightarrow \theta = -40°$; $n = 0 \Rightarrow \theta = 20°$; $n = 1 \Rightarrow 0 = 80°$; ...]

Sometimes, you may have to do some work first.

Example

Find the general solution, in radians, of the equation

$$8 \sin \theta + 15 \cos \theta = 6.$$

Solution

Rewriting the LHS of this equation in the form $R\sin(\theta + \alpha)$, for instance, gives $R = \sqrt{8^2 + 15^2} = 17$ and $\cos\theta = \dfrac{8}{17}$ or $\sin\theta = \dfrac{15}{17}$ or $\tan\theta = \dfrac{15}{8}$ so that $\theta \approx 1.081$ radians. [Check this working through to make sure you can see where it comes from.]

The equation can now be written as

$$17\sin(\theta + 1.081) = 6$$

$$\Rightarrow \quad \sin(\theta + 1.081) = \frac{6}{17} = \sin 0.3607 \qquad \text{(principal value of } \sin^{-1}\frac{6}{17})$$

$$\Rightarrow \quad \theta + 1.081 = n\pi + (-1)^n 0.3607$$

$$\Rightarrow \quad \theta = n\pi + (-1)^n 0.3607 - 1.081$$

One could proceed to make this more appealing to the eye by considering the cases n even and n odd separately, but there is little else to be gained by proceeding in this way.

Note on accuracy: although final, non-exact numerical answers are usually required to three significant places, the 0.3607 and 1.081 in the answer above are really intermediate answers and hence are given to 4 significant figure accuracy. However, unless a specific value of n is to be substituted in order to determine an individual value of θ, you will not be penalised for premature rounding provided your working is clear and the answers correspond appropriately.

This final example illustrates the sort of ingenuity you might have to employ in finding a general solution of some equation.

Example

Find the values of x for which $\cos x - \sin 4x = 0$.

Solution

Using the result $\sin A = \cos\left(\dfrac{\pi}{2} - A\right)$, the above equation can be written as

$$\cos x = \cos\left(\frac{\pi}{2} - 4x\right)$$

whence

$$x = 2n\pi \pm \left(\frac{\pi}{2} - 4x\right)$$

i.e.

$$x = 2n\pi + \frac{\pi}{2} - 4x \quad \text{or} \quad x = 2n\pi - \frac{\pi}{2} + 4x$$

$$\Rightarrow \quad 5x = 2n\pi + \frac{\pi}{2} \quad \text{or} \quad 3x = -2n\pi + \frac{\pi}{2}$$

$$\Rightarrow \quad x = 2n\frac{\pi}{5} + \frac{\pi}{10} \quad \text{or} \quad x = -2n\frac{\pi}{3} + \frac{\pi}{6}$$

Wait a moment! Although the second solution is correct, n is merely an indicator of some integer; positive, negative or zero. It is immaterial then, whether it is denoted as positive or negative: you could write this solution as $x = 2k\frac{\pi}{3} + \frac{\pi}{6}$ $(k = -n)$ for some integer k, or alternatively, as $x = 2n\frac{\pi}{3} + \frac{\pi}{6}$.

In this case, the general solution takes two forms. An alternative approach could have re-written the equation as

$$\sin 4x = \sin\left(\frac{\pi}{2} - x\right)$$

$$\Rightarrow \quad 4x = n\pi + (-1)^n\left(\frac{\pi}{2} - x\right)$$

When n is odd

$$4x = n\pi - \frac{\pi}{2} + x$$

$$\Rightarrow \quad 3x = n\pi - \frac{\pi}{2}$$

$$\Rightarrow \quad x = n\frac{\pi}{3} - \frac{\pi}{6} = (2n - 1)\frac{\pi}{6} \qquad (n \text{ odd})$$

and when n is even

$$4x = n\pi + \frac{\pi}{2} - x$$

$$\Rightarrow \quad 5x = n\pi + \frac{\pi}{2}$$

$$\Rightarrow \quad x = n\frac{\pi}{5} + \frac{\pi}{10} = (2n + 1)\frac{\pi}{10} \qquad (n \text{ even})$$

The very first way might be considered preferable since the general solution for cos is less clumsy than that for sin.

This example also highlights another important point: two equivalent sets of answers may look **very** different from each other and yet still both be correct.

Exercise 1E

1. Find the general solutions, in degrees, of the equations

   (a) $\sin x = 0.766$

   (b) $\tan(\theta - 45°) = \dfrac{1}{\sqrt{3}}$

   (c) $\cos x = 0.17$

   (d) $\cot(60° - 2\theta) = 3$

   (e) $5\sin x + 3\cos x = 4$

   (f) $4\cos\theta + 3\sin\theta = 2$

   (g) $\cos 3\theta + \cos\theta = 0$

   (h) $\tan^2 4x = 3$

   (i) $\sin 7x - \sin x = \cos 4x$

   (e) $\sqrt{6}\sin\theta - \sqrt{2}\cos\theta = 2$

   (f) $10\cos\theta - 24\sin\theta = 13$

   (g) $\cos x - \cos 3x = 0$

   (h) $\tan x + \cot 2x = 0$

   [Note: $\cot A = \tan\left(\dfrac{\pi}{2} - A\right)$ and $\tan(-A) = -\tan A$]

   (i) $3\tan^2\theta + 5\sec\theta + 1 = 0$

   (j) $\cos 4x + \cos 6x = \cos 5x$

2. Find the general solutions, in radians, of the equations

   (a) $\tan x = \sqrt{2}$

   (b) $\cos\left(2x + \dfrac{\pi}{6}\right) = 1$

   (c) $\sin x = 0.35$

   (d) $\sec\left(\dfrac{1}{2}x + \dfrac{\pi}{4}\right) = 2$

3. Prove the identity $\cos 4x + 4\cos 2x = 8\cos^4 x - 3$. Hence find the general solution, in radians, of the equation $2\cos 4\theta + 8\cos 2\theta = 3$.

1.7 Calculus of the inverse trigonometric functions

The prospect of having to differentiate the function $y = \sin^{-1} x$ may seem rather daunting. However, we can write $y = \sin^{-1} x$ as

$\sin y = x$. (Taking the principal range values $-\dfrac{\pi}{2} \le y \le \dfrac{\pi}{2}$ ensures that this can be done.) Then, using the Chain Rule for differentiation,

$$\frac{d}{dx}(\sin y) = \frac{d}{dy}(\sin y)\frac{dy}{dx} = \cos y \frac{dy}{dx}$$

so that $\sin y = x$ differentiates to give

$$\Rightarrow \quad \cos y \frac{dy}{dx} = 1$$

$$\Rightarrow \quad \frac{dy}{dx} = \frac{1}{\cos y}$$

Now, using

$$\cos^2 y = 1 - \sin^2 y,$$

so that $\qquad \cos^2 y = \pm\sqrt{1 - \sin^2 y} = \pm\sqrt{1 - x^2}$

$$\frac{dy}{dx} = \pm\frac{1}{\sqrt{1 - x^2}}$$

A quick look at the graph of $\sin^{-1} x$ shows that the gradient of the inverse-sine curve is always positive (technically speaking, infinitely so at $x = \pm 1$) and so $y = \sin^{-1} x$ differentiates to

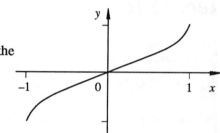

$$\frac{dy}{dx} = \frac{1}{\sqrt{1 - x^2}}$$

Activity 6

Use the above approach to find $\dfrac{dy}{dx}$ when $y = \tan^{-1} x$.

Find the derivative of $\cos^{-1} x$ also, and decide why it is not necessary to learn this result as well as the result for the derivative of $\sin^{-1} x$ when reversing the process and integrating.

The results

$$\frac{d}{dx}\left(\sin^{-1} x\right) = \frac{1}{\sqrt{1 - x^2}}$$

$$\frac{d}{dx}\left(\tan^{-1} x\right) = \frac{1}{1 + x^2}$$

and the corresponding integrations

$$\int \frac{1}{\sqrt{1 - x^2}}\, dx = \sin^{-1} x + C$$

$$\int \frac{1}{1 + x^2}\, dx = \tan^{-1} x + C \qquad (C \text{ constant})$$

are special cases of the more general results:

$$\int \frac{dx}{\sqrt{a^2 - x^2}} = \sin^{-1}\left(\frac{x}{a}\right) + C$$

$$\int \frac{dx}{a^2 + x^2} = \frac{1}{a}\tan^{-1}\left(\frac{x}{a}\right) + C \quad \text{for constant } C.$$

The results, in this form, are given in the AEB's *Booklet of Formulae*, and may be quoted when needed.

Activity 7

(a) Use the substitution $x = a\sin\theta$ to prove the result

$$\int \frac{dx}{\sqrt{a^2 - x^2}} = \sin^{-1}\left(\frac{x}{a}\right) + C.$$

(b) Use the substitution $x = a\tan\theta$ to prove the result

$$\int \frac{dx}{a^2 + x^2} = \frac{1}{a}\tan^{-1}\left(\frac{x}{a}\right) + C.$$

Example

Evaluate $\displaystyle\int_0^{\frac{1}{4}} \frac{dx}{\sqrt{1 - 4x^2}}$

Solution

Now $\sqrt{1 - 4x^2} = \sqrt{4}\sqrt{\dfrac{1}{4} - x^2} = 2\sqrt{\dfrac{1}{4} - x^2}$

so that $\displaystyle\int_0^{\frac{1}{4}} \frac{dx}{\sqrt{1 - 4x^2}} = \frac{1}{2}\int_0^{\frac{1}{4}} \frac{dx}{\sqrt{\dfrac{1}{4} - x^2}}$ (and this is now the standard

format, with $a = \dfrac{1}{2}$)

$$= \frac{1}{2}\left[\sin^{-1}\left(\frac{x}{\frac{1}{2}}\right)\right]_0^{\frac{1}{4}}$$

$$= \frac{1}{2}\left[\sin^{-1} 2x\right]_0^{\frac{1}{4}}$$

$$= \frac{1}{2}\left(\sin^{-1}\frac{1}{2} - \sin^{-1} 0\right)$$

$$= \frac{1}{2}\left(\frac{\pi}{6} - 0\right)$$

$$= \frac{\pi}{12}$$

Example

Evaluate $\displaystyle\int_1^2 \frac{3dx}{2+x^2}$,

giving your answer correct to 4 decimal places.

Solution

$$\int_1^2 \frac{3dx}{2+x^2} = 3\int_1^2 \frac{dx}{\left(\sqrt{2}\right)^2 + x^2} \qquad \text{[so } a = \sqrt{2} \text{ here]}$$

$$= 3\left[\frac{1}{\sqrt{2}}\tan^{-1}\left(\frac{x}{\sqrt{2}}\right)\right]_1^2$$

$$= \frac{3}{\sqrt{2}}\left(\tan^{-1}\sqrt{2} - \tan^{-1}\frac{1}{\sqrt{2}}\right) \qquad \text{[Important note: work in radians]}$$

$$\approx \frac{3}{\sqrt{2}}(0.95532 - 0.61548)$$

$$= 0.7209 \qquad \text{(4 d.p.)}$$

Exercise 1F

Evaluate the following integrals, giving your answers to four significant figures. [Remember to work in radians.]

1. $\displaystyle\int_{\frac{1}{4}}^{\frac{1}{3}} \frac{dx}{\sqrt{1-8x^2}}$

2. $\displaystyle\int_4^8 \frac{4}{8+x^2}\,dx$

3. $\displaystyle\int_2^{\sqrt{5}} \frac{dx}{5+9x^2}$

4. $\displaystyle\int_0^2 \frac{7}{\sqrt{7-x^2}}\,dx$

Evaluate the following integrals exactly:

5. $\displaystyle\int_0^{\sqrt{3}} \frac{3}{6+2x^2}\,dx$

6. $\displaystyle\int_{\frac{3}{2}}^{\sqrt{3}} \frac{2\,dx}{\sqrt{3-x^2}}$

7. $\displaystyle\int_{\sqrt{2}}^{\sqrt{6}} \frac{dx}{6+x^2}$

8. $\displaystyle\int_0^{\frac{\sqrt{5}}{2}} \frac{dx}{\sqrt{5-2x^2}}$

9. $\displaystyle\int_0^1 \frac{dx}{\sqrt{4-3x^2}}$

*10. $\displaystyle\int_{-1}^1 \left(\frac{1-x^2}{1+x^2}\right)dx$

1.8   The '$t = \tan\frac{1}{2}A$' substitution

You will have already encountered the result:

$$\tan 2\theta = \frac{2\tan\theta}{1-\tan^2\theta}$$

which arises from the identity

$$\tan(A+B) = \frac{\tan A + \tan B}{1-\tan A \tan B}$$

Setting $\theta = \frac{1}{2}A$ then yields the result

$$\tan A = \frac{2t}{1-t^2} \text{ where } t = \tan\frac{1}{2}A$$

In the triangle shown opposite, $\tan A = \frac{2t}{1-t^2}$, and the hypotenuse,

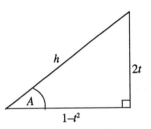

h, is given by Pythagoras' theorem:

$$h^2 = \left(1-t^2\right) + (2t)^2$$
$$= 1 - 2t^2 + t^4 + 4t^2$$
$$= 1 + 2t^2 + t^4$$
$$= \left(1+t^2\right)^2$$

So $h = 1 + t^2$ and

$$\sin A = \frac{2t}{1+t^2} \text{ and } \cos A = \frac{1-t^2}{1+t^2}$$

This would seem, at first sight, to be merely an exercise in trigonometry manipulation, but these results (which are given in the AEB's *Booklet of Formulae*) have their uses, particularly in handling some otherwise tricky trigonometric integrations.

Incidentally, the above working pre-supposes that angle A is acute, and this is generally the case in practice. The identities are valid, however, for all values of A in the range $0 \le A \le 2\pi$ (and hence all values of A).

Although, when $\frac{1}{2}A = \frac{\pi}{2}, 3\frac{\pi}{2}, \ldots \tan\frac{1}{2}A$ is not defined, the limiting values of $\sin A$, $\cos A$ and $\tan A$ are still correct.

Example

Use the substitution $t = \tan \dfrac{1}{2} x$ to show that the indefinite integral

of $\sec x$ is $\ln \left| \tan \left(\dfrac{\pi}{4} + \dfrac{1}{2} x \right) \right|$.

Solution

$$t = \tan \frac{1}{2} x \quad \Rightarrow \quad \frac{dt}{dx} = \frac{1}{2} \sec^2 \frac{1}{2} x$$

$$\Rightarrow \quad 2dt = \left(\sec^2 \frac{1}{2} x \right) dx$$

$$\Rightarrow \quad 2dt = \left(1 + \tan^2 \frac{1}{2} x \right) dx$$

$$\Rightarrow \quad \frac{2dt}{1+t^2} = dx$$

Also, $\sec x = \dfrac{1}{\cos x} = \dfrac{1+t^2}{1-t^2}$, using one of the above results.

Then

$$\int \sec x \, dx = \int \frac{1+t^2}{1-t^2} \cdot \frac{2dt}{1+t^2}$$

$$= \int \frac{2}{1-t^2} \, dt$$

$$= \int \frac{2}{(1-t)(1+t)} \, dt$$

$$= \int \left\{ \frac{1}{1+t} + \frac{1}{1-t} \right\} dt \quad \text{by partial fractions}$$

$$= \ln|1+t| - \ln|1-t|$$

$$= \ln \left| \frac{1+t}{1-t} \right|$$

Now $\qquad \tan \left(\dfrac{\pi}{4} + \dfrac{1}{2} x \right) = \dfrac{\tan \dfrac{\pi}{4} + \tan \dfrac{1}{2} x}{1 - \tan \dfrac{\pi}{4} - \tan \dfrac{1}{2} x} = \dfrac{1+t}{1-t}$ $\qquad$ (since $\tan \dfrac{\pi}{4} = 1$)

so that

$$\int \sec x \, dx = \ln \left| \tan \left(\frac{\pi}{4} + \frac{1}{2} x \right) \right|$$

Activity 8

Use the above identities for cos x and tan x to prove that

$$\sec x + \tan x = \frac{1 + \tan\frac{1}{2}x}{1 - \tan\frac{1}{2}x}$$

The results $\sec x\, dx = \ln\left|\sec x + \tan x\right| = \ln\left|\tan\left(\frac{\pi}{4} + \frac{1}{2}x\right)\right|$ are given

in the AEB's *Booklet of Formulae*, as is the result

$$\int \operatorname{cosec} x\, dx = \ln\left|\tan\frac{1}{2}x\right|$$

Since this latter result is much easier to establish, it has been set as an exercise below.

Example

Use the substitution $t = \tan\frac{1}{2}\theta$ to evaluate exactly

$$\int_0^{\frac{\pi}{2}} \frac{d\theta}{4\cos\theta + 3\sin\theta}$$

Solution

$$t = \tan\frac{1}{2}\theta \Rightarrow \frac{dt}{d\theta} = \frac{1}{2}\sec^2\frac{1}{2}\theta \Rightarrow \frac{2dt}{1 + t^2} = d\theta$$

Also,

$$\cos\theta = \frac{1 - t^2}{1 + t^2} \text{ and } \sin\theta = \frac{2t}{1 + t^2}$$

Changing the limits:

$$\theta = 0 \Rightarrow t = 0 \text{ and } \theta = \frac{\pi}{2} \Rightarrow t = \tan\frac{\pi}{4} = 1$$

so

$$\left(\theta, \frac{\pi}{2}\right) \rightarrow (0, 1)$$

Thus

$$\int_0^{\frac{\pi}{2}} \frac{d\theta}{4\cos\theta + 3\sin\theta} = \int_0^1 \frac{1}{\frac{4 - 4t^2}{1 + t^2} + \frac{6t}{1 + t^2}} \cdot \frac{2dt}{1 + t^2}$$

$$= \int_0^1 \frac{2dt}{4-4t^2+6t}$$

$$= \int_0^1 \frac{dt}{2+3t-2t^2}$$

$$= \int_0^1 \left\{ \frac{\frac{1}{5}}{2-t} + \frac{\frac{2}{5}}{1+2t} \right\} dt$$

$$= \left[-\frac{1}{5}\ln|2-t| + \frac{1}{5}\ln|1+t| \right]_0^1$$

$$= \left(-\frac{1}{5}\ln 1 + \frac{1}{5}\ln 3 \right) - \left(-\frac{1}{5}\ln 2 - \frac{1}{5}\ln 1 \right)$$

$$= \frac{1}{5}\ln 6$$

In the following exercise, you may have to use the $\tan^{-1}$ or $\sin^{-1}$ integrals from the previous section.

Exercise 1G

1. Use the substitution $t = \tan\frac{1}{2}x$ to evaluate

   $\int_{\frac{\pi}{4}}^{\frac{\pi}{3}} \frac{dx}{1+\sin^2 x}$, giving your answer to 4 decimal places.

2. By writing $t = \tan\frac{1}{2}x$, show that

   (a) $\int \cosec x\, dx = \ln\left|\tan\frac{1}{2}x\right| + C$

   (b) $\int \frac{dx}{1+\cos x} = \tan\frac{1}{2}x + C$

   (c) $\int \frac{dx}{\cos\frac{1}{2}x\sqrt{\cos x}} = 2\sin^{-1}\left\{\tan\frac{1}{2}x\right\} + C$

3. Use the $t = \tan\frac{1}{2}\theta$ substitution to evaluate exactly the integrals

   (a) $\int_0^{\frac{2\pi}{3}} \frac{d\theta}{5+4\cos\theta}$ (b) $\int_0^{\frac{\pi}{2}} \frac{\tan\frac{1}{2}\theta}{5+4\cos\theta}d\theta$

   (c) $\int_0^{\frac{\pi}{2}} \frac{1}{3+5\sin\theta}d\theta$

4. (a) By using the identity $\tan A = \frac{2t}{1-t^2}$ where $t = \tan\frac{1}{2}A$, and setting $A = \frac{\pi}{6}$, show that

   $$\tan\frac{\pi}{12} = 2-\sqrt{3}$$

   (b) Evaluate, to four decimal places, the integral

   $$\int_{\frac{\pi}{6}}^{\frac{\pi}{3}} \frac{d\theta}{2+\cos\theta}$$

5. By setting $t = \tan\frac{1}{2}x$, find the indefinite integral

   $$\int \sec\frac{1}{2}x\sqrt{1-\cos x}\, dx$$

1.9   Harder integrations

In this final section of the chapter, all of the integrations involve the standard results for sin^{-1} and tan^{-1}, but you may have to do some work to get them into the appropriate form.

Before you start, here are a few reminders of the algebraic techniques which you will need, and also one or two calculus results. To give you a clear idea of how they work out in practice, they are incorporated into the following set of examples.

Example

By writing $\dfrac{x^2+7x+2}{\left(1+x^2\right)(2-x)}$ in terms of partial fractions, show that

$$\int_0^1 \frac{x^2+7x+2}{\left(1+x^2\right)(2-x)}\,dx = \frac{\pi}{2}\ln 2 - \frac{\pi}{4}$$

Solution

$$\frac{x^2+7x+2}{\left(1+x^2\right)(2-x)} \equiv \frac{Ax+B}{1+x^2} + \frac{C}{2-x}$$

Multiplying throughout by the denominator

$$x^2+7x+2 \equiv (Ax+B)(2-x)+C\left(1+x^2\right)$$

Substituting $x=2$ gives

$$20=5C \quad \Rightarrow \quad C=4$$

Substituting $x=0$ gives

$$2=2B+4 \Rightarrow B=-1$$

Comparing x^2 coefficients:

$$1=-A+4 \Rightarrow A=3$$

Thus $\qquad \dfrac{x^2+7x+2}{\left(1+x^2\right)(2-x)} \equiv \dfrac{3x-1}{1+x^2} + \dfrac{4}{2-x}$

Then $\displaystyle\int_0^1 \frac{x^2+7x+2}{\left(1+x^2\right)(2-x)}\,dx = \int_0^1 \frac{3x}{1+x^2}\,dx - \int_0^1 \frac{1}{1+x^2}\,dx + 4\int_0^1 \frac{1}{2-x}\,dx$

The reason for splitting the integration up in this way is to separate the directly integrable bits. Note that

$$\int \frac{f'(x)}{f(x)}\,dx = \ln\big|f(x)\big| + \text{constant}$$

i.e. when the 'top' is exactly the differential of the 'bottom', the integral is natural log of the 'bottom'. Now $\frac{d}{dx}\left(1+x^2\right) = 2x$ and

$\frac{d}{dx}(2-x) = -1$, so the constants in the numerators need jiggling but, apart from this, you should see that the three integrals are log, $\tan^{-1}$ and log respectively:

$$= \frac{3}{2}\int_0^1 \frac{2x}{1+x^2}\,dx - \int_0^1 \frac{1}{1+x^2}\,dx - 4\int_0^1 \frac{-1}{2-x}\,dx$$

$$= \frac{3}{2}\left[\ln\left(x^2+1\right)\right]_0^1 - \left[\tan^{-1}x\right]_0^1 - 4\left[\ln(2-x)\right]_0^1$$

[Strictly speaking, the log integrals should be $\left|x^2+1\right|$ and $\left|2-x\right|$, but $1+x^2$ is always positive and $2-x$ is positive for x between 0 and 1.]

$$= \frac{3}{2}(\ln 2 - \ln 1) - \left(\tan^{-1}1 - \tan^{-1}0\right) - 4(\ln 1 - \ln 2)$$

$$= \frac{3}{2}\ln 2 - \frac{\pi}{4} + 4\ln 2$$

$$= \frac{11}{2}\ln 2 - \frac{\pi}{4}$$

Example

Evaluate $\int_0^{\frac{1}{3}} \frac{3x+1}{\sqrt{1-3x^2}}\,dx$, giving your answer correct to three significant figures.

Solution

$$\int_0^{\frac{1}{3}} \frac{3x+1}{\sqrt{1-3x^2}}\,dx = \int_0^{\frac{1}{3}} \frac{3x}{\sqrt{1-3x^2}}\,dx + \int_0^{\frac{1}{3}} \frac{1}{\sqrt{1-3x^2}}\,dx$$

Now the second integral on the RHS is clearly a $\sin^{-1}$ integral.

What about the first one?

You might just recognise where the x in the numerator comes from if you think about it long enough. To save time: try calling

$$u = \sqrt{1-3x^2} = \left(1-3x^2\right)^{\frac{1}{2}};$$

then $\quad \dfrac{du}{dx} = \dfrac{1}{2}\left(1-3x^2\right)^{-\frac{1}{2}}(-6x) \quad$ using the Chain Rule

$$= \frac{-3x}{\sqrt{1-3x^2}}$$

So $\quad \displaystyle\int \frac{3x}{\sqrt{1-3x^2}}\,dx = -\sqrt{1-3x^2}$ [This method is referred to as 'integration by recognition']

and

$$\int_0^{\frac{1}{3}} \frac{3x+1}{\sqrt{1-3x^2}}\,dx = \int_0^{\frac{1}{3}} \frac{3x}{\sqrt{1-3x^2}}\,dx + \frac{1}{\sqrt{3}}\int_0^{\frac{1}{3}} \frac{dx}{\sqrt{\frac{1}{3}-x^2}}$$

$$= \left[-\sqrt{1-3x^2}\right]_0^{\frac{1}{3}} + \frac{1}{\sqrt{3}}\left[\sin^{-1}\left(\frac{x}{\frac{1}{\sqrt{3}}}\right)\right]_0^{\frac{1}{3}}$$

$$= \left(-\sqrt{\frac{2}{3}}+1\right) + \frac{1}{\sqrt{3}}\left(\sin^{-1}\frac{1}{\sqrt{3}} - \sin^{-1}0\right)$$

$$= 0.539 \text{ (to 3 s.f.)}$$

Example

Integrate exactly the integrals

(a) $\displaystyle\int_1^2 \frac{dx}{3x^2-6x+4}$ (b) $\displaystyle\int_1^{\frac{3}{2}} \frac{dx}{\sqrt{-2+5x-2x^2}}$

Solution

(a) $\displaystyle\int_1^2 \frac{dx}{3x^2-6x+4} = \frac{1}{3}\int_1^2 \frac{dx}{x^2-2x+\frac{4}{3}}$

[Now $x^2-2x+\frac{4}{3} = (x-1)^2 + \frac{1}{3}$ by completing the square: the factor of 3 was taken out first in order to make this easier to cope with.]

$$= \frac{1}{3}\int_1^2 \frac{dx}{\frac{1}{3}+(x-1)^2}$$

[This is $\displaystyle\int \frac{dx}{a^2+x^2}$ with $a = \dfrac{1}{\sqrt{3}}$ and $'x' = x-1$, which is allowed when a single x is involved.]

$$= \frac{1}{3}\left[\frac{1}{\frac{1}{\sqrt{3}}} \tan^{-1}\left(\frac{x-1}{\frac{1}{\sqrt{3}}}\right)\right]_1^2$$

$$= \frac{\sqrt{3}}{3}\left[\tan^{-1}\left([x-1]\sqrt{3}\right)\right]_1^2$$

$$= \frac{\sqrt{3}}{3}\left(\tan^{-1}\sqrt{3} - \tan^{-1}0\right)$$

$$= \frac{\sqrt{3}}{3}\left(\frac{\pi}{3} - 0\right)$$

$$= \frac{\pi\sqrt{3}}{9}$$

(b) $\displaystyle \int_1^{\frac{3}{2}} \frac{dx}{\sqrt{-2+5x-2x^2}} = \frac{1}{\sqrt{2}}\int_1^{\frac{3}{2}} \frac{dx}{\sqrt{-1+\frac{5}{2}x-x^2}}$

Completing the square:

$$-1+\frac{5}{2}x-x^2 = -\left\{x^2 - \frac{5}{2}x + 1\right\} = -\left\{\left(x-\frac{5}{4}\right)^2 - \frac{25}{16} + 1\right\}$$

$$= \frac{9}{16} - \left(x - \frac{5}{4}\right)^2$$

This gives

$$\text{integral} = \frac{1}{\sqrt{2}}\int_1^{\frac{3}{2}} \frac{dx}{\sqrt{\left(\frac{3}{4}\right)^2 - \left(x-\frac{5}{4}\right)^2}}$$

$$= \frac{1}{\sqrt{2}}\left[\sin^{-1}\left(\frac{\left(x-\frac{5}{4}\right)}{\frac{3}{4}}\right)\right]_1^{\frac{3}{2}}$$

$$= \frac{1}{\sqrt{2}}\left[\sin^{-1}\left(\frac{(4x-5)}{3}\right)\right]_1^{\frac{3}{2}}$$

$$= \frac{1}{\sqrt{2}}\left(\sin^{-1}\frac{1}{3} - \sin^{-1}\left(-\frac{1}{3}\right)\right)$$

$$= \frac{1}{\sqrt{2}}\left(2\sin^{-1}\frac{1}{3}\right)$$

$$= \sqrt{2}\sin^{-1}\frac{1}{3}$$

Exercise 1H

1. By expressing $\dfrac{3x+10}{(2-x)(4+x^2)}$ in terms of partial fractions, evaluate

$$\int_0^1 \frac{3x+10}{(2-x)(4+x^2)}dx$$

giving your answer to three significant figures.

2. Show that $\displaystyle\int_0^{\frac{\sqrt{3}}{2}} \frac{3x+2}{9+2x^2}dx = \frac{3}{4}\ln\left(\frac{4}{3}\right)+\frac{\pi\sqrt{2}}{18}$.

3. Given that $y=\sqrt{4-x^2}$, find an expression for $\dfrac{dy}{dx}$ and deduce that $\displaystyle\int \frac{x}{\sqrt{4-x^2}}dx = C - \sqrt{4-x^2}$ for some constant C. Hence evaluate exactly

$$\int_1^2 \frac{2x-3}{\sqrt{4-x^2}}dx$$

4. Determine the values of the constants A, B and C such that

$$\frac{x^2+2x+7}{1+x^2} \equiv A + \frac{Bx}{1+x^2} + \frac{C}{1+x^2}$$

Show that $\displaystyle\int_1^{\sqrt{3}} \frac{x^2+2x+7}{1+x^2}dx = \sqrt{3}-1+\ln 2+\frac{\pi}{2}$

5. By 'completing the square' in each of the following cases, evaluate exactly the integrals:

(a) $\displaystyle\int_{\frac{1}{2}}^{\frac{3}{2}} \frac{dx}{\sqrt{2x-x^2}}$

(b) $\displaystyle\int_0^1 \frac{dx}{x^2-x+1}$

(c) $\displaystyle\int_0^{\frac{2}{3}} \frac{dx}{\sqrt{1+2x-3x^2}}$

(d) $2x^2-2x+5$

(e) $\displaystyle\int_0^1 \frac{dx}{\sqrt{x-x^2}}$

(f) $\displaystyle\int_0^1 \frac{dx}{x^2+6x+10}$

6. Show that $\displaystyle\int_0^2 \frac{4-3x}{4+3x^2}dx = \frac{2\pi}{3\sqrt{3}} - \frac{1}{2}\ln 13$.

7. Use partial fractions to help evaluate the integral

$$\int_0^{\sqrt{3}} \frac{5}{(1+x^2)(2+x)}dx$$

8. Evaluate the following integrals:

(a) $\displaystyle\int_1^4 \frac{5x+4}{x^2+4}dx$

(b) $\displaystyle\int_0^{\sqrt{2}} \frac{4+3x-x^2}{2+x^2}dx$

9. Determine the values of the constants A, B and C for which

$$f(x) = \frac{x^2+2x-4}{x^2-2x+4} \equiv A + B\left(\frac{2x-2}{x^2-2x+4}\right) + \frac{C}{x^2-2x+4}$$

Hence evaluate $\displaystyle\int_1^4 f(x)$.

10. (a) Prove that $\displaystyle\int_1^2 \frac{4x}{5+x^2}dx = 2\ln\left(\frac{3}{2}\right)$.

(b) Use the result of (a) to evaluate $\displaystyle\int_1^2 \frac{4x+2}{5+x^2}dx$, giving your answer correct to 3 decimal places.

*11. Show that $\displaystyle\int_0^1 \frac{3x\,dx}{\sqrt{1+6x-3x^2}} = \frac{\pi}{\sqrt{3}} - 1$.

*12. Show that $\displaystyle\int_0^{\frac{\sqrt{3}}{2}} \frac{1+x^3}{\sqrt{1-x^2}}dx = \frac{1}{24}(8\pi+5)$.

[Hint: $\displaystyle\int \frac{x^3}{\sqrt{1-x^2}}dx = \int x^2 \times \frac{x}{\sqrt{1-x^2}}dx$]

1.10 Miscellaneous Exercises

1. Prove the identity $\tan\theta + \cot\theta \equiv 2\csc 2\theta$. Find, in radians, all the solutions of the equation $\tan x + \cot x = 8\cos 2x$ in the interval $0 < x < \pi$.
(AEB)

2. Find, in radians, the general solution of the equation $6\tan^2\theta = 4\sin^2\theta + 1$. (AEB)

3. Prove the identity $\cot 2\theta + \tan\theta \equiv \csc 2\theta$. Hence find the values of θ, in the interval $0° < \theta < 180°$ for which $3(\cot 2\theta + \tan\theta)^2 = 4$. (AEB)

4. Find, in terms of π, the general solution of the equation $\tan^4 x - 4\tan^2 x + 3 = 0$. (AEB)

5. Solve the equation $\sqrt{3}\tan\theta - \sec\theta = 1$, giving all solutions in the interval $0° < \theta < 360°$. (AEB)

6. By expanding $\cos(\theta - 60°)$, express $7\cos\theta + 8\cos(\theta - 60°)$ in the form $13\sin(\theta + \alpha)$, where $0° < \alpha < 90°$, and state the value of α to the nearest $0.1°$. Hence find the solutions of the equation $7\cos\theta + 8\cos(\theta - 60°) = 6.5$ in the interval $0° < \theta < 360°$, giving your answer to the nearest $0.1°$. (AEB)

7. Find all solutions in the interval $0° \le \theta \le 360°$ of the equation $\sin\theta - \cos\theta = k$ when
   (a) $k = 0$, and (b) $k = 1$. (AEB)

8. Find the general solution of the equation $\sin 2x + 2\cos^2 x = 0$ for x radians. (AEB)

9. Show that
$$\sin 2x + \sin 4x + \sin 6x \equiv \sin 4x(1 + 2\cos 2x)$$
Hence prove the identity
$$\sin 3x \sin 4x \equiv (\sin 2x + \sin 4x + \sin 6x)\sin x$$
Deduce that $\sin\left(\dfrac{\pi}{12}\right) = \dfrac{1}{\sqrt{6} + \sqrt{2}}$. (AEB)

10. Prove the identity
$$(\cos A + \cos B)^2 + (\sin A + \sin B)^2 \equiv 2 + 2\cos(A - B).$$
Hence solve the equation
$$(\cos 4\theta + \cos\theta)^2 + (\sin 4\theta + \sin\theta)^2 = 2\sqrt{3}\sin 3\theta$$
giving the general solution in degrees.

11. Given that $-1 < x, y < 1$, prove that
$$\tan^{-1}x + \tan^{-1}y = \tan^{-1}\left(\frac{x+y}{1-xy}\right)$$
Deduce the value of $\tan^{-1}\frac{1}{2} + \tan^{-1}\frac{1}{5} + \tan^{-1}\frac{1}{8}$
(AEB)

12. Express $f(x) = \dfrac{3+x}{(1+x^2)(1+2x)}$ in partial fractions.
Prove that the
area of the region enclosed by the curve with equation $y = f(x)$, the coordinate axes and the line $x = 1$ is $\dfrac{\pi}{4} + \dfrac{1}{2}\ln\left(\dfrac{9}{2}\right)$. (AEB)

13. Express $5\cos\theta + 2\sin\theta$ in the form $R\sin(\theta + \alpha)$, where $R > 0$ and $0° < \alpha < 90°$. The function f is defined by $f(\theta) = 6 - 5\cos\theta - 2\sin\theta$ for $0° \le \theta \le 360°$. State the greatest and least values of f and the values of θ, correct to the nearest $0.1°$, at which these occur.

14. Show that $\displaystyle\int_0^1 \frac{x\,dx}{1+x^2} = \frac{1}{2}\ln 2$. Hence using integration by parts, evaluate $\displaystyle\int_0^1 \tan^{-1}x\,dx$. (AEB)

15. Express $\dfrac{16-x}{(2-x)(3+x^2)}$ in partial fractions.
Hence show that
$$\int_0^1 \frac{16-x}{(2-x)(3+x^2)}dx = \ln\frac{16}{3} + \frac{5\pi}{6\sqrt{3}}$$
(AEB)

16. Express $\dfrac{\sin 3\theta}{\sin\theta}$ in terms of $\cos\theta$. Hence show that if $\sin 3\theta = \lambda\sin 2\theta$, where λ is a constant, then either $\sin\theta = 0$ or $4\cos^2\theta - 2\lambda\cos\theta - 1 = 0$. Determine the general solution, in degrees, of the equation $\sin 3\theta = 3\sin 2\theta$. (AEB)

17. Express $3\cos x - 4\sin x$ in the form $A\cos(x + \alpha)$, where $A > 0$ and α is acute, stating the value of α to the nearest $0.1°$.

   (a) Given that $f(x) = \dfrac{24}{3\cos x - 4\sin x + 7}$:
   (i) Write down the greatest and least values of $f(x)$ and the values of x to the nearest $0.1°$ in the interval $-180° < x < 180°$ at which these occur;
   (ii) Find the general solution, in degrees, of the equation $f(x) = \dfrac{16}{3}$.

   (b) Solve the equation $3\cos x - 4\sin x = 5\cos 3x$, giving your answers to the nearest $0.1°$ in the interval $0° < x < 180°$. (Oxford)

18. Given that $3\cos\theta + 4\sin\theta \equiv R\cos(\theta - \alpha)$, where $R > 0$ and $0 \le \alpha \le \dfrac{\pi}{2}$, state the value of R and the value of $\tan\alpha$.

    (a) For each of the following equations, solve for θ in the interval $0 \le \theta \le 2\pi$ and give your answers in radians correct to one decimal place:

    (i) $3\cos\theta + 4\sin\theta = 2$

    (ii) $3\cos 2\theta + 4\sin 2\theta = 5\cos\theta$.

    (b) The curve with equation
    $y = \dfrac{10}{3\cos x + 4\sin x + 7}$, between $x = -\pi$ and $x = \pi$, cuts the y-axis at A, has a maximum point at B and a minimum point at C. Find the coordinates of A, B and C. (AEB)

19. Given that $f(x) = 9\sin\left(x + \dfrac{\pi}{6}\right) + 5\cos\left(x + \dfrac{\pi}{3}\right)$, use the formulae for $\sin(A+B)$ and $\cos(A+B)$ to express $f(x)$ in the form $C\cos x + D\sqrt{3}\sin x$, where C and D are integers. Hence show that $f(x)$ can be written in the form $\sqrt{61}\cos(x - \alpha)$ giving a value for α in radians to three significant figures. (Oxford)

20. Prove the identity $1 + \sin 2\theta \equiv \dfrac{(1 + \tan\theta)^2}{1 + \tan^2\theta}$. By using the substitution $t = \tan\theta$, or otherwise, find the general solution, in radians, of the equation $(2 - \tan\theta)(1 + \sin 2\theta) = 2$. (AEB)

21. (a) Starting from the identity
    $\cos(A+B) \equiv \cos A\cos B - \sin A\sin B$,
    prove the identity
    $\cos 2\theta \equiv 2\cos^2\theta - 1$.

    (b) Find the general solution of the equation $\sin\theta + \tan\theta\cos 2\theta = 0$, giving your answer in radians in terms of π.

    (c) Prove the identity
    $2\cos^2\theta - 2\cos^2 2\theta \equiv \cos 2\theta - \cos 4\theta$.

    (d) By substituting $\theta = \dfrac{\pi}{5}$ in the identity in (c),
    prove that $\cos\left(\dfrac{\pi}{5}\right) - \cos\left(\dfrac{2\pi}{5}\right) = \dfrac{1}{2}$.

    (e) Hence find the value of $\cos\left(\dfrac{\pi}{5}\right)$ in the form $a + b\sqrt{5}$, stating the values of a and b. (AEB)

22. Use identities for $\cos(C+D)$ and $\cos(C-D)$ to prove that $\cos A + \cos B = 2\cos\left(\dfrac{A+B}{2}\right)\cos\left(\dfrac{A-B}{2}\right)$.
    Hence find, in terms of π, the general solution of the equation $\cos 5\theta + \cos\theta = \cos 3\theta$.

    Using both the identity for $\cos A + \cos B$, and the corresponding identity for $\sin A - \sin B$, show that
    $\cos 5\alpha - \sin\alpha = 2\sin\alpha(\cos 4\alpha + \cos 2\alpha)$.

    The triangle PQR has angle $QPR = \alpha(\ne 0)$, angle $PQR = 5\alpha$ and $RP = 3RQ$. Show that $\sin 5\alpha = 3\sin\alpha$ and deduce that $\cos 4\alpha + \cos 2\alpha = 1$.
    By solving a quadratic equation in $\cos 2\alpha$, or otherwise, find the value of α, giving your answer to the nearest $0.1°$. (AEB)

23. Given that $\dfrac{7x - x^2}{(2-x)(x^2+1)} \equiv \dfrac{A}{2-x} + \dfrac{Bx+C}{x^2+1}$,
    determine the values of A, B and C. A curve has equation $y = \dfrac{7x - x^2}{(2-x)(x^2+1)}$. Prove that the area of the region enclosed by the curve, the x-axis and the line $x = 1$ is $\dfrac{7}{2}\ln 2 - \dfrac{\pi}{4}$. (AEB)

24. Use the substitution $x = 1 + 2\tan\theta$ to evaluate the integral $\displaystyle\int_1^3 \dfrac{x}{x^2 - 2x + 5}dx$ giving your answer correct to two decimal places. (AEB)

25. By expressing $2\cos 3\theta\sin\dfrac{\theta}{2}$ and other similar expressions as the difference of two sines, prove the identity
    $(2\cos 3\theta + 2\cos 2\theta + 2\cos\theta + 1)\sin\dfrac{\theta}{2} \equiv \sin\dfrac{7\theta}{2}$.

    Express $\cos 3\theta$ and $\cos 2\theta$ in terms of $\cos\theta$ and deduce the identity
    $(8\cos^3\theta + 4\cos^2\theta - 4\cos\theta - 1)\sin\dfrac{\theta}{2} \equiv \sin\dfrac{7\theta}{2}$.

    Hence, or otherwise, show that $\cos\dfrac{2\pi}{7}$, $\cos\dfrac{4\pi}{7}$ and $\cos\dfrac{6\pi}{7}$ are the roots of the equation
    $8x^3 + 4x^2 - 4x - 1 = 0$. (AEB)

26. Assuming the identities
    $\sin 3\theta \equiv 3\sin\theta - 4\sin^3\theta$ and
    $\cos 3\theta \equiv 4\cos^3\theta - 3\cos\theta$
    prove that
    $\cos 5\theta \equiv 5\cos\theta - 20\cos^3\theta + 16\cos^5\theta$.

(a) Find the set of values of θ in the interval $0 < \theta < \pi$ for which $\cos 5\theta > 16\cos^5 \theta$.

(b) Find the general solution, in radians, of the equation $\cos x + 3\cos 3x + \cos 5x = 0$.   (AEB)

27. Express $f(\theta) = 4\cos\theta + 3\sin\theta$ in the form

    $R\cos(\theta - \alpha)$ where $R > 0$ and $0 < \alpha < \dfrac{\pi}{2}$.

    (a) A rectangle $OABC$ is formed from the origin, the point $A(4\cos\theta, 0)$, the point B, and the point $C(0, 3\sin\theta)$. State the coordinates of B and express the perimeter of the rectangle in terms of $f(\theta)$. Hence find the greatest perimeter of the rectangle as θ varies in the range $0 \le \theta \le \dfrac{\pi}{2}$ and state the coordinates of B for which this greatest perimeter occurs.

    (b) A curve has the equation

    $y = \dfrac{1}{(4\cos x + 3\sin x)^2}\left(0 \le x \le \dfrac{\pi}{2}\right)$. Show that

    the region enclosed by the curve, the x-axis, and the lines $x = 0$ and $x = \dfrac{\pi}{2}$ has area $\dfrac{1}{12}$.

    (AEB)

2 HYPERBOLIC FUNCTIONS

Objectives

After studying this chapter you should

- understand what is meant by a hyperbolic function;
- be able to find derivatives and integrals of hyperbolic functions;
- be able to find inverse hyperbolic functions and use them in calculus applications;
- recognise logarithmic equivalents of inverse hyperbolic functions.

2.0   Introduction

This chapter will introduce you to the hyperbolic functions which you may have noticed on your calculator with the abbreviation *hyp*. You will see some connections with trigonometric functions and will be able to find various integrals which cannot be found without the help of hyperbolic functions. The first systematic consideration of hyperbolic functions was done by the Swiss mathematician *Johann Heinrich Lambert* (1728-1777).

2.1   Definitions

The **hyperbolic cosine function**, written cosh x, is defined for all real values of x by the relation

$$\cosh x = \frac{1}{2}\left(e^x + e^{-x}\right)$$

Similarly the **hyperbolic sine function**, sinh x, is defined by

$$\sinh x = \frac{1}{2}\left(e^x - e^{-x}\right)$$

The names of these two hyperbolic functions suggest that they have similar properties to the trigonometric functions and some of these will be investigated.

Activity 1

Show that $\cosh x + \sinh x = e^x$

and simplify $\cosh x - \sinh x.$

(a) By multiplying the expressions for $(\cosh x + \sinh x)$ and $(\cosh x - \sinh x)$ together, show that

$$\cosh^2 x - \sinh^2 x = 1$$

(b) By considering $(\cosh x + \sinh x)^2 + (\cosh x - \sinh x)^2$

show that $\cosh^2 x + \sinh^2 x = \cosh 2x$

(c) By considering $(\cosh x + \sinh x)^2 - (\cosh x - \sinh x)^2$

show that $2 \sinh x \cosh x = \sinh 2x$

Activity 2

Use the definitions of $\sinh x$ and $\cosh x$ in terms of exponential functions to prove that

(a) $\cosh 2x = 2 \cosh^2 x - 1$

(b) $\cosh 2x = 1 + 2 \sinh^2 x$

Example

Prove that $\cosh(x - y) = \cosh x \cosh y - \sinh x \sinh y$

Solution

$$\cosh x \cosh y = \frac{1}{2}\left(e^x + e^{-x}\right) \times \frac{1}{2}\left(e^y + e^{-y}\right)$$

$$= \frac{1}{4}\left(e^{x+y} + e^{x-y} + e^{-(x-y)} + e^{-(x+y)}\right)$$

$$\sinh x \sinh y = \frac{1}{2}\left(e^x - e^{-x}\right) \times \frac{1}{2}\left(e^y - e^{-y}\right)$$

$$= \frac{1}{4}\left(e^{x+y} - e^{x-y} - e^{-(x-y)} + e^{-(x+y)}\right)$$

Subtracting gives

$$\cosh x \cosh y - \sinh x \sinh y = 2 \times \frac{1}{4}\left(e^{x-y} + e^{-(x-y)}\right)$$

$$= \frac{1}{2}\left(e^{x-y} + e^{-(x-y)}\right) = \cosh(x - y)$$

Exercise 2A

Prove the following identities.

1. (a) $\sinh(-x) = -\sinh x$ (b) $\cosh(-x) = \cosh x$

2. (a) $\sinh(x+y) = \sinh x \, \cosh y + \cosh x \, \sinh y$

    (b) $\sinh(x-y) = \sinh x \, \cosh y - \cosh x \, \sinh y$

3. $\cosh(x+y) = \cosh x \, \cosh y + \sinh x \, \sinh y$

4. $\sinh A + \sinh B = 2\sinh\left(\dfrac{A+B}{2}\right)\cosh\left(\dfrac{A-B}{2}\right)$

5. $\cosh A - \cosh B = 2\sinh\left(\dfrac{A+B}{2}\right)\sinh\left(\dfrac{A-B}{2}\right)$

2.2 Osborn's rule

You should have noticed from the previous exercise a similarity between the corresponding identities for trigonometric functions. In fact, trigonometric formulae can be converted into formulae for hyperbolic functions using **Osborn's rule**, which states that cos should be converted into cosh and sin into sinh, except when there is a product of two sines, when a sign change must be effected.

For example, $\qquad \cos 2x = 1 - 2\sin^2 x$

can be converted, remembering that $\sin^2 x = \sin x . \sin x$,

into $\qquad \cosh 2x = 1 + 2\sinh^2 x$.

But $\qquad \sin 2A = 2\sin A \cos A$

simply converts to $\sinh 2A = 2\sinh A \cosh A$ because there is no product of sines.

Activity 3

Given the following trigonometric formulae, use Osborn's rule to write down the corresponding hyperbolic function formulae.

(a) $\sin A - \sin B = 2\cos\left(\dfrac{A+B}{2}\right)\sin\left(\dfrac{A-B}{2}\right)$

(b) $\sin 3A = 3\sin A - 4\sin^3 A$

(c) $\cos^2 \theta + \sin^2 \theta = 1$

2.3 Further functions

Corresponding to the trigonometric functions $\tan x$, $\cot x$, $\sec x$ and $\operatorname{cosec} x$ we define

$$\tanh x = \frac{\sinh x}{\cosh x}, \quad \coth x = \frac{1}{\tanh x} = \frac{\cosh x}{\sinh x},$$

$$\operatorname{sech}x = \frac{1}{\cosh x} \quad \text{and} \quad \operatorname{cosech}x = \frac{1}{\sinh x}$$

By implication when using Osborn's rule, where the function $\tanh x$ occurs, it must be regarded as involving $\sinh x$.

Therefore, to convert the formula $\sec^2 x = 1 + \tan^2 x$

we must write

$$\operatorname{sech}^2 x = 1 - \tanh^2 x.$$

Activity 4

(a) Prove that

$$\tanh x = \frac{e^x - e^{-x}}{e^x + e^{-x}} \text{ and } \operatorname{sech}x = \frac{2}{e^x + e^{-x}},$$

and hence verify that

$$\operatorname{sech}^2 x = 1 - \tanh^2 x.$$

(b) Apply Osborn's rule to obtain a formula which corresponds to

$$\operatorname{cosec}^2 y = 1 + \cot^2 y.$$

Prove the result by converting $\operatorname{cosech}y$ and $\coth y$ into exponential functions.

2.4 Graphs of hyperbolic functions

You could plot the graphs of $\cosh x$ and $\sinh x$ quite easily on a graphics calculator and obtain graphs as shown opposite.

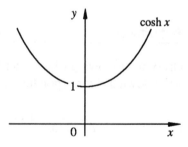

The shape of the graph of $y = \cosh x$ is that of a particular chain supported at each end and hanging freely. It is often called a **catenary** (from the Latin word *catena* for chain or thread).

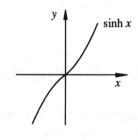

Activity 5

(a) Superimpose the graphs of $y = \cosh x$ and $y = \sinh x$ on the screen of a graphics calculator. Do the curves ever intersect?

(b) Use a graphics calculator to sketch the function
$f : x \mapsto \tanh x$ with domain $x \in \mathbb{R}$. What is the range of the function?

(c) Try to predict what the graphs of
$$y = \operatorname{sech} x, \ y = \operatorname{cosech} x \text{ and } y = \coth x$$
will look like. Check your ideas by plotting the graphs on a graphics calculator.

2.5 Solving equations

Suppose $\sinh x = \dfrac{3}{4}$ and we wish to find the exact value of x.

Recall that $\cosh^2 x = 1 + \sinh^2 x$ and $\cosh x$ is always positive, so

when $\sinh x = \dfrac{3}{4}$, $\cosh x = \dfrac{5}{4}$.

From Activity 1, we have $\sinh x + \cosh x = e^x$

so $\qquad e^x = \dfrac{3}{4} + \dfrac{5}{4} = 2$

and hence $\quad x = \ln 2$.

Alternatively, we can write $\sinh x = \dfrac{1}{2}\left(e^x - e^{-x}\right)$

so $\sinh x = \dfrac{3}{4}$ means

$$\frac{1}{2}\left(e^x - e^{-x}\right) = \frac{3}{4}$$

$$\Rightarrow \quad 2e^x - 3 - 2e^{-x} = 0$$

and multiplying by e^x

$$2e^{2x} - 3e^x - 2 = 0$$

$$\left(e^x - 2\right)\left(2e^x + 1\right) = 0$$

$$e^x = 2 \ \text{ or } \ e^x = -\frac{1}{2}$$

But e^x is always positive so $e^x = 2 \ \Rightarrow \ x = \ln 2$.

Activity 6

Find the values of x for which

$$\cosh x = \frac{13}{5}$$

expressing your answers as natural logarithms.

Example

Solve the equation

$$2\cosh 2x + 10\sinh 2x = 5$$

giving your answer in terms of a natural logarithm.

Solution

$$\cosh 2x = \frac{1}{2}\left(e^{2x} + e^{-2x}\right); \quad \sinh 2x = \frac{1}{2}\left(e^{2x} - e^{-2x}\right)$$

So $\qquad e^{2x} + e^{-2x} + 5e^{2x} - 5e^{-2x} = 5$

$$6e^{2x} - 5 - 4e^{-2x} = 0$$

$$6e^{4x} - 5e^{2x} - 4 = 0$$

$$\left(3e^{2x} - 4\right)\left(2e^{2x} + 1\right) = 0$$

$$e^{2x} = \frac{4}{3} \text{ or } e^{2x} = -\frac{1}{2}$$

The only real solution occurs when $e^{2x} > 0$

So $\qquad 2x = \ln\frac{4}{3} \;\Rightarrow\; x = \frac{1}{2}\ln\frac{4}{3}$

Exercise 2B

1. Given that $\sinh x = \frac{5}{12}$, find the values of

   (a) $\cosh x$ (b) $\tanh x$ (c) $\text{sech}\,x$

   (d) $\coth x$ (e) $\sinh 2x$ (f) $\cosh 2x$

   Determine the value of x as a natural logarithm.

2. Given that $\cosh x = \frac{5}{4}$, determine the values of

   (a) $\sinh x$ (b) $\cosh 2x$ (c) $\sinh 2x$

   Use the formula for $\cosh(2x+x)$ to determine the value of $\cosh 3x$.

3. In the case when $\tanh x = \dfrac{1}{2}$, show that $x = \dfrac{1}{2}\ln 3$.

4. Solve the following equations giving your answers in terms of natural logarithms.

   (a) $4\cosh x + \sinh x = 4$

   (b) $3\sinh x - \cosh x = 1$

   (c) $4\tanh x = 1 + \operatorname{sech} x$

5. Find the possible values of $\sinh x$ for which

   $$12\cosh^2 x + 7\sinh x = 24$$

   (You may find the identity $\cosh^2 x - \sinh^2 x = 1$ useful.)

   Hence find the possible values of x, leaving your answers as natural logarithms.

6. Solve the equations

   (a) $3\cosh 2x + 5\cosh x = 22$

   (b) $4\cosh 2x - 2\sinh x = 7$

7. Express $25\cosh x - 24\sinh x$ in the form $R\cosh(x - \alpha)$ giving the values of R and $\tanh \alpha$.

   Hence write down the minimum value of $25\cosh x - 24\sinh x$ and find the value of x at which this occurs, giving your answer in terms of a natural logarithm.

8. Determine a condition on A and B for which the equation

   $$A\cosh x + B\sinh x = 1$$

   has at least one real solution.

9. Given that a, b, c are all positive, show that when $a > b$ then $a\cosh x + b\sinh x$ can be written in the form $R\cosh(x + \alpha)$.

   Hence determine a further condition for which the equation

   $$a\cosh x + b\sinh x = c$$

   has real solutions.

10. Use an appropriate iterative method to find the solution of the equation

    $$\cosh x = 3x$$

    giving your answer correct to three significant figures.

2.6   Calculus of hyperbolic functions

Activity 7

(a)   By writing $\cosh x = \dfrac{1}{2}\left(e^x + e^{-x}\right)$, prove that

$$\frac{d}{dx}(\cosh x) = \sinh x.$$

(b)   Use a similar method to find $\dfrac{d}{dx}(\sinh x)$.

(c)   Assuming the derivatives of $\sinh x$ and $\cosh x$, use the quotient rule to prove that if $y = \tanh x = \dfrac{\sinh x}{\cosh x}$

then $\dfrac{dy}{dx} = \operatorname{sech}^2 x.$

Note: care must be taken that Osborn's rule is **not** used to obtain corresponding results from trigonometry in calculus.

Activity 8

Use the quotient rule, or otherwise, to prove that

(a) $\dfrac{d}{dx}(\operatorname{sech} x) = -\operatorname{sech} x \,\tanh x$

(b) $\dfrac{d}{dx}(\operatorname{cosech} x) = -\operatorname{cosech} x \,\coth x$

(c) $\dfrac{d}{dx}(\coth x) = -\operatorname{cosech}^2 x$

Example

Integrate each of the following with respect to x.

(a) $\cosh 3x$ (b) $\sinh^2 x$

(c) $x \sinh x$ (d) $e^x \cosh x$

Solution

(a) $\displaystyle \int \cosh 3x \, dx = \frac{1}{3} \sinh 3x + \text{constant}$

(b) $\sinh^2 x \, dx$ can be found by using $\cosh 2x = 1 + 2\sinh^2 x$
giving

$$\frac{1}{2} \int (\cosh 2x - 1) \, dx$$

$$= \frac{1}{4} \sinh 2x - \frac{1}{2} x + \text{constant}$$

Alternatively, you could change to exponentials, giving

$$\sinh^2 x = \frac{1}{4} \left(e^{2x} - 2 + e^{-2x} \right)$$

$$\int \sinh^2 x \, dx = \frac{1}{8} e^{2x} - \frac{1}{2} x - \frac{1}{8} e^{-2x} + \text{constant}$$

Can you show this answer is identical to the one found earlier?

(c) Using integration by parts,

$$\int x \sinh x \, dx = x \cosh x - \int \cosh x \, dx$$

$$= x \cosh x - \sinh x + \text{constant}$$

(d) Certainly this is found most easily by converting to exponentials, giving

$$e^x \cosh x = \frac{1}{2}e^{2x} + \frac{1}{2}$$

$$\int e^x \cosh x \, dx = \frac{1}{4}e^{2x} + \frac{1}{2}x + \text{constant}$$

Exercise 2C

1. Differentiate with respect to x

    (a) $\tanh 4x$ (b) $\operatorname{sech} 2x$

    (c) $\operatorname{cosech}(5x+3)$ (d) $\sinh(e^x)$

    (e) $\cosh^3 2x$ (f) $\tanh(\sin x)$

    (g) $\cosh 5x \sinh 3x$ (h) $\sqrt{(\coth 4x)}$

2. Integrate each of the following with respect to x.

    (a) $\sinh 4x$ (b) $\cosh^2 3x$

    (c) $x^2 \cosh 2x$ (d) $\operatorname{sech}^2 7x$

    (e) $\operatorname{cosech} 2x \coth 3x$ (f) $\tanh x$

    (g) $\tanh^2 x$ (h) $e^2 \sinh 3x$

    (i) $x^2 \cosh(x^3 + 4)$ (j) $\sinh^4 x$

    (k) $\cosh 2x \sinh 3x$ (l) $\operatorname{sech} x$

3. Find the equation of the tangent to the curve with equation

$$y = 3\cosh 2x - \sinh x$$

    at the point where $x = \ln 2$.

4. A curve has equation

$$y = \lambda \cosh x + \sinh x$$

    where λ is a constant.

    (a) Sketch the curve for the cases $\lambda = 0$ and $\lambda = 1$.

    (b) Determine the coordinates of the turning point of the curve in the case when $\lambda = \frac{4}{3}$. Is this a maximum or minimum point?

    (c) Determine the range of values of λ for which the curve has no real turning points.

5. Find the area of the region bounded by the coordinate axes, the line $x = \ln 3$ and the curve with equation $y = \cosh 2x + \operatorname{sech}^2 x$.

2.7   Inverse hyperbolic functions

The function $f : x \mapsto \sinh x \ (x \in \mathbb{R})$ is one-one, as can be seen from the graph in Section 2.4. This means that the inverse function f^{-1} exists. The **inverse hyperbolic sine function** is denoted by $\sinh^{-1} x$. Its graph is obtained by reflecting the graph of $\sinh x$ in the line $y = x$.

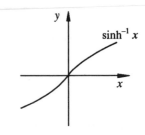

Recall that $\dfrac{d}{dx}(\sinh x) = \cosh x$, so the gradient of the graph of

$y = \sinh x$ is equal to 1 at the origin. Similarly, the graph of $\sinh^{-1} x$ has gradient 1 at the origin.

Similarly, the function $g:x \mapsto \tanh x \ (x \in \mathbb{R})$ is one-one.

You should have obtained its graph in Activity 5. The range of g is $\{y:-1 < y < 1\}$ or the open interval $(-1, 1)$.

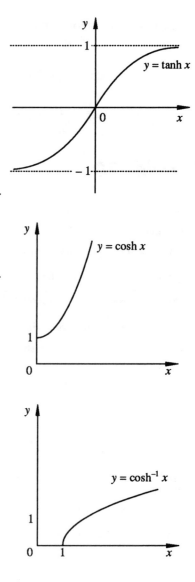

Activity 9

Sketch the graph of the inverse tanh function, $\tanh^{-1} x$.

Its range is now $\mathbb{R}$. What is its domain?

The function $h:x \mapsto \cosh x \ (x \in \mathbb{R})$ is **not** a one-one function and so we cannot define an inverse function. However, if we change the domain to give the function

$$f:x \mapsto \cosh x \text{ with domain } \{x:x \in \mathbb{R}, x \ge 0\}$$

then we do have a one-one function, as illustrated.

So, provided we consider $\cosh x$ for $x \ge 0$, we can define the inverse function $f^{-1}:x \mapsto \cosh^{-1} x$ with domain $\{x:x \in \mathbb{R}, \ x \ge 1\}$.

This is called the **principal value** of $\cosh^{-1} x$.

2.8 Logarithmic equivalents

Activity 10

Let $y = \sinh^{-1} x$ so $\sinh y = x$.

Since $\cosh y$ is always positive, show that $\cosh y = \sqrt{\left(1 + x^2\right)}$

By considering $\sinh y + \cosh y$, find an expression for e^y in terms of x.

Hence show that $\sinh^{-1} x = \ln\left[x + \sqrt{\left(1 + x^2\right)}\right]$

Activity 11

Let $y = \tanh^{-1} x$ so $\tanh y = x$.

Express $\tanh y$ in the terms of e^y and hence show that $e^{2y} = \dfrac{1+x}{1-x}$.

Deduce that $\tanh^{-1} x = \dfrac{1}{2}\ln\left(\dfrac{1+x}{1-x}\right)$.

(Do not forget that $\tanh^{-1} x$ is only defined for $|x| < 1$.)

Activity 12

Let $y = \cosh^{-1} x$, where $x \geq 1$, so $\cosh y = x$.

Use the graph in Section 2.7 to explain why y is positive and hence why $\sinh y$ is positive. Show that $\sinh y = \sqrt{(x^2 - 1)}$.

Hence show that

$$\cosh^{-1} x = \ln\left[x + \sqrt{(x^2 - 1)}\right].$$

The full results are summarised below.

$$\sinh^{-1} x = \ln\left\{x + \sqrt{(x^2+1)}\right\} \quad \text{(all values of } x\text{)}$$

$$\tanh^{-1} x = \frac{1}{2}\ln\left(\frac{1+x}{1-x}\right) \quad (|x| < 1)$$

$$\cosh^{-1} x = \ln\left\{x + \sqrt{(x^2-1)}\right\} \quad (x \geq 1)$$

Exercise 2D

1. Express each of the following in logarithmic form.

   (a) $\sinh^{-1}\left(\dfrac{3}{4}\right)$　　(b) $\cosh^{-1}2$　　(c) $\tanh^{-1}\left(\dfrac{1}{2}\right)$

2. Given that $y = \sinh^{-1}x$, find a quadratic equation satisfied by e^y. Hence obtain the logarithmic form of $\sinh^{-1}x$. Explain why you discard one of the solutions.

3. Express $\text{sech}^{-1}x$ in logarithmic form for $0 < x < 1$.

4. Find the value of x for which
   $$\sinh^{-1}x + \cosh^{-1}(x+2) = 0.$$

5. Solve the equation $2\tanh^{-1}\left(\dfrac{x-2}{x+1}\right) = \ln 2.$

2.9　Derivatives of inverse hyperbolic functions

Let $y = \sinh^{-1}x$ so that $x = \sinh y$.

$$\frac{dx}{dy} = \cosh y \quad \text{but} \quad \cosh^2 y = \sinh^2 y + 1 = x^2 + 1$$

and $\cosh y$ is always positive.

So　$\dfrac{dx}{dy} = \sqrt{(x^2+1)}$ and therefore $\dfrac{dy}{dx} = \dfrac{1}{\sqrt{(x^2+1)}}$

In other words,　$\dfrac{d}{dx}\left(\sinh^{-1}x\right) = \dfrac{1}{\sqrt{(x^2+1)}}$

Activity 13

(a) Show that $\dfrac{d}{dx}\left(\cosh^{-1}x\right) = \dfrac{1}{\sqrt{(x^2-1)}}$

(b) Show that $\dfrac{d}{dx}\left(\tanh^{-1}x\right) = \dfrac{1}{1-x^2}$

An alternative way of showing that $\dfrac{d}{dx}\left(\sinh^{-1}x\right) = \dfrac{1}{\sqrt{(x^2+1)}}$ is to use the logarithmic equivalents.

Since

$$\frac{d}{dx}\left[x+\sqrt{(x^2+1)}\right]=1+\frac{1}{2}.2x(x^2+1)^{-\frac{1}{2}}$$

$$=1+\frac{x}{\sqrt{(x^2+1)}}\ =\ \frac{\sqrt{(x^2+1)}+x}{\sqrt{(x^2+1)}}$$

we can now find the derivative of $\ln\left[x+\sqrt{(x^2+1)}\right]$

$$\frac{d}{dx}\left[\ln\left\{x+\sqrt{(x^2+1)}\right\}\right]=\frac{\sqrt{(x^2+1)}+x}{\sqrt{(x^2+1)}}.\frac{1}{x+\sqrt{(x^2+1)}}$$

which cancels down to

$$\frac{1}{\sqrt{(x^2+1)}}$$

So
$$\boxed{\frac{d}{dx}\left(\sinh^{-1}x\right)=\frac{1}{\sqrt{(x^2+1)}}}$$

You can use a similar approach to find the derivatives of $\cosh^{-1}x$ and $\tanh^{-1}x$ but the algebra is a little messy.

Example
Differentiate

(a) $\cosh^{-1}(2x+1)$ (b) $\sinh^{-1}\left(\frac{1}{x}\right)$ with respect to x $(x>0)$.

Solution
(a) Use the function of a function or chain rule.

$$\frac{d}{dx}\left[\cosh^{-1}(2x+1)\right]=2.\frac{1}{\sqrt{\{(2x+1)^2-1\}}}=\frac{2}{\sqrt{(4x^2+4x)}}=\frac{1}{\sqrt{(x^2+x)}}$$

(b) $\dfrac{d}{dx}\left[\sinh^{-1}\left(\dfrac{1}{x}\right)\right]=\dfrac{-1}{x^2}.\dfrac{1}{\sqrt{\left\{\frac{1}{x^2}+1\right\}}}=-\dfrac{1}{x^2}.\dfrac{x}{\sqrt{(1+x^2)}}$

$$=\frac{-1}{x\sqrt{(1+x^2)}}$$

Exercise 2E

Differentiate each of the expressions in Questions 1 to 6 with respect to x.

1. $\cosh^{-1}(4+3x)$

2. $\sinh^{-1}(\sqrt{x})$

3. $\tanh^{-1}(3x+1)$

4. $x^2\sinh^{-1}(2x)$

5. $\cosh^{-1}\left(\dfrac{1}{x}\right)$ $(x>0)$

6. $\sinh^{-1}(\cosh 2x)$

7. Differentiate $\operatorname{sech}^{-1}x$ with respect to x, by first writing $x = \operatorname{sech}y$.

8. Find an expression for the derivative of $\operatorname{cosech}^{-1}x$ in terms of x.

9. Prove that
$$\frac{d}{dx}\left(\coth^{-1}x\right) = \frac{-1}{\left(x^2-1\right)}.$$

2.10 Use of hyperbolic functions in integration

Activity 14

Use the results from Section 2.9 to write down the values of

(a) $\displaystyle\int \frac{1}{\sqrt{\left(x^2+1\right)}}\,dx$ and   (b) $\displaystyle\int \frac{1}{\sqrt{\left(x^2-1\right)}}\,dx$

Activity 15

Differentiate $\sinh^{-1}\left(\dfrac{x}{3}\right)$ with respect to x.

Hence find $\displaystyle\int \frac{1}{\sqrt{\left(x^2+9\right)}}\,dx.$

What do you think $\displaystyle\int \frac{1}{\sqrt{\left(x^2+49\right)}}\,dx$ is equal to?

Activity 16

Use the substitution $x = 2\cosh u$ to show that

$$\int \frac{1}{\sqrt{\left(x^2-4\right)}}\,dx = \cosh^{-1}\left(\frac{x}{2}\right) + \text{constant}$$

Activity 17

Prove, by using suitable substitutions that, where a is a constant,

(a) $\displaystyle\int \frac{1}{\sqrt{(x^2+a^2)}}\,dx = \sinh^{-1}\left(\frac{x}{a}\right) + \text{constant}$

(b) $\displaystyle\int \frac{1}{\sqrt{(x^2-a^2)}}\,dx = \cosh^{-1}\left(\frac{x}{a}\right) + \text{constant}$

Integrals of this type are found by means of a substitution involving hyperbolic functions. They may be a little more complicated than the ones above and it is sometimes necessary to complete the square.

Activity 18

Express $4x^2 - 8x - 5$ in the form $A(x-B)^2 + C$, where A, B and C are constants.

Example

Evaluate in terms of natural logarithms

$$\int_4^7 \frac{1}{\sqrt{(4x^2-8x-5)}}\,dx$$

Solution

From Activity 18, the integral can be written as

$$\int_4^7 \frac{1}{\sqrt{\{4(x-1)^2-9\}}}\,dx$$

You need to make use of the identity $\cosh^2 A - 1 = \sinh^2 A$ because of the appearance of the denominator.

Substitute $\quad 4(x-1)^2 = 9\cosh^2 u\quad$ in order to accomplish this.

So $\qquad 2(x-1) = 3\cosh u$

and $\qquad 2\dfrac{dx}{du} = 3\sinh x$

The denominator then becomes

$$\sqrt{\{9\cosh^2 u - 9\}} = \sqrt{(9\sinh^2 u)} = 3\sinh u$$

In order to deal with the limits, note that when

$x = 4, \quad \cosh u = 2 \quad \left(\text{so } u = \ln\left[2 + \sqrt{3}\right]\right)$ and when

$x = 7, \quad \cosh u = 4 \quad \left(\text{so } u = \ln\left[4 + \sqrt{15}\right]\right)$

The integral then becomes

$$\int_{\cosh^{-1} 2}^{\cosh^{-1} 4} \frac{\frac{3}{2}\sinh u \, du}{3\sinh u} = \int_{\cosh^{-1} 2}^{\cosh^{-1} 4} \frac{1}{2} du$$

$$= \frac{1}{2}\left[\cosh^{-1} 4 - \cosh^{-1} 2\right] = \frac{1}{2}\left\{\ln\left(2 + \sqrt{3}\right) - \ln\left(4 + \sqrt{15}\right)\right\}$$

Example

Evaluate

$$\int_{-3}^{1} \sqrt{\left(x^2 + 6x + 13\right)} \, dx$$

leaving your answer in terms of natural logarithms.

Solution

Completing the square, $x^2 + 6x + 13 = (x + 3)^2 + 4$

You will need the identity $\sinh^2 A + 1 = \cosh^2 A$ this time because of the + sign after completing the square.

Now make the substitution $x + 3 = 2\sinh\theta$

giving $\qquad \dfrac{dx}{d\theta} = 2\cosh\theta$

When $x = -3, \quad \sinh\theta = 0 \quad \Rightarrow \quad \theta = 0$

When $x = 1, \quad \sinh\theta = 2 \quad \Rightarrow \quad \theta = \sinh^{-1} 2 = \ln\left(2 + \sqrt{5}\right)$

The integral transforms to

$$\int_{0}^{\sinh^{-1} 2} \sqrt{\left(4\sinh^2\theta + 4\right)} \cdot 2\cosh\theta \, d\theta$$

$$= \int_{0}^{\sinh^{-1} 2} 4\cosh^2\theta \, d\theta$$

You can either convert this into exponentials or you can use the identity

$$\cosh 2A = 2\cosh^2 A - 1$$

giving

$$\int_0^{\sinh^{-1}2} (2 + 2\cosh 2\theta)d\theta$$

$$= [2\theta + \sinh 2\theta]_0^{\sinh^{-1}2}$$

$$= 2[\theta + \sinh\theta\cosh\theta]_0^{\sinh^{-1}2}$$

$$= 2\left(\sinh^{-1}2 + 2\sqrt{1 + 2^2}\right)$$

$$= 2\ln\left(2 + \sqrt{5}\right) + 4\sqrt{5}$$

Activity 19

Show that

$$\frac{d}{d\phi}(\sec\phi\tan\phi) = 2\sec^3\phi - \sec\phi$$

and deduce that

$$\int \sec^3\phi\, d\phi = \frac{1}{2}\{\sec\phi\tan\phi + \ln(\sec\phi + \tan\phi)\}$$

Hence use the substitution

$$x + 3 = 2\tan\phi$$

in the integral of the previous example and verify that you obtain the same answer.

Exercise 2F

Evaluate the integrals in Questions 1 to 12.

1. $\displaystyle\int_0^2 \frac{1}{\sqrt{(x^2+1)}}\,dx$

2. $\displaystyle\int_3^4 \frac{1}{\sqrt{(x^2-4)}}\,dx$

3. $\displaystyle\int_0^4 \frac{1}{\sqrt{(x^2+2x+5)}}\,dx$

4. $\displaystyle\int_{-1}^4 \frac{1}{\sqrt{(x^2+6x+8)}}\,dx$

5. $\displaystyle\int_0^2 \sqrt{(4+x^2)}\,dx$

6. $\displaystyle\int_3^4 \sqrt{(x^2-9)}\,dx$

7. $\displaystyle\int_1^2 \sqrt{(x^2+2x+2)}\,dx$

8. $\displaystyle\int_1^2 \frac{1}{\sqrt{(x^2+2x)}}\,dx$

9. $\displaystyle\int_4^5 \frac{x+1}{\sqrt{(x^2-9)}}\,dx$

10. $\displaystyle\int_1^2 \frac{1}{\sqrt{(x^2+x)}}\,dx$

11. $\displaystyle\int_{-1}^0 \frac{1}{\sqrt{(2x^2+4x+7)}}\,dx$

12. $\displaystyle\int_4^5 \sqrt{(3x^2-12x+8)}\,dx$

13. Use the substitution $u = e^x$ to evaluate
$\int_0^1 \operatorname{sech} x\,dx$.

14. (a) Differentiate $\sinh^{-1} x$ with respect to x.
By writing $\sinh^{-1} x$ as $1 \times \sinh^{-1} x$, use
integration by parts to find $\int_1^2 \sinh^{-1} dx$.

(b) Use integration by parts to evaluate
$\int_1^2 \cosh^{-1} x\,dx$.

15. Evaluate each of the following integrals.

(a) $\displaystyle\int_2^3 \frac{1}{\sqrt{(x^2+6x-7)}}\,dx$

(b) $\displaystyle\int_2^3 \sqrt{(x^2+6x-7)}\,dx$

16. Transform the integral
$$\int_1^2 \frac{1}{x\sqrt{4+x^2}}\,dx$$
by means of the substitution $x = \dfrac{1}{u}$. Hence, by
means of a further substitution, or otherwise,
evaluate the integral.

17. The point P has coordinates $(a\cosh t,\ b\sinh t)$.
Show that P lies on the hyperbola with equation
$$\frac{x^2}{a^2} - \frac{y^2}{b^2} = 1.$$
Which branch does it lie on when $a > 0$?

Given that O is the origin, and A is the point
$(a, 0)$, prove that the region bounded by the lines
OA and OP and the arc AP of the hyperbola has
area $\dfrac{1}{2}abt$.

2.11 Miscellaneous Exercises

1. The sketch below shows the curve with equation
$y = 3\cosh x - x\sinh x$, which cuts the y-axis at the
point A. Prove that, at A, y takes a minimum
value and state this value.

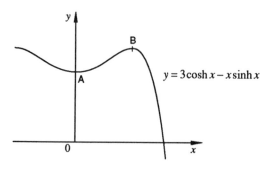

$y = 3\cosh x - x\sinh x$

Given that $\dfrac{dy}{dx} = 0$ at B, show that the
x-coordinate of B is the positive root of the
equation
$$x\cosh x - 2\sinh x = 0.$$
Show that this root lies between 1.8 and 2.
Find, by integration, the area of the finite region
bounded by the coordinate axes, the curve with
equation $y = 3\cosh x - x\sinh x$ and the line $x = 2$,
giving your answer in terms of e.   (AEB)

2. Starting from the definition
$$\cosh\theta = \frac{1}{2}\left(e^{\theta}+e^{-\theta}\right) \text{ and } \sinh\theta = \frac{1}{2}\left(e^{\theta}-e^{-\theta}\right)$$

show that
$$\sinh(A+B) = \sinh A \cosh B + \cosh A \sinh B.$$

There exist real numbers r and α such that
$$5\cosh x + 13\sinh x \equiv r\sinh(x+\alpha).$$

Find r and show that $\alpha = \ln\frac{3}{2}$.

Hence, or otherwise,

(a) solve the equation $5\cosh x + 13\sinh x = 12\sinh 2$

(b) show that
$$\int_{1}^{1}\frac{dx}{5\cosh x+13\sinh x} = \frac{1}{12}\ln\left(\frac{15e-10}{3e+2}\right)$$

(AEB)

3. Given that $|x|<1$, prove that $\frac{d}{dx}\left(\tanh^{-1}x\right) = \frac{1}{1-x^2}$.

Show by integrating the result above that
$$\tanh^{-1}x = \frac{1}{2}\ln\left(\frac{1+x}{1-x}\right)$$

Use integration by parts to find $\int\tanh^{-1}x\,dx$.

4. Given that $t \equiv \tanh\frac{1}{2}x$, prove the identities

(a) $\sinh x = \frac{2t}{1-t^2}$ (b) $\cosh x = \frac{1+t^2}{1-t^2}$

Hence, or otherwise, solve the equation
$$2\sinh x - \cosh x = 2\tanh\frac{1}{2}x$$

5. Solve the equations

(a) $\cosh(\ln x) - \sinh\left(\ln\frac{1}{2}x\right) = 1\frac{3}{4}$

(b) $4\sinh x + 3e^x + 3 = 0$

6. Show that $\cosh x + \sinh x = e^x$

Deduce that $\cosh nx + \sinh nx = \sum_{k=0}^{n}\binom{n}{k}\cosh^{n-k}x\sinh^k x$

Obtain a similar expression for
$$\cosh nx - \sinh nx.$$

Hence prove that
$$\cosh 7x = 64\cosh^7 x - 112\cosh^5 x + 56\cosh^3 x - 7\cosh x$$

7. Define $\operatorname{cosech} x$ and $\coth x$ in terms of exponential functions and from your definitions prove that
$$\coth^2 x \equiv 1 + \operatorname{cosech}^2 x.$$

Solve the equation
$$3\coth^2 x + 4\operatorname{cosech} x = 23$$

8. Solve the equation
$$3\operatorname{sech}^2 x + 4\tanh x + 1 = 0$$
(AEB)

9. Find the area of the region R bounded by the curve with equation $y = \cosh x$, the line $x = \ln 2$ and the coordinate axes. Find also the volume obtained when R is rotated completely about the x-axis. (AEB)

10. Prove that
$$\sinh^{-1}x = \ln\left[x+\sqrt{\left(1+x^2\right)}\right]$$

and write down a similar expression for $\cosh^{-1}x$.

Given that
$$2\cosh y - 7\sinh x = 3 \text{ and } \cosh y - 3\sinh^2 x = 2,$$

find the real values of x and y in logarithmic form. (AEB)

11. Evaluate the following integrals

(a) $\int_{1}^{3}\frac{1}{\sqrt{\left(x^2+6x+5\right)}}dx$

(b) $\int_{1}^{3}\sqrt{\left(x^2+6x+5\right)}dx$

12. Use the definitions in terms of exponential functions to prove that

(a) $\frac{1-\tanh^2 x}{1+\tanh^2 x} = \operatorname{sech} 2x$

(b) $\frac{d}{dx}(\tanh x) = 1 - \tanh^2 x$

Hence, use the substitution $t = \tanh x$ to find
$$\int\operatorname{sech} 2x\,dx$$
(AEB)

13. Sketch the graph of the curve with equation $y = \tanh x$ and state the equations of its asymptotes.

Use your sketch to show that the equation $\tanh x = 10 - 3x$ has just one root α. Show that α lies between 3 and $3\frac{1}{3}$.

Taking 3 as a first approximation for α, use the Newton-Raphson method once to obtain a second approximation, giving your answer to four decimal places.

14. Prove that $\sinh^{-1} x = \ln\left[x + \sqrt{(1+x^2)}\right]$.

 (a) Given that $\exp(z) \equiv e^z$, show that $y = \exp\left(\sinh^{-1} x\right)$ satisfies the differential equation

$$\left(1+x^2\right)\frac{d^2 y}{dx^2} + x\frac{dy}{dx} - y = 0$$

 (b) Find the value of $\int_0^1 \sinh^{-1} x \, dx$, leaving your answer in terms of a natural logarithm.

15. Sketch the graph of $y = \tanh^{-1} x$.

 Determine the value of x, in terms of e, for which $\tanh^{-1} x = \dfrac{1}{2}$.

 The point P is on the curve $y = \tanh^{-1} x$ where $y = \dfrac{1}{2}$. Find the equation of the tangent to the curve at P. Determine where the tangent to the curve crosses the y-axis.

16. Evaluate the following integrals, giving your answers as multiples of π or in logarithmic form.

 (a) $\displaystyle\int_0^2 \frac{dx}{\sqrt{\left(3x^2 - 6x + 4\right)}}$ (b) $\displaystyle\int_0^2 \frac{dx}{\sqrt{\left(1 + 6x - 3x^2\right)}}$

17. Find the value of x for which

$$\sinh^{-1}\frac{3}{4} + \sinh^{-1} x = \sinh^{-1}\frac{4}{3}$$

18. Starting from the definitions of hyperbolic functions in terms of exponential functions, show that

$$\cosh(x - y) = \cosh x \cosh y - \sinh x \sinh y$$

 and that

$$\tanh^{-1} = \frac{1}{2}\ln\left(\frac{1+x}{1-x}\right) \text{ where } -1 < x < 1.$$

 (a) Find the values of R and α such that

$$5\cosh x - 4\sinh x \equiv R\cosh(x - \alpha)$$

 Hence write down the coordinates of the minimum point on the curve with equation

$$y = 5\cosh x - 4\sinh x$$

 (b) Solve the equation

$$9\,\text{sech}^2 y - 3\tanh y = 7,$$

 leaving your answer in terms of natural logarithms. (AEB)

19. Solve the equation $3\,\text{sech}^2 x + 4\tanh x + 1 = 0$. (AEB)

20. Define $\sinh y$ and $\cosh y$ in terms of exponential functions and show that

$$2y = \ln\left\{\frac{\cosh y + \sinh y}{\cosh y - \sinh y}\right\}$$

 By putting $\tanh y = \dfrac{1}{3}$, deduce that

$$\tanh^{-1}\left(\frac{1}{3}\right) = \frac{1}{2}\ln 2 \qquad \text{(AEB)}$$

21. Show that the function $f(x) = (1+x)\sinh(3x - 2)$ has a stationary value which occurs at the intersection of the curve $y = \tanh(3x - 2)$ and the straight line $y + 3x + 3 = 0$. Show that the stationary value occurs between -1 and 0. Use Newton-Raphson's method once, using an initial value of -1 to obtain an improved estimate of the x-value of the stationary point.

22. (a) Given that $\tanh x = \dfrac{\sinh x}{\cosh x}$, express the value of $\tanh x$ in terms of e^x and e^{-x}.

 (b) Given that $\tanh y = t$, show that $y = \dfrac{1}{2}\ln\left(\dfrac{1+t}{1-t}\right)$ for $-1 < t < 1$.

 (c) Given that $y = \tanh^{-1}(\sin x)$ show that

$$\frac{dy}{dx} = \sec x \text{ and hence show that}$$

$$\int_0^{\frac{\pi}{6}} \sec^2 x \tanh^{-1}(\sin x)\,dx = \frac{1}{\sqrt{3}}\left[\sqrt{3} - 2 + \frac{1}{2}\ln 3\right]$$

 (AEB)

23. Solve the simultaneous equations

$$\cosh x - 3\sinh y = 0$$
$$2\sinh x + 6\cosh y = 5$$

 giving your answers in logarithmic form. (AEB)

24. Given that $x = \cosh y$, show that the value of x is either

$$\ln\left[x + \sqrt{\left(x^2 - 1\right)}\right] \text{ or } \ln\left[x - \sqrt{\left(x^2 - 1\right)}\right]$$

 Solve the equations

 (a) $\sinh^2 \theta - 5\cosh \theta + 7 = 0$

 (b) $\cosh(z + \ln 3) = 2$

25. Sketch the curve with equation $y = \operatorname{sech} x$ and determine the coordinates of its point of inflection. The region bounded by the curve, the coordinate axes and the line $x = \ln 3$ is R.

    Calculate

    (a) the area of R

    (b) the volume generated when R is rotated through 2π radians about the x-axis.

26. Solve the equation $\tanh x + 4\operatorname{sech} x = 4$.

27. Prove the identity

    $$\cosh^2 x \cos^2 x - \sinh^2 x \sin^2 x \equiv \frac{1}{2}(1 + \cosh 2x \cos 2x)$$

28. Prove that

    $$16\sinh^2 x \cosh^3 x \equiv \cosh 5x + \cosh 3x - 2\cosh x$$

    Hence, or otherwise, evaluate

    $$\int_0^1 16\sinh^2 x \cosh^3 x \, dx,$$

    giving your answer in terms of e.

29. Show that the minimum value of $\sinh x + n\cosh x$ is $\sqrt{(n^2 - 1)}$ and that this occurs when

    $$x = \frac{1}{2}\ln\left(\frac{n-1}{n+1}\right)$$

    Show also, by obtaining a quadratic equation in e^x, that if $k > \sqrt{(n^2 - 1)}$ then the equation $\sinh x + n\cosh x = k$ has two real roots, giving your answers in terms of natural logarithms.

    (AEB)

3 COMPLEX NUMBERS

Objectives

After studying this chapter you should

- understand how quadratic equations lead to complex numbers and how to plot complex numbers on an Argand diagram;
- be able to relate graphs of polynomials to complex numbers;
- be able to do basic arithmetic operations on complex numbers of the form $a+ib$;
- understand the polar form $[r, \theta]$ of a complex number and its algebra;
- understand Euler's relation and the exponential form of a complex number $re^{i\theta}$;
- be able to use de Moivre's theorem;
- be able to interpret relationships of complex numbers as loci in the complex plane.

3.0   Introduction

The history of complex numbers goes back to the ancient Greeks who decided (but were perplexed) that no number existed that satisfies

$$x^2 = -1$$

For example, *Diophantus* (about 275 AD) attempted to solve what seems a reasonable problem, namely

'Find the sides of a right-angled triangle of perimeter 12 units and area 7 squared units.'

Letting $AB = x$, $AC = h$ as shown,

then   area $= \frac{1}{2} x h$

and   perimeter $= x + h + \sqrt{x^2 + h^2}$

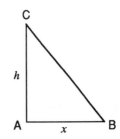

Activity 1

Show that the two equations above reduce to

$$6x^2 - 43x + 84 = 0$$

when perimeter $= 12$ and area $= 7$. Does this have real solutions?

A similar problem was posed by *Cardan* in 1545. He tried to solve the problem of finding two numbers, a and b, whose sum is 10 and whose product is 40;

i.e. $a + b = 10$ (1)

                $ab = 40$ (2)

Eliminating b gives

$$a(10 - a) = 40$$

or $a^2 - 10a + 40 = 0$.

Solving this quadratic gives

$$a = \frac{1}{2}(10 \pm \sqrt{-60}) = 5 \pm \sqrt{-15}$$

This shows that there are no **real** solutions, but if it is agreed to continue using the numbers

$$a = 5 + \sqrt{-15}, \; b = 5 - \sqrt{-15}$$

then equations (1) and (2) are satisfied.

Show that equations (1) and (2) are satisfied by these values of x and y.

So these are solutions of the original problem but they are not **real** numbers. Surprisingly, it was not until the nineteenth century that such solutions were fully understood.

The square root of -1 is denoted by i, so that

$$i = \sqrt{-1}$$

and $a = 5 + \sqrt{15}\,i, \;\; b = 5 - \sqrt{15}\,i$

are examples of **complex numbers**.

Activity 2   The need for complex numbers

Solve if possible, the following quadratic equations by factorising or by using the quadratic formula. If a solution is not possible explain why.

(a) $x^2 - 1 = 0$ (b) $x^2 - x - 6 = 0$

(c) $x^2 - 2x - 2 = 0$ (d) $x^2 - 2x + 2 = 0$

You should have found (a), (b) and (c) straightforward to solve but in (d) a term appears in the solution which includes the square root of a **negative** number and to obtain solutions you need to use the symbol $i = \sqrt{-1}$, or

$$\boxed{i^2 = -1}$$

It is then possible to obtain a solution to (d) in Activity 2.

Example

Solve $x^2 - 2x + 2 = 0$.

Solution

Using the quadratic formula

$$x = \frac{-b \pm \sqrt{b^2 - 4ac}}{2a}$$

$$\Rightarrow \quad x = \frac{-(-2) \pm \sqrt{(-2)^2 - 4(1)(2)}}{2(1)}$$

$$\Rightarrow \quad x = \frac{2 \pm \sqrt{-4}}{2}$$

But $\sqrt{-4} = \sqrt{4(-1)} = \sqrt{4}\sqrt{-1} = 2\sqrt{-1} = 2i$

(using the definition of i).

Therefore $x = \dfrac{2 \pm 2i}{2}$

$$\Rightarrow \quad x = 1 \pm i$$

Therefore the two solutions are

$$x = 1 + i \quad \text{and} \quad x = 1 - i$$

Activity 3

Solve the following equations, leaving your answers in terms of i:

(a) $x^2 + x + 1 = 0$ (b) $3x^2 - 4x + 2 = 0$

(c) $x^2 + 1 = 0$ (d) $2x - 7 = 4x^2$

The set of solutions to a quadratic equation such as

$$ax^2 + bx + c = 0$$

can be related to the intercepts on the x-axis when the graph of the function

$$f(x) = ax^2 + bx + c$$

is drawn.

Activity 4   Quadratic graphs

Using a graphics calculator, a graph drawing program on a computer, a spreadsheet or otherwise, draw the graphs of the following functions and find a connection between the existence or not of real solutions to the related quadratic equations.

(a) $f(x) = x^2 - 1$ (b) $f(x) = x^2 - x - 6$

(c) $f(x) = x^2 - 2x - 2$ (d) $f(x) = x^2 + x + 1$

(e) $f(x) = 3x^2 - 4x + 2$ (f) $f(x) = x^2 + 1$

You should have noted that if the graph of the function either intercepts the x-axis in two places or touches it in one place then the solutions of the related quadratic equation are real, but if the graph does not intercept the x-axis then the solutions are complex.

If the quadratic equation is expressed as $ax^2 + bx + c = 0$, then the expression that determines the type of solution is $b^2 - 4ac$, called the **discriminant**.

In a quadratic equation $ax^2 + bx + c = 0$, if:

$b^2 - 4ac > 0$ then solutions are real and different

$b^2 - 4ac = 0$ then solutions are real and equal

$b^2 - 4ac < 0$ then solutions are complex

3.1 Complex number algebra

A number such as $3+4i$ is called a **complex number**. It is the sum of two terms (each of which may be zero).

The real term (not containing i) is called the **real** part and the coefficient of i is the **imaginary** part. Therefore the real part of $3+4i$ is 3 and the imaginary part is 4.

A number is real when the coefficient of i is zero and is imaginary when the real part is zero.

e.g. $3+0i=3$ is real   and $0+4i=4i$ is imaginary.

Having introduced a complex number, the ways in which they can be combined, i.e. addition, multiplication, division etc., need to be defined. This is termed the **algebra** of complex numbers. You will see that, in general, you proceed as in real numbers, but using

$$i^2 = -1$$

where appropriate.

But first **equality** of complex numbers must be defined.

If two complex numbers, say

$$a+bi, \ c+di$$

are **equal**, then both their real and imaginary parts are equal;

$$\boxed{a+bi=c+di \ \Rightarrow \ a=c \text{ and } b=d}$$

Addition and subtraction

Addition of complex numbers is defined by separately adding real and imaginary parts; so if

$$z = a+bi, \ w = c+di$$

then $z+w=(a+c)+(b+d)i$.

Similarly for **subtraction**.

Example

Express each of the following in the form $x+yi$.

(a) $(3+5i)+(2-3i)$

(b) $(3+5i)+6$

(c) $7i-(4+5i)$

Solution

(a) $(3+5i)+(2-3i) = 3+2+(5-3)i = 5+2i$

(b) $(3+5i)+6 = 9+5i$

(c) $7i-(4+5i) = 7i-4-5i = -4+2i$

Multiplication

Multiplication is straightforward provided you remember that
$i^2 = -1.$

Example

Simplify in the form $x+yi$:

(a) $3(2+4i)$

(b) $(5+3i)i$

(c) $(2-7i)(3+4i)$

Solution

(a) $3(2+4i) = 3(2)+3(4i) = 6+12i$

(b) $(5+3i)i = (5)i+(3i)i = 5i+3\left(i^2\right) = 5i+(-1)3 = -3+5i$

(c) $(2-7i)(3+4i) = (2)(3) - (7i)(3) + (2)(4i) - (7i)(4i)$

$$= 6-21i+8i-(-28)$$

$$= 6-21i+8i+28$$

$$= 34-13i$$

In general, if

$$z = a+bi, \quad w = c+di,$$

then $\quad zw = (a+bi)(c+di)$

$$= ac-bd+(ad+bc)i$$

Activity 5

Simplify the following expressions:

(a) $(2+6i)+(9-2i)$

(b) $(8-3i)-(1+5i)$

(c) $3(7-3i)+i(2+2i)$

(d) $(3+5i)(1-4i)$

(e) $(5+12i)(6+7i)$

(f) $(2+i)^2$

(g) i^3

(h) i^4

(i) $(1-i)^3$

(j) $(1+i)^2+(1-i)^2$

(k) $(2+i)^4+(2-i)^4$

(l) $(a+ib)(a-ib)$

Division

The **complex conjugate** of a complex number is obtained by changing the sign of the imaginary part. So if $z = a+bi$, its complex conjugate, $\bar{z}$, is defined by

Note: an alternative notation often used for the complex conjugate is z^*.

$$\bar{z} = a-bi$$

Any complex number $a+bi$ has a complex conjugate $a-bi$ and from Activity 5 it can be seen that $(a+bi)(a-bi)$ is a real number. This fact is used in simplifying expressions where the denominator of a quotient is complex.

Example

Simplify the expressions:

(a) $\dfrac{1}{i}$ (b) $\dfrac{3}{1+i}$ (c) $\dfrac{4+7i}{2+5i}$

Solution

To simplify these expressions you multiply the numerator and denominator of the quotient by the complex conjugate of the denominator.

(a) The complex conjugate of i is $-i$, therefore

$$\frac{1}{i} = \frac{1}{i} \times \frac{-i}{-i} = \frac{(1)(-i)}{(i)(-i)} = \frac{-i}{-(-1)} = -i$$

(b) The complex conjugate of $1+i$ is $1-i$, therefore

$$\frac{3}{1+i} = \frac{3}{1+i} \times \frac{1-i}{1-i} = \frac{3(1-i)}{(1+i)(1-i)} = \frac{3-3i}{2} = \frac{3}{2} - \frac{3}{2}i$$

(c) The complex conjugate of $2+5i$ is $2-5i$ therefore

$$\frac{4+7i}{2+5i} = \frac{4+7i}{2+5i} \times \frac{2-5i}{2-5i} = \frac{43-6i}{29} = \frac{43}{29} - \frac{6}{29}i$$

Activity 6   Division

Simplify to the form $a+ib$

(a) $\dfrac{4}{i}$ (b) $\dfrac{1-i}{1+i}$ (c) $\dfrac{4+5i}{6-5i}$ (d) $\dfrac{4i}{(1+2i)^2}$

3.2 Solving equations

Just as you can have equations with real numbers, you can have equations with complex numbers, as illustrated in the example below.

Example

Solve each of the following equations for the complex number z.

(a) $4+5i = z-(1-i)$

(b) $(1+2i)z = 2+5i$

Solution

(a) Writing $z = x+iy$,

$$4+5i = (x+yi)-(1-i)$$

$$4+5i = x-1+(y+1)i$$

Comparing real parts $\Rightarrow$ $4 = x-1, \quad x = 5$

Comparing imaginary parts $\Rightarrow$ $5 = y+1, \quad y = 4$

So $z = 5+4i$. In fact there is no need to introduce the real and imaginary parts of z, since

$$4+5i = z-(1-i)$$

$\Rightarrow$ $z = 4+5i+(1-i)$

$\Rightarrow$ $z = 5+4i$

(b) $(1+2i)z = 2+5i$

$$z = \frac{2+5i}{1+2i}$$

$$z = \frac{2+5i}{1+2i} \times \frac{1-2i}{1-2i}$$

$$z = \frac{12+i}{5} = \frac{12}{5} + \frac{1}{5}i$$

Activity 7

(a) Solve the following equations for real x and y

 (i) $3+5i+x-yi = 6-2i$

 (ii) $x+yi = (1-i)(2+8i)$.

(b) Determine the complex number z which satisfies
 $z(3+3i) = 2-i$.

Exercise 3A

1. Solve the equations:

 (a) $x^2+9=0$ (b) $9x^2+25=0$

 (c) $x^2+2x+2=0$ (d) $x^2+x+1=0$

 (e) $2x^2+3x+2=0$

2. Find the quadratic equation which has roots $2\pm\sqrt{3}i$.

3. Write the following complex numbers in the form $x+yi$.

 (a) $(3+2i)+(2+4i)$ (b) $(4+3i)-(2+5i)$

 (c) $(4+3i)+(4-3i)$ (d) $(2+7i)-(2-7i)$

 (e) $(3+2i)(4-3i)$ (f) $(3+2i)^2$

 (g) $(1+i)(1-i)(2+i)$

4. Find the value of the real number y such that
 $(3+2i)(1+iy)$
 is (a) real (b) imaginary.

5. Simplify:

 (a) i^3 (b) i^4 (c) $\frac{1}{i}$ (d) $\frac{1}{i^2}$ (e) $\frac{1}{i^3}$

6. If $z=1+2i$, find

 (a) z^2 (b) $\frac{1}{z}$ (c) $\frac{1}{z^2}$

7. Write in the form $x+yi$:

 (a) $\frac{2+3i}{1+i}$ (b) $\frac{-4+3i}{-2-i}$ (c) $\frac{4i}{2-i}$

 (d) $\frac{1}{2+3i}$ (e) $\frac{3-2i}{i}$ (f) $\frac{p+qi}{r+si}$

8. Simplify:

 (a) $\frac{(2+i)(3-2i)}{1+i}$ (b) $\frac{(1-i)^3}{(2+i)^2}$

 (c) $\frac{1}{3+i} - \frac{1}{3-i}$

9. Solve for z when

 (a) $z(2+i)=3-2i$ (b) $(z+i)(1-i)=2+3i$

 (c) $\frac{1}{z} + \frac{1}{2-i} = \frac{3}{1+i}$

10. Find the values of the real numbers x and y in each of the following:

 (a) $\frac{x}{1+i} + \frac{y}{1-2i} = 1$

 (b) $\frac{x}{2-i} + \frac{yi}{i+3} = \frac{2}{1+i}$

11. Given that p and q are real and that $1+2i$ is a root of the equation

$$z^2 + (p+5i)z + q(2-i) = 0$$

determine:

(a) the values of p and q;

(b) the other root of the equation.

12. The complex numbers u, v and w are related by

$$\frac{1}{u} = \frac{1}{v} + \frac{1}{w}.$$

Given that $v = 3+4i$, $w = 4-3i$, find u in the form $x+iy$.

3.3 Argand diagram

Any complex number $z = a+bi$ can be represented by an ordered pair (a, b) and hence plotted on xy-axes with the real part measured along the x-axis and the imaginary part along the y-axis. This graphical representation of the complex number field is called an **Argand diagram**, named after the Swiss mathematician *Jean Argand* (1768-1822).

Example

Represent the following complex numbers on an Argand diagram:

(a) $z = 3+2i$ (b) $z = 4-5i$ (c) $z = -2-i$

Solution

The Argand diagram is shown opposite.

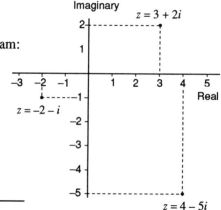

Activity 8

Let $z_1 = 5+2i$, $z_2 = 1+3i$, $z_3 = 2-3i$, $z_4 = -4-7i$.

(a) Plot the complex numbers z_1, z_2, z_3, z_4 on an Argand diagram and label them.

(b) Plot the complex numbers z_1+z_2 and z_1-z_2 on the same Argand diagram. Geometrically, how do the positions of the numbers z_1+z_2 and z_1-z_2 relate to z_1 and z_2?

3.4 Polar coordinates

Consider the complex number $z = 3 + 4i$ as represented on an Argand diagram. The position of A can be expressed as coordinates (3, 4), the cartesian form, or in terms of the length and direction of OA.

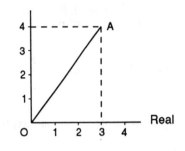

Using Pythagoras' theorem, the length of $OA = \sqrt{3^2 + 4^2} = 5$.

This is written as $|z| = r = 5$. $|z|$ is read as the **modulus** or absolute value of z.

The angle that OA makes with the positive real axis is

$$\theta = \tan^{-1}\left(\frac{4}{3}\right) = 53.13° \text{ (or 0.927 radians)}.$$

This is written as $\arg(z) = 53.13°$. You say $\arg(z)$ is the **argument** or phase of z.

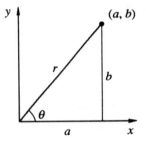

The parameters $|z|$ and $\arg(z)$ are in fact the equivalent of **polar coordinates** r, θ as shown opposite. There is a simple connection between the polar coordinate form and the cartesian or rectangular form (a, b):

$$a = r\cos\theta, \quad b = r\sin\theta.$$

Therefore

$$z = a + bi = r\cos\theta + ri\sin\theta = r(\cos\theta + i\sin\theta)$$

where $|z| = r$, and $\arg(z) = \theta$.

It is more usual to express the angle θ in radians. Note also that it is convention to write the i before $\sin\theta$, i.e. $i\sin\theta$ is preferable to $\sin\theta i$.

In the diagram opposite, the point A could be labelled $\left(2\sqrt{3}, 2\right)$ or as $2\sqrt{3} + 2i$.

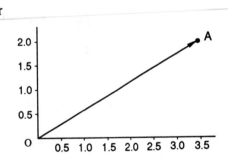

The angle that OA makes with the positive x-axis is given by

$$\theta = \tan^{-1}\left(\frac{2}{2\sqrt{3}}\right) = \tan^{-1}\left(\frac{1}{\sqrt{3}}\right).$$

Therefore $\theta = \dfrac{\pi}{6}$ or $2\pi + \dfrac{\pi}{6}$ or $4\pi + \dfrac{\pi}{6}$ or ... etc. There is an infinite number of possible angles. The one you should normally use is in the interval $-\pi < \theta \leq \pi$, and this is called the **principal argument**.

Using polar coordinates the point A could be labelled with its polar coordinates $[r, \theta]$ as $\left[4, \dfrac{\pi}{6}\right]$. Note the use of squared brackets when using polar coordinates. This is to avoid confusion with Cartesian coordinates.

Thus $2\sqrt{3} + 2i = 4\left(\cos\left(\dfrac{\pi}{6}\right) + i\sin\left(\dfrac{\pi}{6}\right)\right).$

Important note: if you are expressing $a + ib$ in its polar form, where a and b are both positive, then the formula $\theta = \tan^{-1}\dfrac{b}{a}$ is quite sufficient. But in other cases you need to think about the position of $a + ib$ in the Argand diagram.

Example

Write $z = -1 - i$ in polar form.

Solution

Now $z = a + ib$ where $a = -1$ and $b = -1$ and in polar form the modulus of $z = |z| = r = \sqrt{1^2 + 1^2} = \sqrt{2}$ and the argument is $\dfrac{5\pi}{4}$ (or 225°): its principal value is $-\dfrac{3\pi}{4}$.

Hence $z = \left[\sqrt{2}, \dfrac{-3\pi}{4}\right]$ in polar coordinates. (The formula $\tan^{-1}\dfrac{b}{a}$ would have given you $\dfrac{\pi}{4}$.)

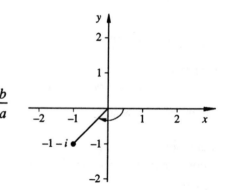

Activity 9

(a) Write the following numbers in $[r, \theta]$ form:

    (i) $7 + 2i$ (ii) $3 - i$ (iii) $-4 + 6i$ (iv) $-\sqrt{3} - i$

(b) Write the following in $a + bi$ form:

    (remember that the angles are in radians)

    (i) $\left[3, \dfrac{\pi}{4}\right]$ (ii) $[5, \pi]$ (iii) $[6, 4.2]$

    (iv) $\left[\sqrt{2}, \dfrac{-2\pi}{3}\right]$

3.5 Complex number algebra

You will now investigate the set of complex numbers in the modulus/argument form, $[r, \theta]$.

Suppose you wish to combine two complex numbers of the form

$$z_1 = [r_1, \theta_1] \quad z_2 = [r_2, \theta_2]$$

Note that, in $a + bi$ form,

$$z_1 = r_1 \cos \theta_1 + i\, r_1 \sin \theta_1$$

and $\quad z_2 = r_2 \cos \theta_2 + ir_2 \sin \theta_2$

So $\quad z_1 z_2 = \left(r_1 \cos \theta_1 + ir_1 \sin \theta_1 \right)\left(r_2 \cos \theta_2 + ir_2 \sin \theta_2 \right)$

$$= r_1 r_2 \left(\cos \theta_1 + i \sin \theta_1 \right)\left(\cos \theta_2 + i \sin \theta_2 \right)$$

$$= r_1 r_2 \Big[\left(\cos \theta_1 \cos \theta_2 - \sin \theta_1 \sin \theta_2 \right)$$
$$+ \left(\sin \theta_1 \cos \theta_2 + \cos \theta_1 \sin \theta_2 \right) i \Big].$$

Simplify the expressions in the brackets.

Using the formulae for angles,

$$\boxed{z_1 z_2 = r_1 r_2 \left[\cos\left(\theta_1 + \theta_2\right) + i \sin\left(\theta_1 + \theta_2\right) \right]}$$

or, in polar notation

$$z_1 z_2 = [r_1 r_2,\ \theta_1 + \theta_2].$$

For example, $[3, 0.5] \times [4, 0.3] = [12, 0.8]$.

That is, the first elements of the ordered pairs are **multiplied** and the second elements are **added**.

Activity 10

Given that $z_1 = [3, 0.7]$, $z_2 = [2, 1.2]$ and $z_3 = [4, -0.5]$,

(a) find $z_1 \times z_2$ and $z_1 \times z_3$

(b) show that $[1, 0] \times z_1 = z_1$

(c) (i) find a complex number $z = [r, \theta]$ such that
$z \times z_2 = [1, 0]$.

(ii) find a complex number $z = [r, \theta]$ such that
$z \times z_3 = [1, 0]$.

(d) for any complex number $[r, \theta]$ show that

$$\left[\frac{1}{r}, -\theta\right] \times [r, \theta] = [1, 0] \quad (r > 0).$$

Activity 11

Use a spreadsheet package to plot numbers on an Argand diagram by entering numbers and formulae into cells A5 to E5 as shown opposite.

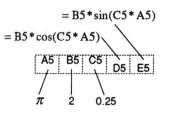

$= B5 * sin(C5 * A5)$

$= B5 * cos(C5 * A5)$

| A5 | B5 | C5 | D5 | E5 |

π 2   0.25

Cells D5 and E5 calculate the x and y coordinates respectively of the complex number whose modulus and argument are in cells B5 and C5 (the argument is entered as a multiple of π).

A second number can be entered in cells B6 and C6 and its (x, y) coordinates calculated by using appropriate formulae in cells D6 and E6.

This can be repeated for further numbers (the spreadsheet facility 'FILL DOWN' is useful here).

Use the appropriate facility on your spreadsheet to plot the (x, y) values.

Label rows and columns if it makes it easier.

Experiment with different values of r and θ.

An example is shown in the graph opposite and the related spreadsheet below.

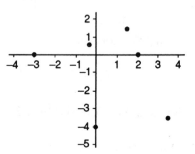

	A	B	C	D	E
1			=B5*cos(C5*A5)		
2					
3				=B5*sin(C5*A5)	
4					
5	3.141593	2	0.25	1.4142134399	1.4142136848
6	3.141593	3	1	-3.000000000	-1.039231E-6
7	3.141593	4	1.5	2.0784612E-6	-4.000000000
8	3.141593	0.6	0.666667	-0.300000664	0.5196148588
9	3.141593	2	2	2.0000000000	1.3856408E-6
10	3.141593	5	1.75	3.5355360492	-3.535531763
11					

Exercise 3B

1. Mark on an Argand diagram the points representing the following numbers:

    (a) 2 (b) $3i$ (c) $-i$ (d) $1+2i$ (e) $3-i$

    (f) $-2+3i$

2. The points A, B, C and D represent the numbers z_1, z_2, z_3 and z_4 and O is the origin.

    (a) If OABC is a parallelogram, and $z_1 = 1+i$, $z_2 = 4+5i$, find z_3.

    (b) Find z_2 and z_4 when ABCD is a square and

    (i) $z_1 = 2+i$, $z_3 = 6+7i$

    (ii) $z_1 = 6-2i$, $z_3 = 6i$

3. Find the modulus and argument of

    (a) $1-i$ (b) $1+\sqrt{3}i$ (c) $3-3i$ (d) $3+2i$

4. Show that

    (a) $|\bar{z}| = |z|$ (b) $\arg \bar{z} = -\arg z$

    and illustrate these results on an Argand diagram.

5. Find the modulus and argument of z_1, z_2, $z_1 z_2$

    and $\dfrac{z_1}{z_2}$ when $z_1 = 1+i$ and $z_2 = \sqrt{3}+i$. What do you notice?

6. Write in the form $a+bi$

    (a) $\left[4, \dfrac{\pi}{3}\right]$ (b) $\left[5, \dfrac{\pi}{2}\right]$

    (c) $\left[3\sqrt{2}, -\dfrac{3\pi}{4}\right]$ (d) $[4, 13\pi]$

7. Write in polar form

    (a) $1+i$ (b) $-2+i$ (c) -5 (d) $4i$ (e) $3+4i$

    (f) $-3-4i$ (g) $3-4i$ (h) $-3+4i$

8. In this question, angles are in radians.

    (a) (i) Plot the following complex numbers on an Argand diagram and label them:

    $$z_1 = [4,0], \quad z_2 = \left[3, \frac{\pi}{2}\right], \quad z_3 = \left[2, \frac{-\pi}{2}\right]$$

    $$z_4 = \left[3, \frac{\pi}{3}\right], \quad z_5 = \left[2, \frac{5\pi}{3}\right]$$

    (ii) Let the complex number $z = \left[1, \dfrac{\pi}{2}\right]$

    Calculate $z \times z_1$, $z \times z_2$, etc. and plot the points on the same diagram as in (i). What do you notice?

    (b) Repeat (a) (ii) using $z = \left[1, \dfrac{\pi}{3}\right]$

    (c) In general, what happens when a complex number is multiplied by $[1, \theta]$? Make up some examples to illustrate your answer.

    (d) Repeat (a) (ii) using $z = \left[0.5, \dfrac{\pi}{2}\right]$

    (e) In general, what happens when a complex number is multiplied by $\left[0.5, \dfrac{\pi}{2}\right]$? Make up some examples to illustrate your answer.

    (f) Repeat (e) for $\left[3, \dfrac{\pi}{3}\right]$

    (g) Describe what happens when a complex number is multiplied by $\left[3, \dfrac{\pi}{3}\right]$. Make up some examples to illustrate your answer.

3.6 De Moivre's theorem

An important theorem in complex numbers is named after the French mathematician, *Abraham de Moivre* (1667-1754). Although born in France, he came to England where he made the acquaintance of *Newton* and *Halley* and became a private teacher of Mathematics. He never obtained the university position he sought but he did produce a considerable amount of research, including his work on complex numbers.

The derivation of de Moivre's theorem now follows.

Consider the complex number $z = \left(\cos\dfrac{\pi}{3} + i\sin\dfrac{\pi}{3} \right)$.

Then
$$z^2 = \left(\cos\frac{\pi}{3} + i\sin\frac{\pi}{3} \right) \times \left(\cos\frac{\pi}{3} + i\sin\frac{\pi}{3} \right)$$

$$= \cos^2\frac{\pi}{3} - \sin^2\frac{\pi}{3} + 2i\cos\frac{\pi}{3}\sin\frac{\pi}{3}$$

$$= \cos\frac{2\pi}{3} + i\sin\frac{2\pi}{3}$$

or with the modulus/argument notation

$$z = \left[1, \frac{\pi}{3} \right]$$

and
$$z^2 = \left[1, \frac{\pi}{3} \right] \times \left[1, \frac{\pi}{3} \right] = \left[1, \frac{2\pi}{3} \right].$$

Remember that any complex number $z = x + yi$ can be written in the form of an ordered pair $[r, \theta]$ where $r = \sqrt{x^2 + y^2}$ and $\theta = \tan^{-1}\left(\dfrac{y}{x} \right)$.

If the modulus of the number is 1, then $z = \cos\theta + i\sin\theta$

and
$$z^2 = (\cos\theta + i\sin\theta)^2$$

$$= \cos^2\theta - \sin^2\theta + 2i\cos\theta\sin\theta$$

$$= \cos 2\theta + i\sin 2\theta$$

i.e.
$$z^2 = [1, \theta]^2 = [1, 2\theta].$$

Activity 12

(a) Use the principle that, with the usual notation,
$$[r_1, \theta_1] \times [r_2, \theta_2] = [r_1 r_2, \theta_1 + \theta_2]$$

to investigate $\left(\cos\dfrac{\pi}{6} + i\sin\dfrac{\pi}{6} \right)^n$ when $n = 0, 1, 2, 3, ..., 12$.

(b) In the same way as in (a), investigate

$$\left(3\cos\frac{\pi}{6}+3i\sin\frac{\pi}{6}\right)^n$$

for $n = 0,\ 1,\ 2,\ ...,\ 6$.

You should find from the last activity that

$$(\cos\theta+i\sin\theta)^n = \cos(n\theta)+i\sin(n\theta).$$

In $[r,\theta]$ form this is $[r,\theta]^n = \left[r^n,n\theta\right]$ and **de Moivre's theorem** states that this is true for any **rational number** n.

A more rigorous way of deriving de Moivre's theorem follows.

Activity 13

Show that $(\cos\theta+i\sin\theta)^n = \cos n\theta+i\sin n\theta$ for $n = 3$ and $n = 4$.

Activity 14

Show that

$$(\cos k\theta+i\sin k\theta)(\cos\theta+i\sin\theta) = \cos(k+1)\theta+i\sin(k+1)\theta.$$

Hence show that if

$$(\cos\theta+i\sin\theta)^k = \cos k\theta+i\sin k\theta$$

then $\quad (\cos\theta+i\sin\theta)^{k+1} = \cos((k+1)\theta)+i\sin((k+1)\theta).$

The principle of **mathematical induction** will be used to prove that $(\cos\theta+i\sin\theta)^n = \cos(n\theta)+i\sin(n\theta)$ for all **positive integers**.

Let $S(k)$ be the statement

$$'(\cos\theta+i\sin\theta)^k = \cos k\theta+i\sin k\theta'.$$

As $S(1)$ is true and you have shown in Activity 14 that $S(k)$ implies $S(k+1)$ then $S(2)$ is also true. But then (again by Activity 14) $S(3)$ is true. But then ... Hence S(n) is true for $n = 1, 2, 3, ...$ This is the principle of mathematical induction (which you meet more fully later in the book). So for all positive integers n,

$$\boxed{(\cos\theta + i\sin\theta)^n = \cos n\theta + i\sin n\theta}$$

If n is a **negative integer**, then let $m = -n$

$$(\cos\theta + i\sin\theta)^n = (\cos\theta + i\sin\theta)^{-m} = \frac{1}{(\cos\theta + i\sin\theta)^m}$$

where m is positive and, from the work above,

$$(\cos\theta + i\sin\theta)^m = (\cos m\theta + i\sin m\theta).$$

Therefore $\quad (\cos\theta + i\sin\theta)^n = \dfrac{1}{(\cos m\theta + i\sin m\theta)}$

Activity 15

Show that

$$\frac{1}{(\cos m\theta + i\sin m\theta)} = \cos m\theta - i\sin m\theta$$

and hence that $(\cos\theta + i\sin\theta)^n = \cos n\theta + i\sin n\theta$ when n is a negative integer.

Hint : multiply top and bottom by $(\cos m\theta - i\sin m\theta)$ and use the fact that $\sin(-A) = -\sin(A)$.

When n is a **rational number**, i.e. $n = \dfrac{p}{q}$ where p and q are integers, then as q is an integer

$$\left\{\cos\left(\frac{p}{q}\right)\theta + i\sin\left(\frac{p}{q}\right)\theta\right\}^q = (\cos p\theta + i\sin p\theta)$$

Since p is an integer

$$\cos p\theta + i\sin p\theta = (\cos\theta + i\sin\theta)^p,$$

and hence

$$\left\{\cos\left(\frac{p}{q}\right)\theta + i\sin\left(\frac{p}{q}\right)\theta\right\}^q = (\cos\theta + i\sin\theta)^p$$

Thus
$$\left\{\cos\left(\frac{p}{q}\right)\theta + i\sin\left(\frac{p}{q}\right)\theta\right\} = (\cos\theta + i\sin\theta)^{\frac{p}{q}}$$

Therefore $\cos n\theta + i\sin n\theta = (\cos\theta + i\sin\theta)^n$ for any rational number n and clearly this leads to

$$\boxed{(r(\cos\theta + i\sin\theta))^n = r^n(\cos n\theta + i\sin n\theta)}$$

3.7 Applications of de Moivre's theorem

There are many applications of de Moivre's theorem, including the proof of trigonometric identities.

Example

Prove that $\cos 3\theta = \cos^3\theta - 3\cos\theta\sin^2\theta$.

Solution

By de Moivre's theorem:

$$\cos 3\theta + i\sin 3\theta = (\cos\theta + i\sin\theta)^3$$
$$= \cos^3\theta + 3\cos^2\theta(i\sin\theta) + 3\cos\theta(i\sin\theta)^2 + (i\sin\theta)^3$$
$$= \cos^3\theta + 3i\cos^2\theta\sin\theta - 3\cos\theta\sin^2\theta - i\sin^3\theta$$
$$= \cos^3\theta - 3\cos\theta\sin^2\theta + i(3\cos^2\theta\sin\theta - \sin^3\theta)$$

Comparing **real parts** of the equation above you obtain

$$\cos 3\theta = \cos^3\theta - 3\cos\theta\sin^2\theta$$

Example

Simplify the following expression:

$$\frac{\cos 2\theta + i\sin 2\theta}{\cos 3\theta + i\sin 3\theta}$$

Solution

$$\frac{\cos 2\theta + i\sin 2\theta}{\cos 3\theta + i\sin 3\theta} = \frac{(\cos\theta + i\sin\theta)^2}{(\cos\theta + i\sin\theta)^3} = \frac{1}{(\cos\theta + i\sin\theta)^1}$$

$$= (\cos\theta + i\sin\theta)^{-1}$$

$$= (\cos(-\theta) + i\sin(-\theta))$$

$$= \cos\theta - i\sin\theta$$

Exercise 3C

1. Use de Moivre's theorem to prove the trig identities:

   (a) $\sin 2\theta = 2\sin\theta\cos\theta$

   (b) $\cos 5\theta = \cos^5\theta - 10\cos^3\theta\sin^2\theta + 5\cos\theta\sin^4\theta$

2. If $z = \cos\theta + i\sin\theta$ then use de Moivre's theorem to show that:

   (a) $z + \dfrac{1}{z} = 2\cos\theta$ \qquad (b) $z^2 + \dfrac{1}{z^2} = 2\cos 2\theta$

   (c) $z^n + \dfrac{1}{z^n} = 2\cos n\theta$

3. Simplify the following expressions:

   (a) $\dfrac{\cos 5\theta + i\sin 5\theta}{\cos 2\theta - i\sin 2\theta}$ \qquad (b) $\dfrac{\cos\theta - i\sin\theta}{\cos 4\theta - i\sin 4\theta}$

Activity 16

Make an educated guess at a complex solution to the equation $z^3 = 1$ and then use the facilities of the spreadsheet to raise it to the power 3 and plot it on the Argand diagram. If it is a solution of the equation then the resultant point will be plotted at distance 1 unit along the real axis. The initial spreadsheet layout from Activity 11 can be adapted. In addition, the cells shown opposite are required.

What does the long formula in cell C7 do? Is it strictly necessary in this context?

Below are two examples of the output from a spreadsheet using these cells – the first one is not a cube root of 1 but the second is.

$$= B7 * \sin(A5 * C7)$$

$$= B7 * \cos(A5 * C7)$$

| B7 | C7 | D7 | E7 |

$$= B5^3$$

$$= C5 * 3 - 2 * \left(\mathrm{int}\left(\tfrac{C5*3}{2}\right)\right)$$

	A	B	C	D	E
5	3.141593	1	0.6666667	-0.5	0.8666025
6					
7		1	2	1	4.14E-13

	A	B	C	D	E
5	3.141593	1	0.8	-0.80902	0.587785
6					
7		1	2.4	0.309017	0.951057

3.8 Solutions of $z^3 = 1$

Write down one solution of $z^3 = 1$.

De Moivre's theorem can be used to find all the solutions of $z^3 = 1$.

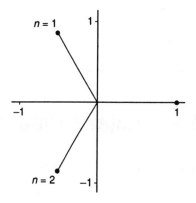

Let $\qquad z = [r, \theta]$

then $\qquad z^3 = [r, \theta]^3 = \left[r^3, 3\theta\right]$

and you can express 1 as $1 = [1, 2n\pi]$ where n is an integer.

Then $\qquad \left[r^3, 3\theta\right] = [1, 2n\pi]$

Therefore $\qquad r^3 = 1$ and $3\theta = 2n\pi$

i.e. $\qquad r = 1$ and $\theta = \dfrac{2n\pi}{3}$

The solutions are then given by letting $n = 0, 1, 2, \ldots$

If $n = 0, \qquad z_1 = [1, 0] = 1$

If $n = 1, \qquad z_2 = \left[1, \dfrac{2\pi}{3}\right] = \cos\dfrac{2\pi}{3} + i\sin\dfrac{2\pi}{3}$

$$= -\frac{1}{2} + \frac{\sqrt{3}}{2}i$$

If $n = 2, \qquad z_3 = \left[1, \dfrac{4\pi}{3}\right] = \cos\dfrac{4\pi}{3} + i\sin\dfrac{4\pi}{3}$

$$= -\frac{1}{2} - \frac{\sqrt{3}}{2}i$$

What happens if $n = 3, 4, \ldots$ **?**

Activity 17   Cube roots of unity

Plot the three distinct cube roots of unity on an Argand diagram. What do you notice?

Activity 18

Use de Moivre's theorem to find all solutions to the following equations and plot the results on an Argand diagram.

(a) $z^4 = 1$ (b) $z^3 = 8$ (c) $z^3 = i$

3.9   Euler's theorem

You have probably already met the series expansion of e^x, namely

$$e^x = 1 + x + \frac{x^2}{2!} + \frac{x^3}{3!} + \frac{x^4}{4!} + \dots$$

Also the series expansions for $\cos\theta$ and $\sin\theta$ are given by

$$\cos\theta = 1 - \frac{\theta^2}{2!} + \frac{\theta^4}{4!} - \frac{\theta^6}{6!} + \dots$$

$$\sin\theta = \theta - \frac{\theta^3}{3!} + \frac{\theta^5}{5!} - \frac{\theta^7}{7!} + \dots$$

Activity 19

(a) For each of the following values of θ, use the series for e^x with x replaced by $i\theta$ to calculate (to 4 d.p.) the value of $e^{i\theta}$. (Write your answer in the form $a + bi$.)

(i) $\theta = 0$ (ii) $\theta = 1$ (iii) $\theta = 2$ (iv) $\theta = -0.4$

(b) Calculate $\cos\theta$ and $\sin\theta$ for each of the values in (a).

(c) Find a connection between the values of $e^{i\theta}$, $\cos\theta$ and $\sin\theta$ for each of the values of θ given in (a) and make up one other example to test your conjecture.

(d) To prove this for all values of θ, write down the series expansions of $e^{i\theta}$, $\cos\theta$ and $\sin\theta$ and show that

$$e^{i\theta} = \cos\theta + i\sin\theta.$$

The previous activity has shown that

$$e^{i\theta} = \cos\theta + i\sin\theta$$

which is sometimes known as **Euler's theorem**.

It is an important result, and can be used to derive de Moivre's theorem in a simple way. If z is any complex number then in polar form

$$z = x + yi = r\cos\theta + ri\sin\theta$$

$$= r(\cos\theta + i\sin\theta)$$

$$= re^{i\theta}, \text{ using Euler's theorem.}$$

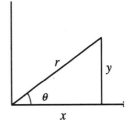

Thus
$$z^n = \left(re^{i\theta}\right)^n = r^n e^{ni\theta} = r^n e^{i(n\theta)}$$

or
$$\left(r\cos\theta + ir\sin\theta\right)^n = r^n\left(\cos(n\theta) + i\sin(n\theta)\right)$$

$$\Rightarrow \quad \left(\cos\theta + i\sin\theta\right)^n = \cos(n\theta) + i\sin(n\theta)$$

which is de Moivre's theoem.

What assumptions about complex number algebra have been made in the 'proof' above?

One interesting result can be obtained from Euler's theorem by putting $\theta = \pi$. This gives

$$e^{i\pi} = \cos\pi + i\sin\pi$$

$$= -1 + i \times 0.$$

So
$$e^{i\pi} + 1 = 0$$

This is often referred to as **Euler's equation**, since it connects the five most 'famous' numbers

$$0, 1, \ \pi, e, i$$

with a '+' and '=' sign!

Try substituting other values of θ in Euler's theorem and see what equation is derived.

3.10 Exponential form of a complex number

When a complex number z has modulus r, which must be non-negative, and argument θ, which is usually taken such that it satisfies $-\pi < \theta \le \pi$, you have already shown that it can be represented in the forms

(i) $r(\cos\theta + i\sin\theta)$

(ii) $[r, \theta]$

(iii) $re^{i\theta}$

Expression (iii) is referred to as the **exponential form** of a complex number.

Activity 20

Write each of the following complex numbers in the exponential form.

(a) $2\left(\cos\dfrac{\pi}{3} + i\cos\dfrac{\pi}{3}\right)$ (b) $\left[5, \dfrac{2\pi}{3}\right]$ (c) $1 - i\sqrt{3}$

3.11 Solving equations

You have already investigated the solutions of the equation $z^3 = 1$ and similar equations using a spreadsheet and by using de Moivre's theorem. A similar approach will now be used to solve more complicated equations.

Example

Write down the modulus and argument of the complex number $4 - 4i$.

Solve the equation $z^5 = 4 - 4i$, expressing your answers in the exponential form.

Solution

$$|4 - 4i| = \sqrt{\left\{4^2 + (-4)^2\right\}} = 4\sqrt{2}$$

As before it is often helpful to make a small sketch of an Argand diagram to locate the correct quadrant for the argument.

So $\qquad \arg(4-4i)=\dfrac{-\pi}{4}$

Therefore the complex number $4-4i$ can be expressed as

$$\left[4\sqrt{2},\ \dfrac{-\pi}{4}\right]$$

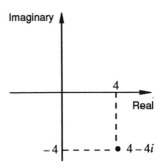

It is quite convenient to work using the polar form of a complex number when solving $z^5=4-4i$.

Let $z=[r,\ \theta]$, then $z^5=\left[r^5,\ 5\theta\right]$.

So as to obtain all five roots of the equation, the argument is considered to be $2n\pi-\dfrac{\pi}{4}$ where n is an integer.

Equating the results

$$\left[r^5,\ 5\theta\right]=\left[4\sqrt{2},\ 2n\pi-\dfrac{\pi}{4}\right]$$

$$r^5=4\sqrt{2}\ \Rightarrow\ r=\sqrt{2}$$

$$5\theta=2n\pi-\dfrac{\pi}{4}\ \Rightarrow\ \theta=(8n-1)\dfrac{\pi}{20}$$

Now choose the five appropriate values of n so that θ lies between $-\pi$ and π.

$$n=-2\quad\Rightarrow\quad\theta\ =\ \dfrac{-17\pi}{20}$$

$$n=-1\quad\Rightarrow\quad\theta\ =\ \dfrac{-9\pi}{20}$$

$$n=0\quad\Rightarrow\quad\theta\ =\ \dfrac{-\pi}{20}$$

$$n=1\quad\Rightarrow\quad\theta\ =\ \dfrac{7\pi}{20}$$

$$n=2\quad\Rightarrow\quad\theta\ =\ \dfrac{15\pi}{20}\ \text{or}\ \dfrac{3\pi}{4}$$

The solutions in exponential form are therefore

$$\sqrt{2}\,e^{-\frac{17\pi}{20}i},\ \sqrt{2}\,e^{-\frac{9\pi}{20}i},\ \sqrt{2}\,e^{-\frac{\pi}{20}i},\ \sqrt{2}\,e^{\frac{7\pi}{20}i}\ \text{and}\ \sqrt{2}\,e^{\frac{3\pi}{4}i}.$$

Activity 21

Show that $1+i$ is a root of the equation $z^4 = -4$ and find each of the other roots in the form $a+bi$ where a and b are real.

Plot the roots on an Argand diagram. By considering the diagonals, or otherwise, show that the points are at the vertices of a square. Calculate the area of the square.

Activity 22

Given that $k \neq 1$ and the roots of the equation $z^3 = k$ are α, β and γ, use the substitution $z = \dfrac{(x-2)}{(x+1)}$ to obtain the roots of the equation

$$(x-2)^3 = k(x+1)^3$$

Exercise 3D

1. By using de Moivre's theorem, find all solutions to the following equations, giving your answers in polar form. Plot each set of roots on an Argand diagram and comment on the symmetry.

   (a) $z^4 = 16$ (b) $z^3 = -27i$ (c) $z^5 = -1$

2. Find the cube roots of

   (a) $1+i$ (b) $2i-2$

   giving your answers in exponential form.

3. Using the answers from Question 1(a), determine the solutions of the equation

   $$(x+1)^4 = 16(x-1)^4$$

   giving your answers in the form $a+bi$.

4. Using the results from Question 1(b), solve the equation

   $$1+27i(x+1)^3 = 0$$

   giving your answers in the form $a+bi$.

5. Solve the equation $z^3 = i(z-1)^3$ giving your answers in the form $a+bi$.

   Plot the solutions on an Argand diagram and comment on your results.

6. Determine the four roots of the equation

   $$(z-2)^4 + (z+1)^4 = 0$$

   and plot them on an Argand diagram.

3.12 Loci in the complex plane

Suppose z is allowed to vary in such a way that $|z-1| = 2$. You could write $z = x+iy$ and obtain

$$\sqrt{\{(x-1)^2 + y^2\}} = 2$$

or $\qquad (x-1)^2 + y^2 = 4$

You can immediately identify this as the cartesian equation of a circle centre $(1, 0)$ and radius 2. In terms of the complex plane, the centre is $1+0i$.

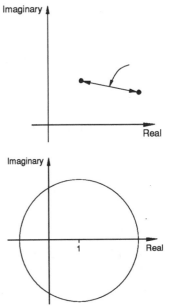

This approach could be adopted for most problems and the exercise is simply one in algebra, lacking any geometrical feel for the locus.

Instead, if ω is a complex number, you can identify $|z-\omega|$ as the distance of z from the point represented by ω on the complex plane. The locus $|z-1|=2$ can be interpreted as the set of points that are 2 units from the point $1+0i$; in other words, a circle centre $1+0i$ and radius 2.

Activity 23

Illustrate the locus of z in the complex plane if z satisfies

(a) $|z-(3+2i)|=5$

(b) $|z-2+i|=|1+3i|$

(c) $|z+2i|=2$

(d) $|z-4|=0$

Activity 24

Describe the path of a point which moves in a fixed plane so that it is always the same distance from two fixed points A and B.

Illustrate the locus of z in the case when z satisfies

$$|z+3|=|z-4i|.$$

You would probably have had some difficulty in writing down a cartesian equation of the locus in Activity 24, even though you could describe the locus geometrically.

Activity 25

Describe the locus of z in the case where z moves in such a way that
$$|z|=|z+2-2i|.$$

Now try to write down the cartesian equation of this locus which should be a straight line.

By writing $z=x+iy$, try to obtain the same result algebraically.

Activity 26

Investigate the locus of P when P moves in the complex plane and represents the complex number z which satisfies

$$|z+1| = k|z-1|$$

for different values of the real number k.

Why does $k = 1$ have to be treated as a special case?

Example

The point P represents the complex number z on an Argand diagram. Describe the locus geometrically and obtain a cartesian equation for the locus in the cases

(a) $|z| = |z-4|$

(b) $|z| + |z-4| = 6$

(c) $|z| = 2|z-4|$

Solution

(a) From your work in Activity 25, you should recognise this as a straight line. In fact, it is the mediator, or perpendicular bisector, of the line segment joining the origin to the point $4+0i$.

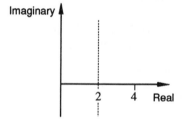

It should be immediately obvious that its cartesian equation is $x = 2$; however, writing

$$z = x+iy$$

$$|z| = |x+iy| = |x-4+iy|$$

Squaring both sides gives

$$x^2 + y^2 = (x-4)^2 + y^2$$

leading to

$$0 = -8x + 16$$

or $\qquad x = 2$.

(b) You may be aware of a curve that is traced out when the sum of the distances from two fixed points is constant. You could try using a piece of string with its ends fastened to two fixed points. The curve is called an ellipse.

A sketch of the locus is shown opposite.

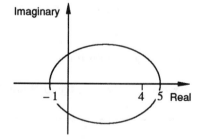

You can obtain a cartesian equation by putting $z = x + iy$

$$|x + iy| + |x - 4 + iy| = 6$$

So $$\sqrt{x^2 + y^2} + \sqrt{\left((x-4)^2 + y^2\right)} = 6$$

$\Rightarrow$ $$(x-4)^2 + y^2 = \left[6 - \left(x^2 + y^2\right)\right]^2$$

$$x^2 - 8x + 16 + y^2 = 36 - 12\sqrt{\left(x^2 + y^2\right)} + x^2 + y^2$$

$$12\sqrt{\left(x^2 + y^2\right)} = 20 + 8x$$

$$3\sqrt{\left(x^2 + y^2\right)} = 5 + 2x$$

$$9\left(x^2 + y^2\right) = 25 + 20x + 4x^2$$

$$5x^2 - 20x + 9y^2 = 25$$

$$5(x-2)^2 + 9y^2 = 45$$

$$\frac{(x-2)^2}{9} + \frac{y^2}{5} = 1$$

(c) You should have discovered in Activity 26 that the locus will be a circle when the relationship is of this form. It is called the **circle of Apollonius**.

You could possibly sketch the locus without finding the cartesian equation.

Let $$z = x + iy$$

$$|x + iy| = 2|x - 4 + iy|$$

$$\sqrt{\left(x^2 + y^2\right)} = 2\sqrt{\left((x-4)^2 + y^2\right)}$$

$$x^2 + y^2 = 4\left(x^2 - 8x + 16 + y^2\right)$$

$$0 = 3x^2 + 3y^2 - 32x + 64$$

In order to find the centre and radius you can complete the square

$$x^2 + y^2 - \frac{32}{3}x + \frac{64}{3} = 0$$

$$\left(x - \frac{16}{3}\right)^2 + y^2 = \frac{256}{9} - \frac{64}{3} = \frac{64}{9}$$

Centre of circle is at $\frac{16}{3} + 0i$ and radius is $\frac{8}{3}$.

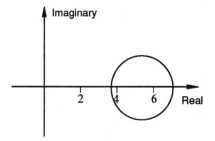

Activity 27

By recognising the locus

$$|z - 2| = 3|z - 10|$$

as the circle of Apollonius, use the idea of simple ratios to determine the coordinates of the centre and the radius of the circle.

Check your answer by finding the cartesian equation of the circle.

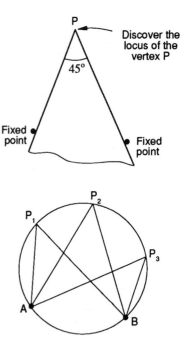

Discover the locus of the vertex P

Activity 28

By folding a piece of paper, create an angle of 45° and cut it out. Now mark two fixed points on a piece of paper and explore the locus of the vertex as you keep the two sides of the cut-out in contact with the fixed points as shown.

You should find that P moves on the arc of a circle.

Alternatively, when you have a circle and two fixed points A and B, if you choose a sequence of points P_1, P_2, P_3, ... on the circumference, what do you notice about the angles AP_1B, AP_2B, AP_3B, etc.?

This is an example of the constant angle locus.

Example

The point P represents z in the complex plane. Find the locus of P in each of the cases below when z satisfies

(a) $\arg z = \dfrac{5\pi}{6}$

(b) $\arg(z - 2 + 3i) = \dfrac{-\pi}{4}$

(c) $\arg\left(\dfrac{z-1}{z+1}\right) = \dfrac{\pi}{4}$

Solution

(a) The locus is a half-line starting at the origin making an angle $\dfrac{5}{6}\pi$ with the real axis.

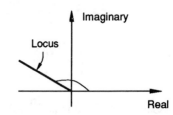

(b) The half-line to be considered here is one which starts at the point $2 - 3i$.

It makes an angle of $\dfrac{\pi}{4}$ below the real axis as shown opposite.

(c) You need to make use of the fact that

$$\arg\left(\frac{z-1}{z+1}\right) = \arg(z-1) - \arg(z+1)$$

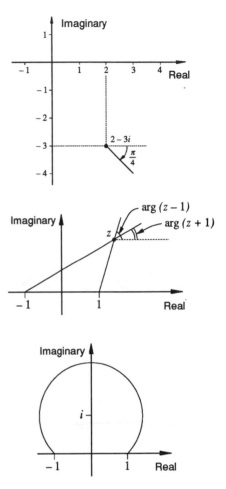

One possible solution for z is shown in the second diagram opposite.

By the results of Activity 28 you can see that the locus of z is the major arc of a circle passing through $1+0i$ and $-1+0i$.

Since the angle at the centre of the circle is twice that on the circumference, it can be seen that the centre of the circle is at $0+i$ and hence the radius of the circle is $\sqrt{2}$.

The problem can be tackled algebraically but there are difficulties that can creep in by assuming

$$\arg(x+iy) = \tan^{-1}\left(\frac{y}{x}\right)$$

Nevertheless, you can obtain the cartesian equation of the full circle of which the locus is only part.

Let $\qquad z = x + iy$

$$\arg\left(\frac{z-1}{z+1}\right) = \arg\left(\frac{x-1+iy}{x+1+iy}\right)$$

$$= \arg\left[\frac{\{(x-1)+iy\}\{(x+1)-iy\}}{(x+1)^2 + y^2}\right]$$

$$= \arg\left[\frac{\left(x^2 - 1 + y^2\right) + 2iy}{(x+1)^2 + y^2}\right] = \frac{\pi}{4}$$

Taking tangents of both sides

$$\frac{2y}{x^2 - 1 + y^2} = 1$$

$$\Rightarrow \quad x^2 + y^2 - 2y = 1$$

$$x^2 + (y-1)^2 = 2$$

from which we see the centre is $0+i$ and the radius is $\sqrt{2}$.

Note: this approach does not indicate whether the locus is the major or minor arc of the circle and so the first approach is recommended.

Exercise 3E

1. Sketch the locus of z described by

   (a) $|z+3-4i|=5$ (b) $|z+2|=|z-5+i|$

   (c) $|z+3i|=3|z-i|$ (d) $|z-2|+|z-3+i|=0$

2. Describe geometrically and obtain a cartesian equation for the locus of z in each of the following cases.

   (a) $|z-3|^2=100$ (b) $|z-1|^2+|z-4|^2=9$

   (c) $|z-1|+|z-4|=5$ (d) $|z-1|-|z-4|=1$

3. Describe geometrically and sketch the region on the complex plane for which

   (a) $2<|z-3+i|\le 5$ (b) $\dfrac{-\pi}{4}\le \arg(z-2i)\le \dfrac{\pi}{3}$

4. Sketch the loci for which

   (a) $\arg\left(\dfrac{z+1}{z-i}\right)=\dfrac{3\pi}{2}$ (b) $\arg(z-2)^3=\dfrac{\pi}{2}$

   (c) $\arg(z+2)-\arg(z-3)=\dfrac{\pi}{3}$

   (d) $\arg\left(\dfrac{z-5+7i}{z+1+i}\right)=\dfrac{\pi}{2}$

3.13 Miscellaneous Exercises

1. Find the modulus and argument of the complex numbers

   $$z_1=1+i \text{ and } z_2=1-\sqrt{3}i.$$

   Hence find in the form $z=[r,\ \theta]$ where $-\pi<\theta\le\pi$ and $r>0$, the complex numbers

   (a) $z_1 z_2$ (b) $\dfrac{z_1}{z_2}$ (c) $\dfrac{z_2}{z_1}$

   (d) z_1^2 (e) z_2^3 (f) $\dfrac{z_1^2}{z_2^4}$

2. Express the numbers 1, $3i$, -4, $z=2+\sqrt{5}i$ in the $[r,\ \theta]$ form. Hence express in the $[r,\ \theta]$ form

   (a) $\dfrac{1}{z}$ (b) $3zi$ (c) $\dfrac{z}{3i}$

   (d) $-4z$ (e) $\dfrac{-4}{z}$

3. Find $\sqrt{3}+i$ in the $[r,\ \theta]$ form. Hence find

   (a) $\left(\sqrt{3}+i\right)^3$ (b) $\left(\sqrt{3}+i\right)^8$

   in the form $a+bi$.

   (c) Find the least value of the positive integer n for which $\left(\sqrt{3}+i\right)^n$ is

   (i) purely real

   (ii) purely imaginary.

4. Find in the form $a+bi$

   (a) $\left(1+\sqrt{3}i\right)^5$ (b) $\left(\sqrt{3}-i\right)^{10}$ (c) $(1-i)^7$

   by making use of de Moivre's theorem.

5. Simplify $(1+i)^{10}-(1-i)^{10}$.

   Given that n is a positive integer, show that

   $$(1+i)^{4n}-(1-i)^{4n}=0.$$

6. Given that $z=\dfrac{\sqrt{3}}{2}+\dfrac{1}{2}i$, simplify z^2, z^3, z^4 and illustrate each of these numbers as points on an Argand diagram.

7. Show that the three roots of $z^3=1$ can be expressed in the form 1, ω, ω^2.

   Hence show that $1+\omega+\omega^2=0$.

   Using this relation and the fact that $\omega^3=1$, simplify the following

   (a) $(1+\omega)^7$ (b) $(1-\omega)(1-\omega^2)$

   (c) $\dfrac{\omega^5}{1+\omega}$ (d) $\left(1-\omega+\omega^2\right)^4$

   (e) $\left(\omega-\omega^2\right)^5$ (f) $\dfrac{\left(1+\omega^2\right)(1-\omega)}{(1+\omega)}$

8. The roots of the equation $z^2+4z+29=0$ are z_1 and z_2. Show that $|z_1|=|z_2|$ and calculate, in degrees, the argument of z_1 and the argument of z_2.

   In an Argand diagram, O is the origin and z_1 and z_2 are represented by the points P and Q.

   Calculate the radius of the circle passing throught the points O, P and Q.   (AEB)

9. Sketch on an Argand diagram the loci given by

$$|z-1-2i|=5$$

$$|z-5+i|=|z+3-5i|$$

Show that these loci intersect at the point z_1 where $z_1 = -2-2i$, and at a second point z_2. Find z_2 in the form $a+bi$, where a and b are real.

Express z_1 in the form $r(\cos\alpha + i\sin\alpha)$ where $r > 0$ and $-\pi < \alpha \le \pi$, giving the value of r and the value of α. Show that z_1 is a root of the equation $z^4 + 64 = 0$.

Express $z^4 + 64$ in the form

$$\left(z^2 + Az + B\right)\left(z^2 + Cz + D\right)$$

where A, B, C and D are real, and find these numbers. (AEB)

10. (a) Find the modulus and argument of the complex number $\dfrac{\sqrt{3}+i}{1+i\sqrt{3}}$ giving the argument in radians between $-\pi$ and π.

(b) Find the value of the real number λ in the case when $\dfrac{\sqrt{3}+i\lambda}{1+i\sqrt{3}}$ is real. (AEB)

11. The complex number $u = -10 + 9i$

(a) Show the complex number u on an Argand diagram.

(b) Giving your answer to the nearest degree, calculate the argument of u.

(c) Find the complex number v which satisfies the equation

$$uv = -11 + 28i.$$

(d) Verify that $|u+v| = 8\sqrt{2}$. (AEB)

12. (a) The complex number z satisfies the equation $|z+1| = \sqrt{2}|z-1|$. The point P represents z on an Argand diagram. Show that the locus of P is a circle with its centre on the real axis, and find its radius.

(b) Find the four roots of the equation

$$(z+1)^4 + 4(z-1)^4 = 0,$$

expressing the roots z_1, z_2, z_3 and z_4 in the form $a+bi$.

Show that the points on an Argand diagram representing z_1, z_2, z_3 and z_4 are the vertices of a trapezium and calculate its area. (AEB)

13. Let z be the complex number $-1 + \sqrt{3}i$.

(a) Express z^2 in the form $a+bi$.

(b) Find the value of the real number p such that $z^2 + pz$ is real.

(c) Find the value of the real number q such that

$$\operatorname{Arg}\left(z^2 + qz\right) = \frac{5\pi}{6}. \qquad \text{(AEB)}$$

14. Use the method of mathematical induction to prove that

$$(\cos\theta + i\sin\theta)^n = \cos n\theta + i\sin n\theta,$$

where n is a positive integer.

Deduce that the result is also true when n is a negative integer.

Show that

$$2\cos n\theta = z^n + z^{-n},$$

where $z = \cos\theta + i\sin\theta$.

By considering $\left(z + z^{-1}\right)^4$, show that

$$\cos^4\theta \equiv \frac{1}{8}(\cos 4\theta + 4\cos 2\theta + 3).$$

Hence evaluate $\displaystyle\int_0^{\frac{\pi}{6}} \cos^4 2\theta \, d\theta.$ (AEB)

15. You are given the complex number

$$\omega = \cos\frac{2\pi}{5} + i\sin\frac{2\pi}{5}.$$

(a) Write down the value of ω^5 and prove that

$$1 + \omega + \omega^2 + \omega^3 + \omega^4 = 0.$$

Simplify $\left(\omega + \omega^4\right)\left(\omega^2 + \omega^3\right)$.

Form a quadratic equation with integer coefficients having roots

$$\left(\omega + \omega^4\right) \text{ and } \left(\omega^2 + \omega^3\right)$$

and hence prove that

$$\cos\frac{2\pi}{5} = \frac{-1+\sqrt{5}}{4}.$$

(b) In an Argand diagram the point P is represented by the complex number z.

Sketch and describe geometrically in each case, the locus of the point P when

(i) $|z - \omega| = |z - 1|$

(ii) $\arg\left(\dfrac{z-\omega}{z-1}\right) = \dfrac{\pi}{5}.$

(AEB)

16. (a) Use de Moivre's theorem to show that

$$\left(\sqrt{3}-i\right)^n = 2^n\left(\cos\frac{n\pi}{6} - i\sin\frac{n\pi}{6}\right),$$

where n is an integer.

    (i) Find the least positive integer m for which $\left(\sqrt{3}-i\right)^m$ is real and positive.

   (ii) Given that $\left(\sqrt{3}-i\right)$ is a root of the equation $z^9 + 16(1+i)z^3 + a + ib = 0,$

      find the values of the real constants a and b.

(b) The point P represents a complex number z on an Argand diagram and

$$\left|z - \omega^6\right| = 3\left|z - \omega^3\right|,$$

where $\omega = \sqrt{3} - i.$

Show that the locus of P is a circle and find its radius and the complex number represented by its centre.

(AEB)

4 VECTORS

Objectives

After studying this chapter you should

*   understand the difference between vectors and scalars;
*   be able to find the magnitude and direction of a vector;
*   be able to add vectors, and multiply by a scalar;
*   appreciate the geometrical representation of vectors;
*   be able to evaluate and interpret the scalar and vector products.

4.0   Introduction

Some physical quantities, such as temperature or time, are completely specified by a number given in appropriate units e.g. 20°C, 14.30 hours. Quantities of this sort, which have only magnitude, are referred to as **scalars**; whereas quantities for which it is also necessary to give a direction as well as magnitude are called **vectors**. Examples include

> wind velocity
>
> force
>
> displacement.

In this text we will print vectors in **bold** type; for example

> **a**, **b**, etc.

Unfortunately, when **writing** vectors you cannot distinguish them from scalars in this way. The standard way of writing vectors is to underline them; for example

> $\underset{\sim}{a}$, $\underset{\sim}{b}$, etc.

It is very important for you to conform to this notation. Always remember to underline your vectors, otherwise great confusion will arise!

Activity 1

Make a list of scalar and vector quantities, distinguishing between them.

4.1   Vector representation

A vector can be represented by a section of a straight line, whose length is equal to the magnitude of the vector, and whose direction represents the direction of the vector.

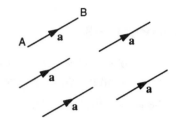

All the lines shown opposite have the same magnitude and direction, and so all represent the same vector **a**. Sometimes the notation

$$\overrightarrow{AB}$$

is used to represent the vector **a**.

Modulus

The **modulus** of a vector **a** is its magnitude. It is written as $|\mathbf{a}|$, and is equal to the length of the line representing the vector.

Equal vectors

The vectors **a** and **b** are equal if, and only if,

> $|\mathbf{a}| = |\mathbf{b}|$ and
>
> **a** and **b** are in the same direction.

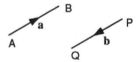

How are the vectors shown opposite, $\mathbf{a} = \overrightarrow{AB}$ and $\mathbf{b} = \overrightarrow{PQ}$, related?

Since $|\mathbf{a}| = |\mathbf{b}|$, and they are in opposite directions, we say that

$$\mathbf{b} = -\mathbf{a}.$$

Multiplication of a vector by a scalar

If λ is a positive real number, then $\lambda\mathbf{a}$ is a vector in the same direction as **a** and is of magnitude $\lambda|\mathbf{a}|$. If $\lambda = 0$, then $\lambda\mathbf{a}$ is the zero vector **0**, and if $\lambda < 0$ then $\lambda\mathbf{a}$ is the vector in the opposite direction to **a** and of magnitude $|\lambda||\mathbf{a}|$.

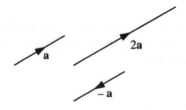

Does the definition make sense when $\lambda = -1$?

Activity 2

Draw any vector **b** on a sheet of paper, and then also draw

(a) $-\mathbf{b}$

(b) $2\mathbf{b}, 3\mathbf{b}, 4\mathbf{b}$

(c) $\frac{1}{2}\mathbf{b}$

(d) $-2\mathbf{b}, -\frac{1}{2}\mathbf{b}$

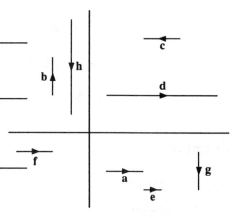

Activity 3

The diagram opposite shows a number of vectors. Express vectors **c**, **d**, **e**, **f**, **g** and **h** in terms of **a** or **b**.

4.2 Vector addition

If the sides AB and BC of a triangle ABC represent the vectors **p** and **q**, then the third side, AC, is defined as the vector sum of **p** and **q**; that is

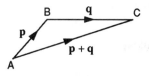

$$\overrightarrow{AB} = \mathbf{p}, \ \overrightarrow{BC} = \mathbf{q} \ \Rightarrow \ \overrightarrow{AC} = \mathbf{p} + \mathbf{q}$$

This definition of vector addition is referred to as the **triangle law of addition**. You can then subtract vectors, for $\mathbf{a} - \mathbf{b}$ simply means $\mathbf{a} + (-\mathbf{b})$. For example

$$\overrightarrow{AB} = \overrightarrow{BC} - \overrightarrow{AC}.$$

As an example, consider the displacement vectors. If you walk in the direction North for 5 miles, then East for 10 miles, you can

represent these two displacements as vectors, $\overrightarrow{OA}$ and $\overrightarrow{AB}$, as

shown opposite. The vector addition of $\overrightarrow{OA}$ and $\overrightarrow{AB}$ is $\overrightarrow{OB}$, and this indeed is the final displacement from O.

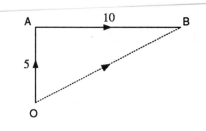

Example

In the triangle ABC, $\overrightarrow{AB}$ represents **a**, $\overrightarrow{BC}$ represents **b**. If D is

the midpoint of AB, express $\overrightarrow{AC}$, $\overrightarrow{CA}$ and $\overrightarrow{DC}$ in terms of **a** and **b**.

Solution

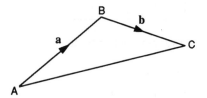

$$\vec{AC} = \vec{AB} + \vec{AC} = \mathbf{a} + \mathbf{b}$$

$$\vec{CA} = -\vec{AC} = -\mathbf{a} - \mathbf{b}$$

$$\vec{DC} = \vec{DA} + \vec{AC}$$

$$= -\vec{AD} + \vec{AC}$$

$$= -\tfrac{1}{2}\mathbf{a} + (\mathbf{a} + \mathbf{b}) \text{ (since D is the midpoint of AB)}$$

$$= \tfrac{1}{2}\mathbf{a} + \mathbf{b}$$

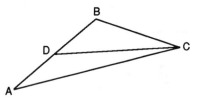

Example

ABCD is a parallelogram. $\vec{AB}$ represents $\mathbf{a}$ and $\vec{BC}$ represents $\mathbf{b}$. If M is the midpoint of AC, and N is the midpoint of BD, find $\vec{AM}$ and $\vec{AN}$ in terms of $\mathbf{a}$ and $\mathbf{b}$, and hence show that M and N are coincident.

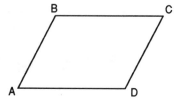

Solution

$$\vec{AC} = \vec{AB} + \vec{BC} = \mathbf{a} + \mathbf{b}$$

so

$$\vec{AM} = \tfrac{1}{2}(\mathbf{a} + \mathbf{b}).$$

Similarly,

$$\vec{BD} = \vec{BA} + \vec{AD} = -\vec{AB} + \vec{BC} = -\mathbf{a} + \mathbf{b},$$

so

$$\vec{BN} = \tfrac{1}{2}(-\mathbf{a} + \mathbf{b})$$

and

$$\vec{AN} = \vec{AB} + \vec{BN}$$

$$= \mathbf{a} + \tfrac{1}{2}(-\mathbf{a} + \mathbf{b})$$

$$= \mathbf{a} - \tfrac{1}{2}\mathbf{a} + \tfrac{1}{2}\mathbf{b}$$

$$= \tfrac{1}{2}(\mathbf{a} + \mathbf{b})$$

$$= \vec{AM}.$$

Since $\vec{AN} = \vec{AM}$, N and M must be coincident.

Exercise 4A

1. Four points, O, A, B and C are such that

   $\vec{OA} = 10a$, $\vec{OB} = 5b$, $\vec{OC} = 4a + 3b$.

   Find $\vec{AB}$ and $\vec{BC}$ in terms of **a** and **b** and hence show that A, B and C are collinear.

2. ABCD is a quadrilateral. Find a single vector which is equivalent to

   (a) $\vec{AB} + \vec{BC}$ (b) $\vec{BC} + \vec{CD}$ (c) $\vec{AB} + \vec{BC} + \vec{CD}$

   Hence deduce that

   $\vec{AB} + \vec{BC} + \vec{CD} + \vec{DA} = \mathbf{0}$.

3. If **a**, **b** and **c** are represented by $\vec{AB}$, $\vec{AD}$ and $\vec{AF}$ in the cube shown, find in terms of **a**, **b** and **c**, the vectors represented by other edges.

   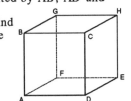

4. OABC is a tetrahedron with

   $\vec{OA} = a$, $\vec{OB} = b$, $\vec{OC} = c$.

   Find $\vec{AC}$, $\vec{AB}$ and $\vec{CB}$ in terms of **a**, **b** and **c** and hence show that

   $\vec{AB} + \vec{BC} + \vec{CA} = \mathbf{0}$.

5. In a regular hexagon ABCDEF, $\vec{AB} = a$ and $\vec{BC} = b$. Find expressions for $\vec{DE}$, $\vec{DC}$, $\vec{AD}$ and $\vec{BD}$ in terms of **a** and **b**.

6. Given that $\vec{OA} + \vec{OC} = \vec{OB} + \vec{OD}$, show that the quadrilateral ABCD is a parallelogram.

4.3   Position vectors

In general, a vector has no specific location in space. However, if

$a = \vec{OA}$, where O is a fixed origin, then **a** is referred to as the position vector of A, relative to O.

Is the position vector unique?

The use of position vectors for solving geometry problems has already been illustrated in the previous section. Here, you will see many more examples of this type, but first an important result.

Theorem

If A and B are points with position vectors **a** and **b** and point C divides A and B in the ratio $\lambda : \mu$, then C has position vector

$$\boxed{\dfrac{\mu a + \lambda b}{(\lambda + \mu)}}$$

Proof

If C divides AB in the ratio $\lambda : \mu$, then

$$AC = \frac{\lambda}{(\lambda + \mu)} AB$$

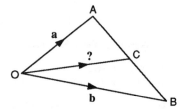

(and $CB = \dfrac{\mu}{(\lambda + \mu)} AB$)

Hence $\vec{AC} = \dfrac{\lambda}{(\lambda + \mu)} \vec{AB}$

since $\vec{AC}$ and $\vec{AB}$ are in the same direction. Thus

$$\vec{AC} = \frac{\lambda}{(\lambda + \mu)}\left(\vec{OB} - \vec{OA}\right)$$

$$= \frac{\lambda}{(\lambda + \mu)}(\mathbf{b} - \mathbf{a})$$

and $\vec{OC} = \vec{OA} + \vec{AC}$

$$= \mathbf{a} + \frac{\lambda}{(\lambda + \mu)}(\mathbf{b} - \mathbf{a})$$

$$= \frac{\mathbf{a}(\lambda + \mu - \lambda) + \lambda\mathbf{b}}{(\lambda + \mu)}$$

$$= \frac{\mu\mathbf{a} + \lambda\mathbf{b}}{(\lambda + \mu)}, \text{ as required.}$$

Note that, in the special case $\lambda = \mu$, when C is the midpoint of AB, then

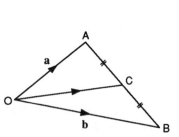

$$\vec{OC} = \tfrac{1}{2}(\mathbf{a} + \mathbf{b})$$

and this result has already been developed in the last section.

Example

In the triangle OAB, $\vec{OA} = \mathbf{a}$ and $\vec{OB} = \mathbf{b}$. If C divides the line AB in the ratio 1:2 and D divides the line OB in the ratio 1:2, find $\vec{DC}$ and hence show that DC is parallel to OA.

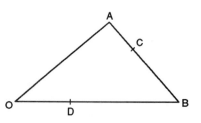

Solution

From the result in the theorem above

$$\vec{OC} = \frac{2\mathbf{a}+\mathbf{b}}{3} = \frac{2}{3}\mathbf{a} + \frac{1}{3}\mathbf{b}$$

Clearly $\quad \vec{OD} = \frac{1}{3}\mathbf{b},$

so $\quad \vec{DC} = \vec{DO} + \vec{OC} = -\frac{1}{3}\mathbf{b} + \left(\frac{2}{3}\mathbf{a} + \frac{1}{3}\mathbf{b}\right) = \frac{2}{3}\mathbf{a}$

Since $\vec{DC}$ is a multiple of $\mathbf{a}$, it is in the same direction as $\mathbf{a}$; that is, DC is parallel to OA.

Example

In the figure opposite, X and Y are the midpoints of OA and OB respectively. If $\vec{OA} = \mathbf{a}$ and $\vec{OB} = \mathbf{b}$ find the position vector of the point Z, the intersection of XB and YA.

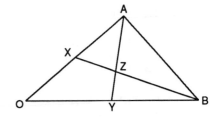

Solution

$$\vec{OX} = \frac{1}{2}\mathbf{a} \text{ and } \vec{OY} = \frac{1}{2}\mathbf{b}.$$

Thus $\quad \vec{XB} = \vec{XO} + \vec{OB}$

$$= -\frac{1}{2}\mathbf{a} + \mathbf{b} \ = \mathbf{b} - \frac{1}{2}\mathbf{a}$$

Since Z lies on XB, for some scalar number, say t,

$$\vec{XZ} = t\vec{XB} = t\left(\mathbf{b} - \frac{1}{2}\mathbf{a}\right)$$

and $\quad \vec{OZ} = \vec{OX} + \vec{XZ}$

$$= \frac{1}{2}\mathbf{a} + t\left(\mathbf{b} - \frac{1}{2}\mathbf{a}\right)$$

$$= \frac{1}{2}(1-t)\mathbf{a} + t\mathbf{b}.$$

Similarly, for some scalar number s, using the fact that Z lies on $\overrightarrow{AY}$ gives

$$\overrightarrow{OZ} = s\mathbf{a} + \frac{1}{2}(1-s)\mathbf{b}.$$

But these vectors are equal, so equating coefficients of $\mathbf{a}$ and $\mathbf{b}$,

$$\left. \begin{array}{ll} \frac{1}{2}(1-t) = s & \Rightarrow \quad 2s + t = 1 \\[2mm] t = \frac{1}{2}(1-s) & \Rightarrow \quad s + 2t = 1 \end{array} \right\} \quad s = t = \frac{1}{3}.$$

Hence $\qquad \overrightarrow{OZ} = \frac{1}{3}(\mathbf{a}+\mathbf{b})$

Example 4B

1. In the diagram

    $TA = 2BT$

    $\overrightarrow{OA} = \mathbf{a}$

    $\overrightarrow{OB} = \mathbf{b}$

    $\overrightarrow{AC} = 2\mathbf{b}$

    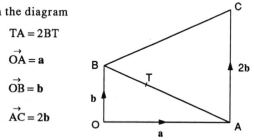

    (a) Find in terms of $\mathbf{a}$ and $\mathbf{b}$

    (i) $\overrightarrow{AB}$ (ii) $\overrightarrow{TB}$ (iii) $\overrightarrow{BC}$ (iv) $\overrightarrow{OT}$ (v) $\overrightarrow{TC}$.

    (b) From (iv) and (v), what can you deduce about O, T and C?

2. From an origin O the points A, B and C have position vectors $\mathbf{a}$, $\mathbf{b}$ and $2\mathbf{b}$ respectively. The points O, A and B are not collinear. The midpoint of AB is M, and the point of trisection of AC nearer to A is T. Draw a diagram to show O, A, B, C, M, T.

    Find, in terms of $\mathbf{a}$ and $\mathbf{b}$, the position vectors of M and T. Use your results to prove that O, M and T are collinear, and find the ratio in which M divides OT.

3. The vertices A, B and C of a triangle have position vectors $\mathbf{a}$, $\mathbf{b}$, $\mathbf{c}$ respectively relative to an origin O. The point P is on BC such that BP:PC=3:1; the point Q is on CA such that CQ: QA=2:3; the point R is on BA produced such that BR: AR=2:1.

    The position vectors of P, Q and R are $\mathbf{p}$, $\mathbf{q}$ and $\mathbf{r}$ respectively. Show that $\mathbf{q}$ can be expressed in terms of $\mathbf{p}$ and $\mathbf{r}$ and hence, or otherwise, show that P, Q and R are collinear. State the ratio of the lengths of the line segments PQ and QR.

4. The points A, B and C have position vectors $\mathbf{a}$, $\mathbf{b}$, $\mathbf{c}$ respectively referred to an origin O.

    (a) Given that the point X lies on AB produced so that AB: BX=2:1, find $\mathbf{x}$, the position vector of X, in terms of $\mathbf{a}$ and $\mathbf{b}$.

    (b) If Y lies on BC, between B and C so that BY: YC=1:3, find $\mathbf{y}$, the position vector of Y, in terms of $\mathbf{b}$ and $\mathbf{c}$.

    (c) Given that Z is the midpoint of AC, show that X, Y and Z are collinear.

    (d) Calculate XY: YZ.

5. The position vectors of three points A, B and C relative to an origin O are $\mathbf{p}$, $3\mathbf{q} - \mathbf{p}$, and $9\mathbf{q} - 5\mathbf{p}$ respectively. Show that the points A, B and C lie on the same straight line, and state the ratio AB: BC. Given that OBCD is a parallelogram and that E is the point such that $\overrightarrow{DB} = \frac{1}{3}\overrightarrow{DE}$, find the position vectors of D and E relative to O.

4.4   Components of a vector

In this section, the idea of a **unit vector** is first introduced. This is a vector which has unit magnitude. So if **a** is any vector, its magnitude is $|\mathbf{a}|$, and (provided that $\mathbf{a} \neq \mathbf{0}$) the vector

$$\hat{\mathbf{a}} = \frac{\mathbf{a}}{|\mathbf{a}|}$$

is a unit vector, parallel to **a**.

Introducing cartesian axes Oxyz in the usual way, unit vectors in the direction Ox, Oy and Oz are represented by

$$\mathbf{i}, \mathbf{j}\ \text{and}\ \mathbf{k}\ .$$

Suppose P is any point with coordinates (x, y, z) relative to O as illustrated.

What is the magnitude and direction of the vector x =xi ?

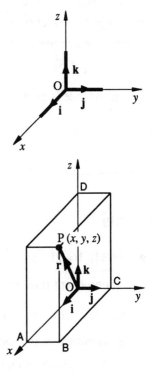

Clearly $\qquad \overrightarrow{OA} = x\mathbf{i}\ \ (=\mathbf{x})$

and $\qquad \overrightarrow{OA} + \overrightarrow{AB} = x\mathbf{i} + \overrightarrow{OC}$

$$= x\mathbf{i} + y\mathbf{j}$$

and $\qquad \overrightarrow{OA} + \overrightarrow{AB} + \overrightarrow{BP} = x\mathbf{i} + y\mathbf{j} + \overrightarrow{OD}$

$$= x\mathbf{i} + y\mathbf{j} + z\mathbf{k}$$

What is the vector $\overrightarrow{OA} + \overrightarrow{AB} + \overrightarrow{BP}$?

Thus

$$\mathbf{r} = \overrightarrow{OP} = x\mathbf{i} + y\mathbf{i} + z\mathbf{k}$$

This vector is often written as a 3×1 column matrix

$$\mathbf{r} = \begin{bmatrix} x \\ y \\ z \end{bmatrix}$$

and the notation $\mathbf{r} = (x, y, z)$ is also sometimes used.

Activity 4

For vectors with two dimensions, using unit vector **i** and **j** as shown opposite, express **a**, **b**, **c**, **d** and **e** in terms of **i** and **j**.

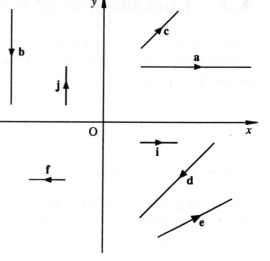

From the activity above, you should have shown that, for example,

$$\mathbf{c} = \mathbf{i} + \mathbf{j} \text{ and } \mathbf{e} = 2\mathbf{i} + \mathbf{j}.$$

Then the vector **c** + **e** is simply $3\mathbf{i} + 2\mathbf{j}$: adding vectors in form is just a matter of adding components.

For vectors in 2 dimensions, in general

$$\mathbf{r} = \overrightarrow{OP} = x\mathbf{i} + y\mathbf{j}$$

and its magnitude is given by the length OP,

where $\qquad OP = \sqrt{x^2 + y^2}$

$$\Rightarrow \quad |\mathbf{r}| = \sqrt{x^2 + y^2}$$

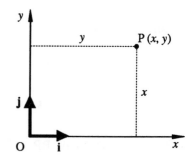

Example

If $\mathbf{a} = \mathbf{i} + 3\mathbf{j}$, $\mathbf{b} = 2\mathbf{i} - 5\mathbf{j}$, $\mathbf{c} = -2\mathbf{i} + 4\mathbf{j}$, find

(a)   the component form of the vectors

(i) $\mathbf{a} + \mathbf{b}$ (ii) $\mathbf{b} + \mathbf{c}$ (iii) $\mathbf{a} - \mathbf{b}$ (iv) $\mathbf{a} + \mathbf{b} - \mathbf{c}$ (v) $3\mathbf{a} + 2\mathbf{b}$;

(b)   the magnitude of the vectors in (a);

(c)   unit vectors in the direction of $\mathbf{a} + \mathbf{b}$ and $\mathbf{b} + \mathbf{c}$.

Solution

(a)   (i) $\mathbf{a} + \mathbf{b} = (\mathbf{i} + 3\mathbf{j}) + (2\mathbf{i} - 5\mathbf{j}) = 3\mathbf{i} - 2\mathbf{j}$

(ii) $\mathbf{b} + \mathbf{c} = (2\mathbf{i} - 5\mathbf{j}) + (-2\mathbf{i} + 4\mathbf{j}) = 0\mathbf{i} - \mathbf{j} = -\mathbf{j}$

(iii) $\mathbf{a} - \mathbf{b} = (\mathbf{i} + 3\mathbf{j}) - (2\mathbf{i} - 5\mathbf{j}) = -\mathbf{i} + 8\mathbf{j}$

(iv) $\mathbf{a} + \mathbf{b} - \mathbf{c} = (\mathbf{a} + \mathbf{b}) - \mathbf{c} = 3\mathbf{i} - 2\mathbf{j} - (-2\mathbf{i} + 4\mathbf{j}) = 5\mathbf{i} - 6\mathbf{j}$

(v) $3\mathbf{a} + 2\mathbf{b} = 3(\mathbf{i} + 3\mathbf{j}) + 2(2\mathbf{i} - 5\mathbf{j}) = 3\mathbf{i} + 9\mathbf{j} + 4\mathbf{i} - 10\mathbf{j} = 7\mathbf{i} - \mathbf{j}$

(b)   (i) $|\mathbf{a} + \mathbf{b}| = \sqrt{3^2 + (-2)^2} = \sqrt{9 + 4} = \sqrt{13}$

(ii) $|\mathbf{b} + \mathbf{c}| = 1$

(iii) $|\mathbf{a} - \mathbf{b}| = \sqrt{(-1)^2 + 8^2} = \sqrt{65}$

(iv) $|\mathbf{a} + \mathbf{b} + \mathbf{c}| = \sqrt{25 + (-6)^2} = \sqrt{61}$

(v) $|3\mathbf{a}+2\mathbf{b}| = \sqrt{7^2 + (-4)^2} = \sqrt{65}$

(c) If $\mathbf{n}=\mathbf{a}+\mathbf{b}$, $\hat{\mathbf{n}} = \dfrac{1}{\sqrt{13}}(3\mathbf{i}-2\mathbf{j}) = \dfrac{3}{\sqrt{13}}\mathbf{i} - \dfrac{2}{\sqrt{13}}\mathbf{j}$

If $\mathbf{n}=\mathbf{b}+\mathbf{c}$, $\hat{\mathbf{n}} = \dfrac{1}{1}(-\mathbf{j}) = -\mathbf{j}$

For vectors in 3 dimensions, the position vector of the point P with coordinates (x, y, z) is given by

$$\mathbf{r} = x\mathbf{i} + y\mathbf{j} + z\mathbf{k}$$

and its magnitude is given by

$$\boxed{|\mathbf{r}| = \sqrt{x^2 + y^2 + z^2}}$$

Why is this result true?

You can perform algebraic operations in the usual way; for example, if

$$\mathbf{a} = 3\mathbf{i} + 2\mathbf{j} + \mathbf{k}$$
$$\mathbf{b} = \mathbf{i} - 2\mathbf{j} + \mathbf{k}$$

thus

$$\mathbf{a} + \mathbf{b} = (3\mathbf{i} + 2\mathbf{j} + \mathbf{k}) + (\mathbf{i} - 2\mathbf{j} + \mathbf{k})$$
$$= 4\mathbf{i} + 2\mathbf{k}$$
$$\mathbf{a} - \mathbf{b} = (3\mathbf{i} + 2\mathbf{j} + \mathbf{k}) - (\mathbf{i} - 2\mathbf{j} + \mathbf{k})$$
$$= 2\mathbf{i} + 4\mathbf{j}$$
$$|\mathbf{a}| = \sqrt{3^2 + 2^2 + 1^2} = \sqrt{14}$$

$$|\mathbf{b}| = \sqrt{1^2 + \left(-2^2\right) + 1^2} = \sqrt{6}$$

Note that two vectors, $\mathbf{a}$ and $\mathbf{b}$ are **parallel** if $\mathbf{a} = \lambda\mathbf{b}$ for some non-zero λ; furthermore, if $\lambda > 0$ they are actually in the same direction.

Also note that two vectors

$$\mathbf{a} = a_1\mathbf{i} + a_2\mathbf{j} + a_3\mathbf{k} \quad \text{and} \quad \mathbf{b} = b_1\mathbf{i} + b_2\mathbf{j} + b_3\mathbf{k}$$

are equal if, and only if, their components are equal,

i.e. $a_1 = b_1$, $a_2 = b_2$, $a_3 = b_3$.

Activity 5

If $\mathbf{a} = 2\mathbf{i} + \mathbf{j} - \mathbf{k}$, $\mathbf{b} = \mathbf{i} - 2\mathbf{j} + 3\mathbf{k}$, which of the vectors below are parallel to $\mathbf{a}$ or $\mathbf{b}$?

(i) $-2\mathbf{i} - \mathbf{j} + \mathbf{k}$ (ii) $5\mathbf{i} - 10\mathbf{j} + 15\mathbf{k}$

(iii) $4\mathbf{i} - 2\mathbf{j} - 2\mathbf{k}$ (iv) $6\mathbf{i} + 3\mathbf{j} - 3\mathbf{k}$

(v) $-2\mathbf{i} + 4\mathbf{j} - 6\mathbf{k}$ (vi) $-4\mathbf{i} - 2\mathbf{j} + 2\mathbf{k}$

Exercise 4C

1. Write in the form $x\mathbf{i} + y\mathbf{j} + z\mathbf{k}$, the vectors represented by $\overrightarrow{OP}$ if P is the point

    (a) (1, 1, 1)   (b) (2, 1, –1)   (c) (1, –1, 0)

2. $\overrightarrow{OP}$ represents the vector $\mathbf{r}$. Write down the coordinates of P if

    (a) $\mathbf{r} = 3\mathbf{i} - 4\mathbf{j} + \mathbf{k}$ (b) $\mathbf{r} = \mathbf{i} + 2\mathbf{j} - \mathbf{k}$ (c) $\mathbf{r} = -4\mathbf{k}$

3. Find the magnitude of the vectors

    (a) $\mathbf{a} = 6\mathbf{i} + 2\mathbf{j} + 3\mathbf{k}$ (b) $\mathbf{b} = 2\mathbf{i} - \mathbf{j} - 2\mathbf{k}$

    (c) $\mathbf{c} = \mathbf{a} + \mathbf{b}$ (d) $\mathbf{d} = \mathbf{a} - \mathbf{b}$

    Also find unit vectors in the direction of $\mathbf{a}$ and $\mathbf{b}$.

4. If $\mathbf{a} = 2\mathbf{i} + 5\mathbf{j} - \mathbf{k}$, $\mathbf{b} = \mathbf{i} + \mathbf{j} + 2\mathbf{k}$, $\mathbf{c} = -2\mathbf{i} + 3\mathbf{j} - \mathbf{k}$ find

    (a) $\mathbf{a} + \mathbf{b}$ (b) $(\mathbf{a} + \mathbf{b}) + \mathbf{c}$ (c) $\mathbf{a} + (\mathbf{b} + \mathbf{c})$

    (d) $\mathbf{a} - 5\mathbf{b} + 11\mathbf{c}$

5. Show that the points A(4, –2, –16), B(0, –10, –4) and C(–6, –22, 14) are collinear.

4.5   Products of vectors

The 'algebra' of vectors has been developed in previous sections. You can add and subtract vectors, multiply a vector by a scalar $(\lambda\mathbf{a})$, but as yet not 'multiply' vectors. There are, in fact, two ways of multiplying vectors: one, the **scalar product** leading to a scalar quantity; the other, the **vector product**, being a vector.

Scalar product

For any two vectors $\mathbf{a}$ and $\mathbf{b}$, the **scalar product**, denoted by $\mathbf{a}.\mathbf{b}$ is defined by

$$\boxed{\mathbf{a}.\mathbf{b} = |\mathbf{a}||\mathbf{b}|\cos\theta}$$

Here $|\mathbf{a}|$ is the modulus of $\mathbf{a}$, $|\mathbf{b}|$ is the modulus of $\mathbf{b}$, and θ is the angle between the direction of the two vectors. (Some texts refer to the scalar product as the 'dot' product, and you say 'a dot b' for $\mathbf{a}.\mathbf{b}$)

Example

If $\mathbf{a} = 2\mathbf{i}$, $\mathbf{b} = 5\mathbf{j}$ and $\mathbf{c} = \mathbf{i} + \mathbf{j}$, find

(a) $\mathbf{a}.\mathbf{b}$ (b) $\mathbf{a}.\mathbf{c}$ (c) $\mathbf{b}.\mathbf{c}$

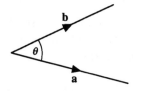

Solution

(a) $\mathbf{a}.\mathbf{b} = |\mathbf{a}||\mathbf{b}|\cos 90°$

$= 2 \times 5 \times 0 = 0$

(b) $\mathbf{a}.\mathbf{c} = |\mathbf{a}||\mathbf{c}|\cos 45°$

$= 2 \times \sqrt{2} \times \dfrac{1}{\sqrt{2}}$ $\left(\text{since } |\mathbf{c}| = \sqrt{2}\right)$

$= 2$

(c) $\mathbf{b}.\mathbf{c} = |\mathbf{b}||\mathbf{c}|\cos 45°$

$= 5 \times \sqrt{2} \times \dfrac{1}{\sqrt{2}}$

$= 5$

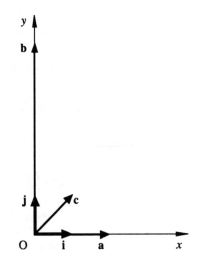

From the definition of the scalar product:

(i)   If $\mathbf{a}$ and $\mathbf{b}$ are perpendicular (as in (a) above), then
$\theta = 90°$ and $\cos \theta = 0$, which gives $\mathbf{a}.\mathbf{b} = 0$.

(ii) If, for non-zero vectors $\mathbf{a}$ and $\mathbf{b}$, $\mathbf{a}.\mathbf{b} = 0$, then
$|\mathbf{a}||\mathbf{b}|\cos \theta = 0 \Rightarrow \cos \theta = 0$, since $|\mathbf{a}| \neq 0, |\mathbf{b}| \neq 0$;
then $\theta = 90°$ and $\mathbf{a}$ and $\mathbf{b}$ are perpendicular.

To summarise, for non-zero vectors $\mathbf{a}$ and $\mathbf{b}$

$$\boxed{\mathbf{a}.\mathbf{b} = 0 \Leftrightarrow \mathbf{a}, \mathbf{b} \text{ perpendicular}}$$

Also it is clear that

$$\boxed{\mathbf{a}.\mathbf{a} = |\mathbf{a}|^2}$$

Activity 6

Evaluate the scalar products

(a) $\mathbf{i}.\mathbf{i}$, $\mathbf{i}.\mathbf{j}$, $\mathbf{i}.\mathbf{k}$

(b) $\mathbf{j}.\mathbf{i}$, $\mathbf{j}.\mathbf{j}$, $\mathbf{j}.\mathbf{k}$

(c) $\mathbf{k}.\mathbf{i}$, $\mathbf{k}.\mathbf{j}$, $\mathbf{k}.\mathbf{k}$

(d) $(\mathbf{i}+\mathbf{j}).\mathbf{j}$, $(2\mathbf{i}+\mathbf{k}).\mathbf{k}$

Check, in (d), that for example,

$$(2\mathbf{i}+\mathbf{k}).\mathbf{k} = 2\mathbf{i}.\mathbf{k}+\mathbf{k}.\mathbf{k}$$

Assuming that the scalar product always behaves in this natural way, deduce a formula for **a.b** when **a** and **b** are expressed in component form

$$\mathbf{a} = a_1\mathbf{i}+a_2\mathbf{j}+a_3\mathbf{k}, \ \mathbf{b} = b_1\mathbf{i}+b_2\mathbf{j}+b_3\mathbf{k}$$

You should have found in Activity 6 that

$$\mathbf{i}.\mathbf{i} = \mathbf{j}.\mathbf{j} = \mathbf{k}.\mathbf{k} = 1, \quad (\mathbf{i}, \mathbf{j}, \mathbf{k} \text{ are unit vectors})$$

$$\mathbf{i}.\mathbf{j} = \mathbf{j}.\mathbf{k} = \mathbf{k}.\mathbf{i} = 0 \quad (\mathbf{i}, \mathbf{j}, \mathbf{k} \text{ are mutually perpendicular})$$

So if **a** and **b** are expressed in component form

$$\mathbf{a}.\mathbf{b} = (a_1\mathbf{i}+a_2\mathbf{j}+a_3\mathbf{k}).(b_1\mathbf{i}+b_2\mathbf{j}+b_3\mathbf{k})$$

$$= a_1(b_1\mathbf{i}.\mathbf{i}+b_2\mathbf{i}.\mathbf{j}+b_3\mathbf{i}.\mathbf{k})$$

$$+a_2(b_1\mathbf{j}.\mathbf{i}+b_2\mathbf{j}.\mathbf{j}+b_3\mathbf{j}.\mathbf{k})$$

$$+a_3(b_1\mathbf{k}.\mathbf{i}+b_2\mathbf{k}.\mathbf{j}+b_3\mathbf{k}.\mathbf{k})$$

$$= a_1 b_1 + a_2 b_2 + a_3 b_3 \qquad \text{(using the results above)}$$

So

$$\boxed{\mathbf{a}.\mathbf{b} = a_1 b_1 + a_2 b_2 + a_3 b_3}$$

Example

If $\mathbf{a} = 2\mathbf{i}+\mathbf{j}+3\mathbf{k}$, $\mathbf{b} = -3\mathbf{i}+\mathbf{j}-2\mathbf{k}$, find **a.b** and the cosine of the angle between **a** and **b**.

Solution

$$\mathbf{a}.\mathbf{b} = (2\mathbf{i}+\mathbf{j}+3\mathbf{k}).(-3\mathbf{i}+\mathbf{j}-2\mathbf{k})$$

$$= 2\times(-3)+1\times1+3\times(-2) = -6+1-6 = -11$$

So
$$\mathbf{a}.\mathbf{b} = |\mathbf{a}||\mathbf{b}|\cos\theta = -11$$

$$\Rightarrow \quad \sqrt{14}\sqrt{14}\cos\theta = -11$$

$$\Rightarrow \quad \cos\theta = -\frac{11}{14}$$

Example

Show that the vectors, $\mathbf{a} = \mathbf{i} + 2\mathbf{j} - \mathbf{k}$ and $\mathbf{b} = 2\mathbf{i} - 2\mathbf{j} - 2\mathbf{k}$, are perpendicular.

Solution

$$\mathbf{a} . \mathbf{b} = (\mathbf{i} + 2\mathbf{j} - \mathbf{k}) . (2\mathbf{i} - 2\mathbf{j} - 2\mathbf{k})$$
$$= 1 \times 2 + 2 \times (-2) + (-1) \times (-2)$$
$$= 2 - 4 + 2$$
$$= 0$$

Hence vectors $\mathbf{a}$ and $\mathbf{b}$ are perpendicular.

Activity 7

For the vector $\mathbf{x} = 3\mathbf{i} + 2\mathbf{j}$, $\mathbf{y} = \mathbf{i} + m\mathbf{j}$, determine the values of m for which

(a) $\mathbf{x}$ is perpendicular to $\mathbf{y}$

(b) $\mathbf{x}$ is parallel to $\mathbf{y}$

(c) the angle between $\mathbf{x}$ and $\mathbf{y}$ is $30°$.

Example

If $\mathbf{a} = 3\mathbf{i} - \mathbf{j} + 2\mathbf{k}$ and $\mathbf{b} = m\mathbf{i} - 2\mathbf{j} - 3\mathbf{k}$, find the value of m for which $\mathbf{a}$ and $\mathbf{b}$ are perpendicular.

Solution

$$\mathbf{a} . \mathbf{b} = (3\mathbf{i} - \mathbf{j} + 2\mathbf{k}) . (m\mathbf{i} - 2\mathbf{j} - 3\mathbf{k})$$
$$= 3m + (-1)(-2) + 2(-3)$$
$$= 3m + 2 - 6$$
$$= 3m - 4$$
$$= 0 \quad \Rightarrow \quad m = \frac{4}{3}$$

So $\mathbf{a}$ and $\mathbf{b}$ are perpendicular when $m = \frac{4}{3}$.

Vector product

For any two vectors, **a** and **b**, the vector product, denoted by $\mathbf{a} \times \mathbf{b}$ (or $\mathbf{a} \wedge \mathbf{b}$) is defined by

$$\boxed{\mathbf{a} \times \mathbf{b} = |\mathbf{a}||\mathbf{b}|\sin\theta\,\hat{\mathbf{n}}}$$

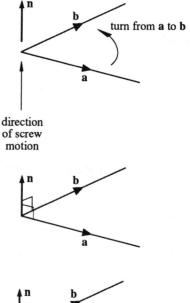

Here $|\mathbf{a}|$ is the magnitude of **a**, $|\mathbf{b}|$ is the magnitude of **b**, and $\hat{\mathbf{n}}$ is a unit vector, perpendicular to both **a** and **b** and in the sense of direction of linear motion when a screw turns from **a** to **b** as illustrated. In the figure if **a** and **b** are in a horizontal plane, then **n** is vertical.

This implies that **a**, **b** and $\hat{\mathbf{n}}$ form a right-handed system similar to the **i**, **j**, **k** system.

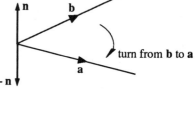

What is the magnitude of the vectors $\mathbf{a} \times \mathbf{b}$ **and** $\mathbf{b} \times \mathbf{a}$**?**

What is the direction of the vector $\mathbf{b} \times \mathbf{a}$**?**

To follow the direction of a screw's motion turning from **b** to **a** gives the direction $-\hat{\mathbf{n}}$, that is

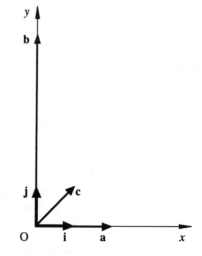

$$\mathbf{b} \times \mathbf{a} = |\mathbf{a}||\mathbf{b}|\sin\theta(-\hat{\mathbf{n}})$$

$$= -\mathbf{a} \times \mathbf{b}.$$

So $\mathbf{b} \times \mathbf{a} + \mathbf{a} \times \mathbf{b} = 0$

and the vector product is not, in general, commutative ($\mathbf{a} \times \mathbf{b} \neq \mathbf{b} \times \mathbf{a}$).

Example

If $\mathbf{a} = 2\mathbf{i}$, $\mathbf{b} = 5\mathbf{j}$ and $\mathbf{c} = \mathbf{i} + \mathbf{j}$, find

(a) $\mathbf{a} \times \mathbf{b}$ (b)   (c) $\mathbf{a} \times \mathbf{c}$ (d) $\mathbf{a} \times \mathbf{a}$

Solution   ᑲ ❰ᵡᑕ

(a) $\mathbf{a} \times \mathbf{b} = 2 \times 5 \times \sin 90° \,\mathbf{k} = 10\mathbf{k}$ (**k** is perpendicular to **a** and **b**)

(b) $\mathbf{b} \times \mathbf{c} = 5 \times \sqrt{2} \times \sin 45°(-\mathbf{k}) = -5\mathbf{k}$

(c) $\mathbf{a} \times \mathbf{c} = 2 \times \sqrt{2} \times \sin 45°(\mathbf{k}) = 2\mathbf{k}$

(d) $|\mathbf{a} \times \mathbf{a}| = 2 \times 2 \times \sin 0° = 0 \Rightarrow \mathbf{a} \times \mathbf{a} = 0$

In a similar way, you can see that

$$\mathbf{i} \times \mathbf{j} = |\mathbf{i}||\mathbf{j}|\sin 90°\mathbf{k} = \mathbf{k}$$

(since **k** is perpendicular to **i** and **j**, and **i**, **j**, **k** form a right-handed system).

Activity 8

Determine all the vector products

(a) $\mathbf{i} \times \mathbf{i}, \ \mathbf{i} \times \mathbf{j}, \ \mathbf{i} \times \mathbf{k}$

(b) $\mathbf{j} \times \mathbf{i}, \ \mathbf{j} \times \mathbf{j}, \ \mathbf{j} \times \mathbf{k}$

(c) $\mathbf{k} \times \mathbf{i}, \ \mathbf{k} \times \mathbf{j}, \ \mathbf{k} \times \mathbf{k}$

You should have found that

$$\mathbf{i} \times \mathbf{j} = \mathbf{k}, \ \mathbf{j} \times \mathbf{k} = \mathbf{i}, \ \mathbf{k} \times \mathbf{i} = \mathbf{j}$$

whereas

$$\mathbf{j} \times \mathbf{i} = -\mathbf{k}, \ \mathbf{k} \times \mathbf{j} = -\mathbf{i}, \ \mathbf{i} \times \mathbf{k} = -\mathbf{j}$$

and

$$\mathbf{i} \times \mathbf{i} = \mathbf{j} \times \mathbf{j} = \mathbf{k} \times \mathbf{k} = \mathbf{0}$$

Again assuming that addition and subtraction behave in a natural way, you can use these results to find a formula for $\mathbf{a} \times \mathbf{b}$ in terms of their components. If

$$\mathbf{a} = a_1\mathbf{i} + a_2\mathbf{j} + a_3\mathbf{k}, \ \ \mathbf{b} = b_1\mathbf{i} + b_2\mathbf{j} + b_3\mathbf{k}$$

then it can be shown that

$$\mathbf{a} \times \mathbf{b} = (a_2b_3 - a_3b_2)\mathbf{i} + (a_3b_1 - a_1b_3)\mathbf{j} + (a_1b_2 - a_2b_1)\mathbf{k}$$

Activity 9

Prove the formula above for $\mathbf{a} \times \mathbf{b}$.

Writing out an array

$$\begin{bmatrix} \mathbf{i} & \mathbf{j} & \mathbf{k} \\ a_1 & a_2 & a_3 \\ b_1 & b_2 & b_3 \end{bmatrix}$$

work out an easy way of remembering the formula for $\mathbf{a} \times \mathbf{b}$.

Example

If $\mathbf{a} = \mathbf{i} + \mathbf{j} + \mathbf{k}$, $\mathbf{b} = 2\mathbf{i} + 3\mathbf{j} - \mathbf{k}$, find $\mathbf{a} \times \mathbf{b}$.

Solution

$$\mathbf{a} \times \mathbf{b} = (\mathbf{i} + \mathbf{j} + \mathbf{k}) \times (2\mathbf{i} + 3\mathbf{j} - \mathbf{k})$$

$$= \mathbf{i} \times (2\mathbf{i} + 3\mathbf{j} + \mathbf{k}) \times \mathbf{j}(2\mathbf{i} + 3\mathbf{j} - \mathbf{k}) + \mathbf{k} \times (2\mathbf{i} + 3\mathbf{j} - \mathbf{k})$$

$$= 20 + 3\mathbf{k} - (-\mathbf{j}) + (-2\mathbf{k}) + 30 - \mathbf{i} + 2\mathbf{j} - 3\mathbf{i} - 0$$

$$= -4\mathbf{i} + 3\mathbf{j} + \mathbf{k}$$

Alternatively you can quickly evaluate the vector product using the formula from Activity 9; this gives

$$\mathbf{a} \times \mathbf{b} = (-1 - 3)\mathbf{i} + (2 - (-1))\mathbf{j} + (3 - 2)\mathbf{k}$$

$$= -4\mathbf{i} + 3\mathbf{j} + \mathbf{k}$$

Note that if two vectors **a** and **b** are parallel (or anti-parallel) then $\theta = 0$ or π, and

$$\mathbf{a} \times \mathbf{b} = 0\hat{\mathbf{n}} = \mathbf{0}$$

Conversly, for non-zero vectors **a** and **b**,

$$\mathbf{a} \times \mathbf{b} = \mathbf{0} \Rightarrow \sin \theta = 0 \Rightarrow \theta = 0, \pi$$

Hence

$$\boxed{\mathbf{a} \times \mathbf{b} = \mathbf{0} \Leftrightarrow \mathbf{a} = \mathbf{0} \text{ or } \mathbf{b} = \mathbf{0} \text{ or } \mathbf{a}, \mathbf{b} \text{ parallel}}$$

Example

If $\mathbf{a} = \mathbf{i} - 3\mathbf{j} + 2\mathbf{k}$ and $\mathbf{b} = -2\mathbf{i} + 6\mathbf{j} - 4\mathbf{k}$, find $\mathbf{a} \times \mathbf{b}$. What can you say about **a** and **b**?

Solution

$$\mathbf{a} \times \mathbf{b} = (\mathbf{i} - 3\mathbf{j} + 2\mathbf{k}) \times (-2\mathbf{i} + 6\mathbf{j} - 4\mathbf{k})$$

$$= \mathbf{i} \times (-2\mathbf{i} + 6\mathbf{j} - 4\mathbf{k}) - 3\mathbf{j} \times (-2\mathbf{i} + 6\mathbf{j} - 4\mathbf{k}) + 2\mathbf{k} \times (-2\mathbf{i} + 6\mathbf{j} - 4\mathbf{k})$$

$$= -20 + 6\mathbf{k} + 4\mathbf{j} - 6\mathbf{k} - 180 + 12\mathbf{i} - 4\mathbf{j} - 12\mathbf{i} - 80$$

$$= \mathbf{0}$$

Hence **a** and **b** are parallel. In fact you can readily see that $\mathbf{b} = -2\mathbf{a}$.

Exercise 4D

1. If $\mathbf{a} = 2\mathbf{i} + \mathbf{j} - 2\mathbf{k}$ and $\mathbf{b} = -3\mathbf{i} + 4\mathbf{k}$, find

   (a) $\mathbf{a}.\mathbf{b}$

   (b) the acute angle between these vectors (to the nearest degree)

   (c) a unit vector which is perpendicular to both $\mathbf{a}$ and $\mathbf{b}$.

2. For $\mathbf{a}$ and $\mathbf{b}$ in Question 1, find $\mathbf{a} \times \mathbf{b}$. Use this to find the angle between these vectors (to the nearest degree).

3. Let $\mathbf{a} = \mathbf{i} - 2\mathbf{j} + \mathbf{k}$, $\mathbf{b} = 2\mathbf{i} + \mathbf{j} - \mathbf{k}$. Given that $\mathbf{c} = \lambda\mathbf{a} + \mu\mathbf{b}$ and that $\mathbf{c}$ is perpendicular to $\mathbf{a}$, find the ratio of λ to μ.

4. Find the value of λ for which the vectors $2\mathbf{i} - 3\mathbf{j} + \mathbf{k}$ and $3\mathbf{i} + 6\mathbf{j} + \lambda\mathbf{k}$ are perpendicular.

5. Given the vectors $\mathbf{u} = 3\mathbf{i} + 2\mathbf{j}$ and $\mathbf{v} = 2\mathbf{i} + \lambda\mathbf{j}$, determine the value of λ so that

   (a) $\mathbf{u}$ and $\mathbf{v}$ are at right angles

   (b) $\mathbf{u}$ and $\mathbf{v}$ are parallel

   (c) the acute angle between $\mathbf{u}$ and $\mathbf{v}$ is $45°$.

6. The angle between the vectors $\mathbf{i} + \mathbf{j}$ and $\mathbf{i} + \mathbf{j} + \lambda\mathbf{k}$ is $45°$. Find the possible values of λ.

7. Given that $\mathbf{a} = 2\mathbf{i} + \mathbf{k}$, $\mathbf{b} = \mathbf{i} - 2\mathbf{j} + 3\mathbf{k}$ calculate

   (a) the scalar product $\mathbf{a}.\mathbf{b}$

   (b) the vector product $\mathbf{a} \times \mathbf{b}$

8. The vectors $\mathbf{u}$ and $\mathbf{v}$ are given by $\mathbf{u} = 2\mathbf{i} - \mathbf{j} + 2\mathbf{k}$, $\mathbf{v} = p\mathbf{i} + q\mathbf{k}$.

   Given that $\mathbf{u} \times \mathbf{v} = \mathbf{i} + s\mathbf{k}$, find p, q and s. Find also the cosine of the angle between $\mathbf{u}$ and $\mathbf{v}$.

4.6 Applications

In Chapter 5 you will see how vectors can be used to solve problems in 3-dimensional space concerned with lines and planes. Using vectors for these problems is very convenient but it is not the principal application of vectors, which is for solving problems in mechanics. These applications, and that of vector calculus to problems in fluid mechanics, are beyond the scope of this text, but if you pursue mathematics in Higher Education you will appreciate their importance. Here we look at some simpler applications.

Projection of a vector

Let P be the foot of the perpendicular from A to the line OB. OP is called the **projection** of $\mathbf{a}$ onto the line OB.

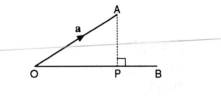

Note that

$$OP = |\mathbf{a}|\cos\theta, \text{ where } \mathbf{a} = \overrightarrow{OA} \text{ and } \theta \text{ is angle AOP}$$

If $\mathbf{i}$ is a unit vector in the direction OB, then

$$\mathbf{a}.\mathbf{i} = |\mathbf{a}||\mathbf{i}|\cos\theta = |\mathbf{a}|\cos\theta = OP$$

So

$$\text{Projection of } \mathbf{a} \text{ onto the line OB } = \mathbf{a}.\mathbf{i}$$

Example

The force $\mathbf{F} = 10\hat{\mathbf{c}}$, where $\hat{\mathbf{c}}$ is a unit vector in a direction making an angle of 45° with each of the positive x and y axes. Find the projection of $\mathbf{F}$ on the x-axis.

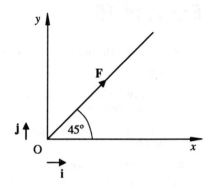

Solution

$$\hat{\mathbf{c}} = \frac{1}{\sqrt{2}}(\mathbf{i} + \mathbf{j})$$

So
$$\mathbf{F} = \frac{10}{\sqrt{2}}(\mathbf{i} + \mathbf{j})$$

and
$$\mathbf{F}.\mathbf{i} = \frac{10}{\sqrt{2}}(\mathbf{i} + \mathbf{j}).\mathbf{i}$$

$$= \frac{10}{\sqrt{2}}.1 + \frac{10}{\sqrt{2}}.0$$

$$= \frac{10}{\sqrt{2}}$$

Area of a triangle

For the triangle AOB, let

$$\mathbf{a} = \vec{OA}, \mathbf{b} = \vec{OB}$$

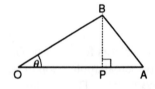

So
$$|\mathbf{a} \times \mathbf{b}| = |\mathbf{a}||\mathbf{b}|\sin\theta$$

$$= OA \times (OB\sin\theta)$$

$$= OA \times BP \quad (= \text{ base } \times \text{ height})$$

So

$$\boxed{\text{Area of } \triangle OAB = \tfrac{1}{2}|\mathbf{a} \times \mathbf{b}|}$$

Example

If A is the point (5, 0), B is the point (3, 0), find the area of the triangle OAB.

Solution

$$\mathbf{a} = 5\mathbf{i}, \ \mathbf{b} = 3\mathbf{i} + 6\mathbf{j}$$

$$\text{Area of triangle } = \tfrac{1}{2}|\mathbf{a} \times \mathbf{b}|$$

$$= \tfrac{1}{2}|5\mathbf{i} \times (3\mathbf{i} + 6\mathbf{j})|$$

$$= \tfrac{1}{2}|150 + 30\mathbf{k}|$$

$$= \tfrac{1}{2}|30\mathbf{k}| = \tfrac{1}{2}.30 = 15$$

Example

The triangle ABC is defined by the points A(0, 1, 2), B(1, 5, 5) and C(2, 3, 1). Find the area of ABC.

Solution

$\overrightarrow{AB} = (1,\ 4,\ 3)$ and $\overrightarrow{AC} = (2,\ 2,\ -1)$.

So you can think of $\overrightarrow{AB}$ as $\mathbf{i} + 4\mathbf{j} + 3\mathbf{k}$ and $\overrightarrow{AC}$ as $2\mathbf{i} + 2\mathbf{j} - \mathbf{k}$ and calculate $\overrightarrow{AB} \times \overrightarrow{AC}$ as

$$\left(4.(-1) - 3.2\right)\mathbf{i} + \left(3.2 - 1.(-1)\right)\mathbf{j} + (1.2 - 4.2)\mathbf{k}$$

or $-10\mathbf{i} + 7\mathbf{j} - 6\mathbf{k}$.

Hence area of $\triangle ABC = \tfrac{1}{2}\left|(-10,\ 7,\ -6)\right|$

$$= \tfrac{1}{2}\sqrt{100 + 49 + 36}$$

$$= \tfrac{1}{2}\sqrt{185}$$

Work done by a force

Work is done when a force moves a particle through a distance. If **F** is the constant force being applied, and the particle is moved from A to B where $\overrightarrow{AB} = \mathbf{d}$, then

$$\boxed{\text{work done} = \mathbf{F}.\mathbf{d}}$$

Example

A block slides down an inclined plane from A to B. Ignoring friction, the forces acting on the block are its weight, **W** and a normal reaction **R**. Calculate the work done by the forces in terms of *h*.

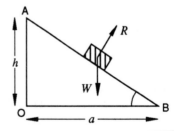

Solution

$$\mathbf{W} = -W\mathbf{j},\ \mathbf{d} = -h\mathbf{j} + a\mathbf{i}$$

$$\mathbf{W}.\mathbf{d} = -W\mathbf{j}.(-h\mathbf{j} + a\mathbf{i}) = Wh$$

and

$$\mathbf{R}.\mathbf{d} = 0$$

since **R** and **d** are perpendicular.

So the work done is simply Wh.

4.7 Miscellaneous Exercises

1. Find the sum of the vectors $2\mathbf{i}+\mathbf{j}-\mathbf{k}$, $\mathbf{i}+3\mathbf{j}+\mathbf{k}$, $3\mathbf{i}+2\mathbf{j}$.

2. Find the magnitude of the vector $\mathbf{a}=3\mathbf{i}-2\mathbf{j}+6\mathbf{k}$.

3. If $(a+2)\mathbf{i}+(b-1)\mathbf{j}$ and $(b-1)\mathbf{i}-a\mathbf{j}$ are equal vectors, find the values of a and b.

4. If $\lambda\mathbf{i}-4\mathbf{j}$ is parallel to $2\mathbf{i}-6\mathbf{j}$, find the value of λ.

5. Find the unit vector in the direction of $2\mathbf{i}-\mathbf{j}+2\mathbf{k}$.

6. Find the vector with magnitude three and parallel to $6\mathbf{i}-3\mathbf{j}+2\mathbf{k}$.

7. If $\overrightarrow{OA}=4\mathbf{i}+14\mathbf{j}-5\mathbf{k}$, $\overrightarrow{OB}=\mathbf{i}+2\mathbf{j}+7\mathbf{k}$, and $\overrightarrow{OC}=2\mathbf{i}+6\mathbf{j}+37\mathbf{k}$, show that the vectors $\overrightarrow{BC}$, $\overrightarrow{CA}$ are parallel. Hence deduce that the points A, B and C are collinear.

8. $\overrightarrow{QP}=\mathbf{p}$, $\overrightarrow{OR}=3\mathbf{p}$, $\overrightarrow{OQ}=\mathbf{q}$. M is the midpoint of QR.

   (a) Express $\overrightarrow{OP}$ and $\overrightarrow{RQ}$ in terms of $\mathbf{p}$ and $\mathbf{q}$.

   (b) Express $\overrightarrow{MQ}$ in terms of $\mathbf{p}$ and $\mathbf{q}$.

   (c) If S lies on $\overrightarrow{QP}$ produced so that $\overrightarrow{QS}=k\,\overrightarrow{QP}$, express $\overrightarrow{MS}$ in terms of $\mathbf{p}$, $\mathbf{q}$ and k.

   (d) Find the value of k if $\overrightarrow{MS}$ is parallel to $\overrightarrow{QO}$.

9. Show that $3\mathbf{i}+7\mathbf{j}+2\mathbf{k}$ is perpendicular to $5\mathbf{i}-\mathbf{j}-4\mathbf{k}$.

10. The points A, B and C have coordinates (2, 1, –1), (1, –7, 3) and (–2, 5, 1) respectively. Find the area of the triangle ABC.

11. If L, M, N and P are the midpoints of AD, BD, BC and AC respectively, show that $\overrightarrow{LM}$ is parallel to $\overrightarrow{NP}$.

12. The position vectors of points P and R are $2\mathbf{i}-3\mathbf{j}+7\mathbf{k}$ and $4\mathbf{i}+5\mathbf{j}+3\mathbf{k}$ respectively. Given that R divides PQ in the ratio 2:1, find the position vector of Q if

    (a) R divides PQ internally.

    (b) R divides PQ externally.

13. Given that $\overrightarrow{OA}=\mathbf{i}+\mathbf{j}$, $\overrightarrow{OB}=5\mathbf{i}+7\mathbf{j}$, find the position vectors of the other two vertices of the square of which A and B are one pair of opposite vertices.

14. Given that $\mathbf{p}=t^2\mathbf{i}+(2t+1)\mathbf{j}+\mathbf{k}$ and $\mathbf{q}=(t-1)\mathbf{i}+3t\mathbf{j}-\left(t^2+3t\right)\mathbf{k}$ where t is a scalar variable, determine

    (a) the values of t for which $\mathbf{p}$ and $\mathbf{q}$ are perpendicular.

    (b) the angle between the vectors $\mathbf{p}$ and $\mathbf{q}$ when $t=1$, giving your answer to the nearest 0.1°.
    (AEB)

15. The point P has position vector
    $$(1+\mu)\mathbf{i}+(3-2\mu)\mathbf{j}+(4+2\mu)\mathbf{k}$$
    where μ is a variable parameter. The point Q has position vector $4\mathbf{i}+2\mathbf{j}+3\mathbf{k}$.

    (a) The points P_0 and P_1 are the positions of P when $\mu=0$ and $\mu=1$ respectively. Calculate the size of angle P_0QP_1, giving your answer to the nearest degree.

    (b) Show that $PQ^2=(3\mu-1)^2+10$ and hence, or otherwise, find the position vector of P when it is closest to Q.
    (AEB)

16. Referred to a fixed origin O, the points A, B and C have position vectors $\mathbf{i}-2\mathbf{j}+2\mathbf{k}$, $3\mathbf{i}-\mathbf{k}$ and $-\mathbf{i}+\mathbf{j}+4\mathbf{k}$ respectively.

    Calculate the cosine of the angle BAC.

    Hence, or otherwise, find the area of the triangle ABC, giving your answer to three significant figures.
    (AEB)

5 VECTOR GEOMETRY

Objectives

After studying this chapter you should

- be able to find and use the vector equation of a straight line;
- be able to find the equation of a plane in various forms;
- be able to interchange between cartesian and vector equations;
- be able to find the perpendicular distance of a point from a plane;
- be able to find the angle between two planes.

5.0   Introduction

This chapter deals with the use of vectors in geometric problems. The key to confidence in answering problems is to be able to visualise the situations. It is usually very helpful to illustrate the situation with a drawing, even though drawing planes can be quite difficult. First, though, try the activity below, which should help you to think geometrically.

Activity 1

Consider the following statements, decide whether each is sometimes true, always true or false, and discuss your answers with your tutor. Think carefully before giving your answers.

(a)   A line and a plane intersect at a point.

(b)   Two lines intersect at a point.

(c)   Two planes intersect in a line.

(d)   A line is uniquely defined by two distinct points on it.

(e)   A plane is uniquely defined by three distinct points on it.

(f)   A plane is defined by giving the direction perpendicular to the plane and a point on the plane.

5.1 Straight line

A straight line, L, is uniquely defined by giving two distinct points on the line.

Are there other ways to define uniquely a straight line?

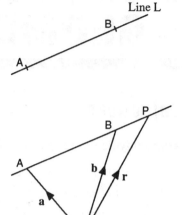

If the coordinates of A and B are given, then the vectors $\mathbf{a} = \vec{OA}$ and $\mathbf{b} = \vec{OB}$ are known. Let P be any point on the line AB with position vector

$$\mathbf{r} = x\mathbf{i} + y\mathbf{j} + z\mathbf{k}.$$

Then $$\mathbf{r} = \vec{OP} = \vec{OA} + \vec{AP}$$

$$\Rightarrow \quad \mathbf{r} = \mathbf{a} + \vec{AP}$$

But $\vec{AP}$ is a linear multiple of $\vec{AB} = \mathbf{b} - \mathbf{a}$;

so $$\mathbf{r} = \mathbf{a} + \lambda(\mathbf{b} - \mathbf{a})$$

for some parameter λ. This is the form of the vector equation of a line. The parameter can take any real value, giving different points on the line.

What value of λ gives the point A?

What value of λ gives the point B?

Example

Find the vector equation of the straight line passing through the points A $(1, 0, 1)$ and B $(0, 1, 3)$.

Solution

Here $$\mathbf{a} = \mathbf{i} + \mathbf{k}$$

$$\mathbf{b} = \mathbf{j} + 3\mathbf{k}$$

so $$\mathbf{r} = (\mathbf{i} + \mathbf{k}) + \lambda\left((\mathbf{j} + 3\mathbf{k}) - (\mathbf{i} + \mathbf{k})\right)$$

$$\mathbf{r} = (\mathbf{i} + \mathbf{k}) + \lambda(-\mathbf{i} + \mathbf{j} + 2\mathbf{k}) \quad (\text{or } (1, 0, 1) + \lambda(-1, 1, 2))$$

The vector equation of a line can readily be turned into a cartesian equation by noting that the coordinates of the point on the line are

$$(x, y, x) = (1 - \lambda, \lambda, 1 + 2\gamma)$$

This gives

$$\left.\begin{array}{l} x = 1 - \lambda \\ y = \lambda \\ z = 1 + 2\lambda \end{array}\right\} \quad \text{or} \quad \frac{x-1}{(-1)} = \frac{y-0}{1} = \frac{z-1}{2} \quad (= \lambda)$$

This is the form of the cartesian equation of a straight line. In general, the vector equation can be written as

$$\boxed{\mathbf{r} = \mathbf{a} + \lambda\, \mathbf{t}}$$

where $\mathbf{t}$ is a vector in the direction of the line.

If
$$\mathbf{a} = a_1\mathbf{i} + a_2\mathbf{j} + a_3\mathbf{k} \quad \text{and} \quad \mathbf{t} = t_1\mathbf{i} + t_2\mathbf{j} + t_3\mathbf{k}$$

then

$$\left.\begin{array}{l} x = a_1 + \lambda\, t_1 \\ y = a_2 + \lambda\, t_2 \\ z = a_3 + \lambda\, t_3 \end{array}\right\} \quad \text{or} \quad \frac{x - a_1}{t_1} = \frac{y - a_2}{t_2} = \frac{z - a_3}{t_3}$$

Example

The cartesian equation of a straight line is given by

$$\frac{x-1}{2} = \frac{y+1}{4} = \frac{z-2}{(-2)}$$

Rewrite it in vector form.

Solution

Writing $\dfrac{x-1}{2} = \dfrac{y+1}{4} = \dfrac{z-2}{(-2)} = \lambda$ for some parameter λ, then

$$\left.\begin{array}{l} x = 1 + 2\lambda \\ y = -1 + 4\lambda \\ z = 2 - 2\lambda \end{array}\right\} \quad \text{or} \quad \mathbf{r} = (\mathbf{i} - \mathbf{j} + 2\mathbf{k}) + \lambda(2\mathbf{i} + 4\mathbf{j} - 2\mathbf{k})$$

Note that this equation is not unique (although the line is unique).

For example, you can write

$$\mathbf{r} = (\mathbf{i} - \mathbf{j} + 2\mathbf{k}) + 2\lambda(\mathbf{i} + 2\mathbf{j} - \mathbf{k})$$

and with $\mu = 2\lambda$,

$$\mathbf{r} = (\mathbf{i} - \mathbf{j} + 2\mathbf{k}) + \mu(\mathbf{i} + 2\mathbf{j} - \mathbf{k})$$

Similarly, check for yourself that

$$\mathbf{r} = (-3\mathbf{j} + 3\mathbf{k}) + \sigma(\mathbf{i} + 2\mathbf{j} - \mathbf{k})$$

and

$$\mathbf{r} = (3\mathbf{i} + 3\mathbf{j}) + \rho(-\mathbf{i} - 2\mathbf{j} + \mathbf{k})$$

describe the same line. In all cases the first vector is on the line and the second is parallel to the line.

Example

Find a vector equation of the line which passes through the point A (1, −1, 0) and is parallel to the line $\overrightarrow{BC}$ where B and C are the points with coordinates (−3, 2, 1) and (2, 1, 0). Show that the point D (−14, 2, 3) lies on the line.

Solution

The line required is parallel to the line $\overrightarrow{BC}$, which has equation

$$(2 - (-3))\mathbf{i} + (1 - 2)\mathbf{j} + (0 - 1)\mathbf{k} = 5\mathbf{i} - \mathbf{j} - \mathbf{k}.$$

Its equation is given by

$$\mathbf{r} = \mathbf{i} - \mathbf{j} + \lambda(5\mathbf{i} - \mathbf{j} - \mathbf{k}).$$

To show that the point D lies on the line, you must check whether

$$\mathbf{r} = \mathbf{i} - \mathbf{j} + \lambda(5\mathbf{i} - \mathbf{j} - \mathbf{k})$$

can ever equal $-14\mathbf{i} + 2\mathbf{j} + 3\mathbf{k}$ for some value of λ.

So you need

$$[\mathbf{i}]\ 1 + 5\lambda = -14 \quad [\mathbf{j}]\ 2 = -1 - \lambda \quad [\mathbf{k}]\ 3 = -\lambda$$

and all three of these **are** satisfied when $\lambda = -3$. Hence D does lie on the line.

Intersection of two lines

Two non-parallel lines either do not intersect or intersect at a point. Lines which do not intersect are called **skew lines**.

Example

The lines L and M have vector equations

$$\text{L:} \quad \mathbf{r} = 2\mathbf{j} - 2\mathbf{k} + \lambda(\mathbf{i} - \mathbf{j})$$

$$\text{M:} \quad \mathbf{r} = \mathbf{i} + \mathbf{j} - 2\mathbf{k} + \mu(\mathbf{j} - \mathbf{k}) \qquad (\lambda, \mu \text{ parameters})$$

Show that these two lines intersect and find their point of intersection.

Solution

If the lines intersect, then for some value of λ and μ,

$$\mathbf{r} = \lambda\mathbf{i} + (2 - \lambda)\mathbf{j} - 2\mathbf{k} = \mathbf{i} + (1 + \mu)\mathbf{j} - (2 + \mu)\mathbf{k}.$$

Equating coefficients of $\mathbf{i}, \mathbf{j}, \mathbf{k}$ gives

$$[\mathbf{i}] \quad \lambda = 1$$

$$[\mathbf{j}] \quad 2 - \lambda = 1 + \mu$$

$$[\mathbf{k}] \quad -2 = -(2 + \mu)$$

The first equation gives $\lambda = 1$ and the second then gives $\mu = 0$. These values of λ and μ also satisfy the third equation and so the lines intersect. To find the point of intersection, put $\lambda = 1$ in the equation for the line L. This gives

$$\mathbf{r} = \mathbf{i} + \mathbf{j} - 2\mathbf{k}$$

[You can check this answer by substituting $\mu = 0$ in the equation for M. This gives $\mathbf{r} = \mathbf{i} + \mathbf{j} - 2\mathbf{k}$ as before.]

Activity 2

The three lines, L, M and N, have vector equations

$$\text{L:} \quad \mathbf{r} = (1 + t)\mathbf{i} + (1 - t)\mathbf{j} - 2\mathbf{k}$$

$$\text{M:} \quad \mathbf{r} = (3 - \mu)\mathbf{i} - (1 - \mu)\mathbf{j} - (\mu - 2)\mathbf{k}$$

$$\text{N:} \quad \mathbf{r} = (1 + s)\mathbf{i} - (1 + 3s)\mathbf{j} - s\mathbf{k}$$

for parameters t, μ and s. Which pairs of lines intersect?

Exercise 5A

1. Find the vector and cartesian equations of the straight line joining the points A and B, whose coordinates are $(-2, 1, 4)$ and $(1, 7, 6)$ respectively.

2. If $\vec{OA} = \mathbf{i} - 2\mathbf{j} + \mathbf{k}$, $\vec{OB} = -\mathbf{i} - 3\mathbf{k}$,

   $\vec{OC} = 3\mathbf{i} + \mathbf{j} - 2\mathbf{k}$, $\vec{OD} = 8\mathbf{i} + \mathbf{j} + 4\mathbf{k}$

   find the vector equation of a straight line

   (a) through A and B;

   (b) through D parallel to BC;

   (c) through C parallel to AB.

3. The three lines, L, M and N, are given by the equations

   L: $\mathbf{r} = 7\mathbf{i} - 3\mathbf{j} + 3\mathbf{k} + \lambda(3\mathbf{i} - 2\mathbf{j} + \mathbf{k})$

   M: $\mathbf{r} = 7\mathbf{i} - 2\mathbf{j} + 4\mathbf{k} + \mu(-2\mathbf{i} + \mathbf{j} - \mathbf{k})$

   N: $\mathbf{r} = \mathbf{i} + \nu(\mathbf{j} - \mathbf{k})$

(a) Show that L and M intersect and find their point of intersection.

(b) Show that L and N do not intersect.

(c) Do M and N intersect?

*4. Prove that a necessary and sufficient condition for three points to be collinear is that their position vectors satisfy the equation

$$\lambda \mathbf{a} + \mu \mathbf{b} + \nu \mathbf{c} = \mathbf{0}$$

where λ, μ and ν are scalars such that
$$\lambda + \mu + \nu = 0.$$

5.2   Equation of a plane

There are a number of ways of specifying a plane – you can deduce its equation in each case. Here you will consider two specific ways:

(1)   a point on the plane and a perpendicular vector to the plane are given;

(2)   three non-collinear points on the plane are given.

Point and perpendicular vector

Let the given point on the plane be A with $\vec{OA} = \mathbf{a}$. Also let $\mathbf{n}$ be a vector perpendicular to the plane, i.e. a **normal** to the plane.

If P is any point on the plane, with position vector $\mathbf{r}$, then

$$\vec{AP} = \mathbf{r} - \mathbf{a}$$

is perpendicular to $\mathbf{n}$; so

$$(\mathbf{r} - \mathbf{a}).\mathbf{n} = 0.$$

Thus the vector equation of a plane is of the form

$$\boxed{\mathbf{r}.\mathbf{n} = \mathbf{a}.\mathbf{n}}$$

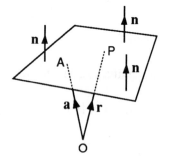

Example

Find the vector equation of a plane which passes through the point
$(0, 1, 1)$ and has normal vector $\mathbf{n} = \mathbf{i} + \mathbf{j} + \mathbf{k}$. Also find its
cartesian equation and show that the points $(1, 0, 1)$ and $(1, 1, 0)$
lie on the plane. Sketch the plane.

Solution

The equation is given by

$$\mathbf{r} \cdot (\mathbf{i} + \mathbf{j} + \mathbf{k}) = (0\mathbf{i} + 1\mathbf{j} + 1\mathbf{k}) \cdot (\mathbf{i} + \mathbf{j} + \mathbf{k})$$

$$\Rightarrow \quad \mathbf{r} \cdot (\mathbf{i} + \mathbf{j} + \mathbf{k}) = 0 + 1 + 1 = 2$$

$$\Rightarrow \quad \mathbf{r} \cdot (\mathbf{i} + \mathbf{j} + \mathbf{k}) = 2.$$

The cartesian equation is found by writing $\mathbf{r}$ as

$$\mathbf{r} = x\mathbf{i} + y\mathbf{j} + z\mathbf{k}$$

giving $\quad (x\mathbf{i} + y\mathbf{j} + z\mathbf{k}) \cdot (\mathbf{i} + \mathbf{j} + \mathbf{k}) = 2$

$$\Rightarrow \quad x + y + z = 2.$$

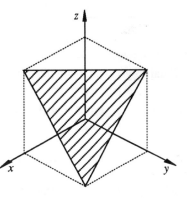

For the point $(1, 0, 1)$, $x = 1$, $y = 0$ and $z = 1$, which satisfies the
equation. Similarly for $(1, 1, 0)$.

A sketch of the plane is shown opposite.

Note that for any particular choice of the normal $\mathbf{n}$, the equation

$$\mathbf{r} \cdot \mathbf{n} = \mathbf{a} \cdot \mathbf{n}$$

gives a unique equation for the plane despite the fact that $\mathbf{a}$ is the
position vector of any point on the plane. For example, another
point on the plane has coordinates $(3, 1, -2)$. In this case, the
equation is

$$\mathbf{r} \cdot (\mathbf{i} + \mathbf{j} + \mathbf{k}) = (3\mathbf{i} + \mathbf{j} - 2\mathbf{k}) \cdot (\mathbf{i} + \mathbf{j} + \mathbf{k}) = 2$$

as before. Different choices for the normal $\mathbf{n}$ (which must be a
scalar multiple of $\mathbf{i} + \mathbf{j} + \mathbf{k}$) will give essentially the same equation.

Three non-collinear points

Three non-collinear points are sufficient to define uniquely a
plane.

What shape will be defined by four non-collinear points?

Suppose the points A, B and C all lie on the plane and

$$\overrightarrow{OA} = \mathbf{a}, \ \overrightarrow{OB} = \mathbf{b}, \ \overrightarrow{OC} = \mathbf{c}.$$

Now the vector $\vec{AB} = \mathbf{b} - \mathbf{a}$ lies in the plane. Similarly

$\vec{AC} = \mathbf{c} - \mathbf{a}$ lies in the plane. Now if P is any point in the plane with position vector $\mathbf{r}$, then

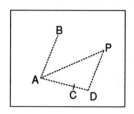

$$\vec{OP} = \vec{OA} + \vec{AP}$$

$$\mathbf{r} = \mathbf{a} + \vec{AP}$$

By construction you can see that

$$\vec{AP} = \vec{AD} + \vec{DP}$$

where D is on AC, produced such that DP is parallel to AB.

So, if

$$AD = n\,AC \quad \text{and} \quad DP = m\,AB$$

for some parameters m and n, then

$$\vec{AP} = m\,\vec{AB} + n\,\vec{AC}$$

$$= m(\mathbf{b} - \mathbf{a}) + n(\mathbf{c} - \mathbf{a})$$

Finally, you can write the equation as

$$\mathbf{r} = \mathbf{a} + m(\mathbf{b} - \mathbf{a}) + n(\mathbf{c} - \mathbf{a})$$

or

$$\mathbf{r} = (1 - m - n)\mathbf{a} + m\mathbf{b} + n\mathbf{c}$$

where m and n are parameters.

Example

Find the vector equation of the plane that passes through the points $(0, 1, 1)$, $(1, 1, 0)$ and $(1, 0, 1)$. Deduce its cartesian form.

Solution

With $\mathbf{a} = \mathbf{j} + \mathbf{k}$, $\mathbf{b} = \mathbf{i} + \mathbf{j}$, $\mathbf{c} = \mathbf{i} + \mathbf{k}$,

$$\mathbf{r} = \mathbf{j} + \mathbf{k} + m(\mathbf{i} - \mathbf{k}) + n(\mathbf{i} - \mathbf{j})$$

$$\mathbf{r} = (m + n)\mathbf{i} + (1 - n)\mathbf{j} + (1 - m)\mathbf{k}.$$

To find the cartesian equation of the plane, note that

$$\mathbf{r} = x\mathbf{i} + y\mathbf{j} + z\mathbf{k}$$

so $\qquad x = m + n, \; y = 1 - n, \; z = 1 - m.$

Eliminating m and n,

$$x = (1-z) + (1-y)$$

$$\Rightarrow \quad x + y + z = 2$$

as deduced in the previous example.

Activity 3

Deduce the general equation of a plane passing through the point A, where $\vec{OA} = \mathbf{a}$, and such that the vectors $\mathbf{s}$ and $\mathbf{t}$ are parallel to the plane.

Example

The lines L_1 and L_2 have equations

$$\mathbf{r} = (3\mathbf{i}+\mathbf{j}-\mathbf{k}) + \alpha(\mathbf{i}+2\mathbf{j}+3\mathbf{k})$$

and

$$\mathbf{r} = (2\mathbf{i}+5\mathbf{j}) + \beta(\mathbf{i}-\mathbf{j}+\mathbf{k})$$

respectively.

(a) Prove that L_1 and L_2 intersect and find the point of intersection.

(b) Determine the equation of the plane π containing L_1 and L_2, giving your answer in the form $\mathbf{r}.\mathbf{n} = d$.

(AEB)

Solution

(a) If L_1 and L_2 intersect, then

$$(3\mathbf{i}+\mathbf{j}-\mathbf{k}) + \alpha(\mathbf{i}+2\mathbf{j}+3\mathbf{k}) = (2\mathbf{i}+5\mathbf{j}) + \beta(\mathbf{i}-\mathbf{j}+\mathbf{k}).$$

Equating coefficients,

$$
\left.
\begin{array}{l}
[\mathbf{i}] \ \ 3 + \alpha = 2 + \beta \\
[\mathbf{j}] \ \ 1 + 2\alpha = 5 - \beta
\end{array}
\right\}
\left.
\begin{array}{l}
\alpha - \beta = -1 \\
2\alpha + \beta = 4
\end{array}
\right\}
\ 3\alpha = 3 \ \Rightarrow \ \alpha = 1, \ \beta = 2
$$

$$[\mathbf{k}] \ \ -1 + 3\alpha = \beta$$

Now $\alpha = 1$, $\beta = 2$ satisfies the third equation, and so the lines intersect at the point $(4, 3, 2)$.

(b)   The plane contains the point with position vector

$$4\mathbf{i}+3\mathbf{j}+2\mathbf{k}$$

and the directions of $(\mathbf{i}+2\mathbf{j}+3\mathbf{k})$ and $(\mathbf{i}-\mathbf{j}+\mathbf{k})$.

Hence

$$\mathbf{r} = 4\mathbf{i}+3\mathbf{j}+2\mathbf{k} + m(\mathbf{i}+2\mathbf{j}+3\mathbf{k}) + n(\mathbf{i}-\mathbf{j}+\mathbf{k})$$

for parameters m and n.

[Note that you can find the cartesian form by writing
$\mathbf{r} = x\mathbf{i} + y\mathbf{i} + z\mathbf{k}$, giving

$$\left.\begin{array}{l} x = 4+m+n \\ y = 3+2m-n \\ z = 2+3m+n \end{array}\right\} \quad \left.\begin{array}{l} x+y=7+3m \\ \\ y+z=5+5m \end{array}\right\} \quad \Rightarrow \quad 5x+2y-3z = 20$$

Activity 4

Show that the equation of a plane, containing the points A, B and C
where $\overrightarrow{OA} = \mathbf{a}$, $\overrightarrow{OB} = \mathbf{b}$, $\overrightarrow{OC} = \mathbf{c}$, can be written in the form

$$\mathbf{r} = \lambda\mathbf{a} + \mu\mathbf{b} + \nu\mathbf{c}$$

where $\lambda + \mu + \nu = 1$.

Exercise 5B

1. Find the equation of the plane that contains the points

    A $(2, -1, 0)$, B $(-1, 3, 4)$ and C $(3, 0, 2)$.

2. Find the equation of the plane that contains the point A $(2, -1, 0)$ and for which the vector

    $$\mathbf{r} = 4\mathbf{i}+10\mathbf{j}-7\mathbf{k}$$

    is perpendicular to the plane.

3. Compare your answers to Questions 1 and 2. What do you deduce?

4. Find the equation of the plane passing through $(0, 0, 0)$ and with normal vector $\mathbf{i}+2\mathbf{j}-3\mathbf{k}$.

5. Show that the line with equation

    $$\mathbf{r} = \mathbf{k}+\lambda(2\mathbf{i}+6\mathbf{j}+8\mathbf{k})$$

    is perpendicular to the plane with equation

    $$x+3y+4z = 8$$

6. Show that the point A $(2, 3, 1)$ lies on the plane

    $$\mathbf{r}.(2\mathbf{i}-\mathbf{k}) = 3$$

    Also show that the line with vector equation

    $$\mathbf{r} = 3\mathbf{i}+\mathbf{j}+3\mathbf{k} + \lambda(\mathbf{i}-2\mathbf{j}+2\mathbf{k})$$

    is contained in the plane.

7. Find the point of intersection of the line

    $$\mathbf{r} = \mathbf{k} + \lambda(2\mathbf{i}+\mathbf{j}+\mathbf{k})$$

    with the plane $\mathbf{r}.\mathbf{i} = 4$.

8. The planes

    $$\mathbf{r}.(2\mathbf{i}-3\mathbf{j}-\mathbf{k}) = 19 \quad \text{and} \quad \mathbf{r}.(-\mathbf{i}+2\mathbf{j}+2\mathbf{k}) = -9$$

    intersect in a line L. Find the cartesian equation of the plane which contains L and is parallel to the vector $\mathbf{i}$.

5.3 Miscellaneous problems

Line of intersection of planes

In general, two planes, π_1 and π_2, intersect in a line, L, as shown opposite.

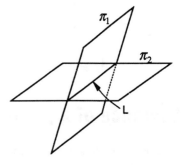

What else can happen?

The following example illustrates how you can determine the equation of L.

Example

Show that the two planes

$$\mathbf{r}.(\mathbf{i}+\mathbf{j}+\mathbf{k}) = 2$$

and $\qquad \mathbf{r}.(\mathbf{i}+2\mathbf{j}+3\mathbf{k}) = 3$

intersect in a line. Find the vector equation of this line.

Solution

The cartesian form of these equations is

$$x+y+z = 2$$

and $\qquad x+2y+3z = 3.$

Writing $x = \lambda$, (alternatively, you could use $y = \mu$, etc.)

$$y+z = 2-\lambda \;\Rightarrow\; 2y+2z = 4-2\lambda$$

$$2y+3z = 3-\lambda.$$

Hence

$$z = 3-\lambda-(4-2\lambda) = -1+\lambda$$

and $\qquad y = 2-\lambda-z = 2-\lambda-(-1+\lambda) = 3-2\lambda.$

So the cartesian equation of the line is

$$\frac{x}{1} = \frac{y-3}{(-2)} = \frac{z+1}{1} \;\;(=\lambda)$$

or, in vector form

$$\mathbf{r} = \mathbf{a} + \lambda\,\mathbf{t}$$

where $\quad\mathbf{a} = 3\mathbf{j} - \mathbf{k}$

$$\mathbf{t} = \mathbf{i} - 2\mathbf{j} + \mathbf{k}.$$

Distance of a point from a plane

To find the distance of the point B with position vector
$\mathbf{b} = (b_1, b_2, b_3)$ from the plane with equation

$$\mathbf{r}.\mathbf{n} = \mathbf{a}.\mathbf{n} = d$$

you first find the equation of the line BN, which is perpendicular to
the plane. Hence it is in the direction of $\mathbf{n}$, and so its equation is of
the form

$$\mathbf{r} = \mathbf{b} + \lambda\,\mathbf{n}.$$

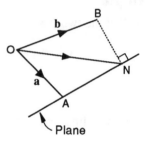

But N also lies on the plane, so it satisfies

$$\mathbf{r}.\mathbf{n} = d \;\Rightarrow\; (\mathbf{b} + \lambda\,\mathbf{n}).\mathbf{n} = d$$

$$\mathbf{b}.\mathbf{n} + \lambda\,\mathbf{n}.\mathbf{n} = d$$

$$\lambda\,\mathbf{n}.\mathbf{n} = d - \mathbf{b}.\mathbf{n}$$

$$\lambda = \frac{d - \mathbf{b}.\mathbf{n}}{|\mathbf{n}|^2}$$

But the length of BN is $|\lambda\,\mathbf{n}| = \dfrac{|d - \mathbf{b}.\mathbf{n}|}{|\mathbf{n}|}$, so

$$\boxed{\text{distance} = \frac{|d - \mathbf{b}.\mathbf{n}|}{|\mathbf{n}|}}$$

Example

Find the distance of the point $(4, 2, 3)$ from the plane

$$\mathbf{r}.(6\mathbf{i} + 2\mathbf{j} - 9\mathbf{k}) = 46.$$

Solution

Here $d = 46$, $\mathbf{n} = 6\mathbf{i} + 2\mathbf{j} - 9\mathbf{k}$, $|\mathbf{n}| = \sqrt{36 + 4 + 81} = 11$, and
$\mathbf{b} = 4\mathbf{i} + 2\mathbf{j} + 3\mathbf{k}$.

So $\qquad$ $\mathbf{b}.\mathbf{n} = 24 + 4 - 27 = 1$

and $\qquad$ distance $= \dfrac{|46-1|}{11} = \dfrac{45}{11}$

This section is completed by looking at a typical exam-type question.

Example

The points A, B and C have position vectors

$$\mathbf{i}+2\mathbf{j}-3\mathbf{k}, \quad \mathbf{i}+5\mathbf{j} \quad \text{and} \quad 5\mathbf{i}+6\mathbf{j}-\mathbf{k}$$

respectively, relative to an origin O.

(a) Show that AB is perpendicular to BC and find the area of the triangle ABC.

(b) Find the vector product $\overrightarrow{AB} \times \overrightarrow{BC}$. Hence find an equation of the plane ABC in the form $\mathbf{r}.\mathbf{n} = p$.

(c) The point D has position vector $4\mathbf{i}-\mathbf{j}+3\mathbf{k}$. Find the distance of the point D from the plane ABC. Hence show that the volume of the tetrahedron ABCD is equal to 21.

(d) Give, in cartesian form, the equation of the plane π which contains D and which has the property that for each point E in π the volume of the tetrahedron ABCE is still 21.

$\qquad\qquad\qquad\qquad\qquad\qquad\qquad\qquad\qquad$ (AEB)

Solution

(a) $\qquad$ $\overrightarrow{AB} = \mathbf{b} - \mathbf{a}$

$\qquad\qquad\qquad = (\mathbf{i}+5\mathbf{j}) - (\mathbf{i}+2\mathbf{j}-3\mathbf{k})$

$\qquad\qquad\qquad = 3\mathbf{j} + 3\mathbf{k}$

$\qquad\qquad$ $\overrightarrow{BC} = \mathbf{c} - \mathbf{b}$

$\qquad\qquad\qquad = (5\mathbf{i}+6\mathbf{j}-\mathbf{k}) - (\mathbf{i}+5\mathbf{j})$

$\qquad\qquad\qquad = 4\mathbf{i} + \mathbf{j} - \mathbf{k}$

and $\qquad$ $\overrightarrow{AB}.\overrightarrow{BC} = (3\mathbf{j}+3\mathbf{k}).(4\mathbf{i}+\mathbf{j}-\mathbf{k})$

$\qquad\qquad\qquad\quad = 0\times4 + 3\times1 + 3\times(-1)$

$\qquad\qquad\qquad\quad = 0$

Hence AB and BC are perpendicular.

Therefore triangle ABC has a right angle at B and area of triangle ABC $= \frac{1}{2} |\vec{AB}| \, |\vec{BC}|$

$$= \tfrac{1}{2} \left(\sqrt{9+9}\right)\left(\sqrt{16+1+1}\right)$$

$$= \tfrac{1}{2}\sqrt{18}\,\sqrt{18}$$

$$= 9$$

(b) $\vec{AB} \times \vec{BC} = (3\mathbf{j}+3\mathbf{k}) \times (4\mathbf{i}+\mathbf{j}-\mathbf{k})$

$$= \big(3.(-1)-3.1\big)\mathbf{i} + \big(3.4 - 0.(-1)\big)\mathbf{j} + (0.1 - 3.4)\mathbf{k}$$

$$= -6\mathbf{i} + 12\mathbf{j} - 12\mathbf{k}.$$

This is perpendicular to the plane ABC and so the equation of the plane takes the form

$$\mathbf{r}.(-6\mathbf{i}+12\mathbf{j}-12\mathbf{k}) = \mathbf{a}.(-6\mathbf{i}+12\mathbf{j}-12\mathbf{k})$$

$$= (\mathbf{i}+2\mathbf{j}-3\mathbf{k}).(-6\mathbf{i}+12\mathbf{j}-12\mathbf{k})$$

$$= -6 + 24 + 36$$

$$= 54$$

[Note that you could have used **b** or **c** instead of **a**. You would still obtain 54 on the right-hand-side.]

Thus the equation of the plane is

$$\mathbf{r}.(-\mathbf{i}+2\mathbf{j}-2\mathbf{k}) = 9 \qquad \text{(dividing by 6)}$$

(You could have saved a little effort by noting that $-\mathbf{i}+2\mathbf{j}-2\mathbf{k}$, being a multiple of $-6\mathbf{i}-12\mathbf{j}-12\mathbf{k}$, is perpendicular to the plane and used that for your **n**.)

(c)   Using the formula for the distance of $\mathbf{d} = 4\mathbf{i}-\mathbf{j}+3\mathbf{k}$ from the plane $\mathbf{r}.(-\mathbf{i}+2\mathbf{j}-2\mathbf{k})=9$
gives

$$\text{distance} = \frac{\left|9 - (4\mathbf{i}-\mathbf{j}+3\mathbf{k}).(-\mathbf{i}+2\mathbf{j}-2\mathbf{k})\right|}{\sqrt{1+4+4}}$$

$$= \frac{21}{\sqrt{1+4+4}}$$

$$= 7$$

Volume of tetrahedron ABCD $= \frac{1}{3} \times$ base area $\times$ height

$$= \frac{1}{3} \times 9 \times 7$$

$$= 21$$

(d)   The required plane is parallel to the plane ABC, and so, using the equation of the plane found in (b), has equation

$$\mathbf{r}.(-\mathbf{i}+2\mathbf{j}-2\mathbf{k}) = \text{constant}, K$$

Since it contains D,

$$(4\mathbf{i}-\mathbf{j}+3\mathbf{k}).(-\mathbf{i}+2\mathbf{j}-2\mathbf{k}) = K$$

$$\Rightarrow \quad -4-2-6 = K$$

$$\Rightarrow \quad K = -12$$

and the equation is

$$\mathbf{r}.(-\mathbf{i}+2\mathbf{j}-2\mathbf{k}) = -12.$$

In cartesian form, $r = x\mathbf{i}+y\mathbf{j}+z\mathbf{k}$, gives

$$-x+2y-2z = -12$$

(or $x-2y+2z = 12$).

Use of vector product

The vector product can be useful when we need a vector perpendicular to two given vectors. For instance, when we are finding the line of intersection of two planes with equations

$$\mathbf{r}.\mathbf{n}_1 = d_1 \text{ and } \mathbf{r}.\mathbf{n}_2 = d_2$$

the direction of the line of intersection will be $\mathbf{n}_1 \times \mathbf{n}_2$.

Can you explain why?

Example

Find a vector equation for the line of intersection of the planes with equations

$$\mathbf{r}.(\mathbf{i}+2\mathbf{j}+3\mathbf{k}) = 6 \text{ and } \mathbf{r}.(3\mathbf{i}-2\mathbf{k}) = 1.$$

Solution

The direction of the line is given by the vector product

$$(\mathbf{i}+2\mathbf{j}+3\mathbf{k})\times(3\mathbf{i}-2\mathbf{k})$$

$$=\begin{bmatrix}1\\2\\3\end{bmatrix}\times\begin{bmatrix}3\\0\\-2\end{bmatrix}=\begin{bmatrix}-4\\11\\-6\end{bmatrix}\qquad\text{(writing the vectors as}\\3\times1\text{ column matrices)}$$

The line of intersection is therefore of the form

$$\mathbf{r}=\mathbf{a}+\lambda(-4\mathbf{i}+11\mathbf{j}-6\mathbf{k})$$

where $\mathbf{a}$ is the position vector of any point on both of the planes and hence on the line of intersection.

For instance,

$$(1,\ 1,\ 1)\ ,\ \left(\frac{1}{3},\ \frac{17}{6},\ 0\right),\ \left(0,\ \frac{15}{4},\ -\frac{1}{2}\right)$$

all lie on each of the planes.

A possible equation for the line of intersection is therefore

$$\mathbf{r}=(1+\mathbf{j}+\mathbf{k})+\lambda(-4\mathbf{i}+11\mathbf{j}-6\mathbf{k})$$

Angle between two planes

The two planes

$$\mathbf{r}.\mathbf{n}_1=d_1\ \text{ and }\ \mathbf{r}.\mathbf{n}_2=d_2$$

have normals $\mathbf{n}_1$ and $\mathbf{n}_2$ respectively.

The angle between the two planes is equal to the angle between $\mathbf{n}_1$ and $\mathbf{n}_2$.

Can you draw a diagram to explain why?

Example

Find the cosine of the acute angle between the two planes

$$\mathbf{r}.(\mathbf{i}-\mathbf{j}+5\mathbf{k})=2\ \text{ and }\ \mathbf{r}.(3\mathbf{i}+2\mathbf{j}-\mathbf{k})=5.$$

Solution

Let $\quad\quad\mathbf{n}_1 = \mathbf{i} - \mathbf{j} + 5\mathbf{k}$ and $\mathbf{n}_2 = 3\mathbf{i} + 2\mathbf{j} - \mathbf{k}$

$$\mathbf{n}_1.\mathbf{n}_2 = 3 - 2 - 5 = -4$$

$$|\mathbf{n}_1| = \sqrt{(1 + 1 + 25)} = \sqrt{27} \; ; \quad |\mathbf{n}_2| = \sqrt{(9 + 4 + 1)} = \sqrt{14}$$

If θ is the angle between $\mathbf{n}_1$ and $\mathbf{n}_2$,

$$\cos\theta = \frac{\mathbf{n}_1.\mathbf{n}_2}{|\mathbf{n}_1||\mathbf{n}_2|} = \frac{-4}{\sqrt{27}\times\sqrt{14}} = \frac{-4}{\sqrt{378}}$$

When two lines intersect, the angle between the lines could be taken as the acute or obtuse angle. The answer above gives the obtuse angle since cosine is negative.

The acute angle is given by

$$\cos^{-1}\left(\frac{4}{\sqrt{378}}\right)$$

But this is equal to the angle between the two planes.

The cosine of the acute angle between the planes is

$$\frac{4}{\sqrt{378}}$$

Angle between a line and a plane

Let the acute angle between the line L with equation

$$\mathbf{r} = \mathbf{a} + \lambda\mathbf{d}$$

and the plane π with equation $\mathbf{r}.\mathbf{n} = p$ be θ.

Let the acute angle between the direction vector of the line $\mathbf{d}$ and $\mathbf{n}$, the normal to the plane π, be ϕ.

Can you see why $\theta + \phi = 90°$?

Therefore $\quad\quad\cos\phi = \dfrac{\mathbf{n}.\mathbf{d}}{|\mathbf{n}||\mathbf{d}|}$

or $\quad\quad\quad\sin\phi = \dfrac{\mathbf{n}.\mathbf{d}}{|\mathbf{n}||\mathbf{d}|}$

The angle between L and π is therefore

$$\sin^{-1}\left(\frac{\mathbf{n}.\mathbf{d}}{|\mathbf{n}||\mathbf{d}|}\right)$$

Example

Find the angle betweeen the line with equation

$$\mathbf{r} = (2\mathbf{i}+\mathbf{k}) + \lambda(3\mathbf{i}-4\mathbf{j}+\mathbf{k})$$

and the plane with equation

$$\mathbf{r}.(5\mathbf{i}+\mathbf{j}-6\mathbf{k}) = 2$$

Solution

Direction of line $\mathbf{d} = 3\mathbf{i}-4\mathbf{j}+\mathbf{k}$

Normal to plane $\mathbf{n} = 5\mathbf{i}+\mathbf{j}-6\mathbf{k}$

$$\mathbf{d}.\mathbf{n} = 15-4-6 = 5 \quad\Rightarrow\quad |\mathbf{d}| = \sqrt{26}, \quad |\mathbf{n}| = \sqrt{62}$$

Angle between line and normal to plane

$$= \cos^{-1}\left(\frac{5}{\sqrt{26}\ \sqrt{62}}\right)$$
$$\approx 82.8°$$

$\Rightarrow$ Angle between line and plane

$$= 90° - 82.8°$$
$$\approx 7.2°$$

5.4   Miscellaneous Exercises

1. Referred to a fixed origin O, the position vectors of the points A, B, C and D are respectively:

   $$-\mathbf{j}+\mathbf{k}, \ 2\mathbf{i}-\mathbf{j}+3\mathbf{k}, \ -\mathbf{i}-2\mathbf{j}+2\mathbf{k}, \ 7\mathbf{i}-4\mathbf{j}+2\mathbf{k}.$$

   (a) Find a vector which is perpendicular to the plane ABC.

   (b) Show that the length of the perpendicular from D to the plane ABC is of length $2\sqrt{6}$.

   (c) Show that the planes ABC and BCD are perpendicular.

   (d) Find the acute angle between the line BD and the plane ABC, giving your answer to the nearest degree.   (AEB)

2. The point A has position vector $\mathbf{i}+4\mathbf{j}-3\mathbf{k}$ referred to the origin O. The line L has vector equation $\mathbf{r} = t\mathbf{i}$. The plane π contains the line L and the point A. Find:

   (a) a vector which is normal to the plane π;

   (b) a vector equation for the plane π;

   (c) the cosine of the acute angle between OA and the line L.

3. The lines l_1 and l_2 have vector equations

    l_1: $\mathbf{r} = 2\mathbf{i} + 3\mathbf{j} + 5\mathbf{k} + \lambda(\mathbf{i} + \mathbf{j} + 2\mathbf{k})$

    l_2: $\mathbf{r} = 4\mathbf{j} + 6\mathbf{k} + \mu(-\mathbf{i} + 2\mathbf{j} + 3\mathbf{k})$

    (a) Show that l_1 and l_2 intersect and find the position vector of the point of intersection.

    (b) Find the acute angle between l_1 and l_2, giving your answer correct to the nearest degree. (AEB)

4. The points P and Q have position vectors

    $\mathbf{p} = 3\mathbf{i} - \mathbf{j} + 2\mathbf{k}$ and $\mathbf{q} = 4\mathbf{i} - 2\mathbf{j} - \mathbf{k}$

    respectively, relative to a fixed origin O.

    (a) Determine a vector equation of the line l_1, passing through P and Q in the form $\mathbf{r} = \mathbf{a} + s\mathbf{b}$, where s is a scalar parameter.

    (b) The line l_2 has vector equation

    $\mathbf{r} = 2\mathbf{i} - 2\mathbf{j} - 3\mathbf{k} + t(2\mathbf{i} - \mathbf{j} - 2\mathbf{k})$.

    Show that l_1 and l_2 intersect and find the position vector of the point of intersection V.

    (c) Show that PV has length $3\sqrt{11}$.

    (d) The acute angle between l_1 and l_2 is θ. Show that
    $$\cos\theta = \frac{3}{\sqrt{11}}$$

    (e) Calculate the perpendicular distance from P to l_2. (AEB)

5. The position vectors of the points A, B and C are

    $\mathbf{a} = 4\mathbf{i} + 10\mathbf{j} + 6\mathbf{k}$, $\mathbf{b} = 6\mathbf{i} + 8\mathbf{j} - 2\mathbf{k}$, $\mathbf{c} = \mathbf{i} + 10\mathbf{j} + 3\mathbf{k}$

    with respect to a fixed origin O.

    (a) Show that the angle ACB is a right angle.

    (b) Find the area of the triangle ABC and hence, or otherwise, show that the shortest distance from C to AB is $3\sqrt{\left(\frac{3}{2}\right)}$.

    (c) The point D lies on the straight line through A and C. Show that the vector $\overrightarrow{AD} = \lambda(\mathbf{i} + \mathbf{k})$ for some scalar λ.

    Given that the lengths AB and AD are equal, dtermine the possible position vectors of D. (AEB)

6. Referred to a fixed origin O, the points A, B and C have position vectors

    $3\mathbf{i} - \mathbf{j} + 2\mathbf{k}$, $7\mathbf{i} + 2\mathbf{j} + 7\mathbf{k}$ and $\mathbf{i} + \mathbf{j} + 3\mathbf{k}$

    respectively. The vector $\mathbf{n}$ is the vector product

    $$\overrightarrow{AB} \times \overrightarrow{AC}.$$

    Express $\mathbf{n}$ in terms of $\mathbf{i}$, $\mathbf{j}$ and $\mathbf{k}$ and describe the direction of $\mathbf{n}$ in relation to the plane ABC.

Find an equation for the plane ABC in the form $\mathbf{r}.\mathbf{n} = p$. Hence find the shortest distance from O to the plane ABC.

Show that the plane OCA has equation

$$\mathbf{r}.(5\mathbf{i} + 7\mathbf{j} - 4\mathbf{k}) = 0.$$

Hence find, to $0.1°$, the angle between the plane OCA and the plane ABC. (AEB)

7. The line l has vector equation $\mathbf{r} = \mathbf{a} + \lambda\mathbf{d}$, where $\mathbf{a} = 3\mathbf{i} + 4\mathbf{j} - 3\mathbf{k}$ and $\mathbf{d} = 2\mathbf{i} - \mathbf{j} - 2\mathbf{k}$. The points P and Q have position vectors $\mathbf{p} = 4\mathbf{j} + 3\mathbf{k}$ and $\mathbf{q} = 2\mathbf{i} + 6\mathbf{j} + 2\mathbf{k}$ respectively. The plane π contains the line l and the point P.

    (a) Find the vector product $\mathbf{d} \times (\mathbf{a} - \mathbf{p})$. Hence, or otherwise, find the equation of the plane π in the form $\mathbf{r}.\mathbf{n} = k$.

    (b) Determine the angle between the lines passing through the points P and Q and the plane π.

    (c) Prove that the point P is equidistant from the line l and the point Q. (AEB)

8. Referred to a fixed origin O, the points

    A (4, 1, 3), B (−2, 7, 6) and C (1, 1, 4)

    have position vectors $\mathbf{a}$, $\mathbf{b}$ and $\mathbf{c}$ respectively.

    Find $(\mathbf{b} - \mathbf{a}) \times (\mathbf{c} - \mathbf{a})$ and hence, or otherwise, determine in the form $\mathbf{r}.\mathbf{n} = p$ an equation of the plane ABC.

    The point D with position vector $\mathbf{d} = 5\mathbf{i} - 3\mathbf{j} + \lambda\mathbf{k}$ lies in the plane ABC. Find the value of λ.

    Prove that ABCD is a trapezium and find its area. (AEB)

9. With respect to a fixed origin O, the lines l_1 and l_2 are given by the vector equations

    l_1: $\mathbf{r} = 9\mathbf{i} - 4\mathbf{j} + 5\mathbf{k} + t(2\mathbf{i} - \mathbf{j} + \mathbf{k})$

    l_2: $\mathbf{r} = 2\mathbf{i} - 8\mathbf{j} + 12\mathbf{k} + s(\mathbf{i} + 2\mathbf{j} - 3\mathbf{k})$,

    where t and s are scalar parameters. The point A lies on l_1 and OA is perpendicular to l_1. Determine the position vector of A and hence find in the form $\mathbf{r}.\mathbf{n} = p$ an equation of the plane π_1 which passes through A and is perpendicular to OA.

    Show that l_1 and l_2 intersect and find the position vector of B, their point of intersection.

    Find a vector which is perpendicular to both l_1 and l_2 and hence find an equation for the plane π_2 which contains l_1 and l_2.

    Find, to the nearest one tenth of a degree, the acute angle between the planes π_1 and π_2. (AEB)

10. With respect to a fixed origin O, the points L and M have position vectors $6\mathbf{i}+3\mathbf{j}+2\mathbf{k}$ and $2\mathbf{i}+2\mathbf{j}+\mathbf{k}$ respectively.

   (a) Form the scalar product $\overrightarrow{OL}.\overrightarrow{OM}$ and hence find the cosine of angle LOM.

   (b) The point N is on the line LM, produced such that angle MON is 90°. Find an equation for the line LM in the form $\mathbf{r}=\mathbf{a}+\mathbf{b}t$ and hence calculate the position vector of N.   (AEB)

11. The plane π_1 contains the points

   $(1, 4, 2)$, $(1, 0, 5)$ and $(0, 8, -1)$.

   Find its equation in cartesian form.

   The plane π_2 contains the point $(2, 2, 3)$ and has normal vector $(\mathbf{i}+2\mathbf{j}+2\mathbf{k})$. Find its equation in cartesian form.

   The point $(p, 0, q)$ lies in both the planes π_1 and π_2. Find p and q and express the equation of the line of intersection of the two planes in the form $\mathbf{r}=\mathbf{a}+\lambda\mathbf{b}$.

   The point $(1, 1, \mu)$ is equidistant from the planes π_1 and π_2. Find the two possible values of μ.   (AEB)

12. The points A, B and C have position vectors

   $\mathbf{a}=\mathbf{i}+2\mathbf{j}+4\mathbf{k}$, $\mathbf{b}=-2\mathbf{i}+3\mathbf{j}+5\mathbf{k}$, $\mathbf{c}=3\mathbf{i}-\mathbf{j}+2\mathbf{k}$

   respectively, with respect to a fixed origin.

   (a) Show that the point P $(1-3\lambda, 2+\lambda, 4+\lambda)$ lies on the straight line through A and B.

   Express PC^2 in terms of λ and show that, as λ varies, the least value of PC^2 is 6. Verify that in this case the line PC is perpendicular to the line AB.

   (b) Find a vector perpendicular to AB and AC and hence, or otherwise, find an equation for the plane ABC in the form $\mathbf{r}.\mathbf{n}=p$.

   (c) Find a cartesian equation of the plane π which contains the line AB and which is perpendicular to the plane ABC.

   (d) Verify that the point D with position vector $2\mathbf{i}-2\mathbf{j}+11\mathbf{k}$ lies in the plane π and is such that DA is perpendicular to AB. Hence, or otherwise, calculate the volume of the tetrahedron ABCD.   (AEB)

13. The points A, B and C have position vectors

   $\mathbf{a}=\mathbf{i}+2\mathbf{j}+2\mathbf{k}$, $\mathbf{b}=3\mathbf{i}+6\mathbf{j}-5\mathbf{k}$, $\mathbf{c}=7\mathbf{i}+20\mathbf{j}-7\mathbf{k}$

   respectively, relative to a fixed origin. The point D has position vector $\mathbf{d}$ and is such that ABCD is a parallelogram.

   (a) Find $\mathbf{d}$ in terms of $\mathbf{i}$, $\mathbf{j}$ and $\mathbf{k}$.

   (b) Calculate $(\mathbf{b}-\mathbf{a}).(\mathbf{c}-\mathbf{a})$ and hence determine the size of angle BAC, giving your answer to the nearest 0.1°.

   (c) Calculate the area of the parallelogram ABCD.

   (d) Show that a general point P on the diagonal AC is $(1+2\lambda, 2+6\lambda, 2-3\lambda)$. Write down the vector $\overrightarrow{BP}$ and hence, or otherwise, determine the position vector of the point on the line AC that is closest to B.   (AEB)

14. With respect to a fixed origin, O, the points A and B have position vectors

   $(2\mathbf{i}+3\mathbf{j}+6\mathbf{k})$ and $(2\mathbf{i}+4\mathbf{j}+4\mathbf{k})$ respectively.

   (a) Calculate $|\overrightarrow{OA}|$, $|\overrightarrow{OB}|$ and, by using the scalar product $\overrightarrow{OA}.\overrightarrow{OB}$, calculate the value of the cosine of angle AOB.

   (b) The point C has position vector $5\mathbf{i}+12\mathbf{j}+6\mathbf{k}$.

   Show that OC and AB are perpendicular. Show also that the line through O and C intersects the line through A and B, and find the position vector of the point E where they intersect.

   (c) Given that $\overrightarrow{AE}=\lambda\overrightarrow{EB}$, find the value of λ and explain briefly why λ is negative.   (AEB)

6 SEQUENCES AND SERIES

Objectives

After studying this chapter you should

* be able to work with both finite and infinite series;

* understand, and be able to apply, the method of proof by mathematical induction;

* be able to use the method of differences to sum finite series, and extend its use to infinite series;

* know how to obtain Maclaurin series for well known functions, including the general binomial expansion;

* appreciate that some of the standard series are valid for all real values of x, while others are only valid for specified ranges of values of x;

* be able to determine general terms in these standard cases.

6.0   Introduction and revision

In *Pure Mathematics*, Chapter 13, you were introduced to the notion of a sequence, and its related series. You will also have encountered the use of the Σ notation as a shorthand for writing out series with a large number of terms (possibly infinitely many). The first section of this chapter will remind you of the essential points that you will need in order to develop further the work in this area.

Definition

A **sequence** is simply an ordered list $u_1, u_2, u_3, \ldots, u_n$, of numbers (or terms). This is often abbreviated to $\{u_n\}$. For our purposes each term u_n is usually given in one of two ways:

    (i)   as a function of the preceding term(s),   or

    (ii)   as a function of its position in the sequence.

Example

The sequence $\{u_n\}$ defined by

$$u_1 = 1 \text{ and } u_n = (u_1 u_2 ... u_{n-1}) + 1 \text{ for } n \geq 2$$

is   1, 2, 3, 7, 43, 1807, ...,

where each term (after the first) is one greater than the product of all the previous terms of the sequence.

You will appreciate however that, in such cases, should you wish to know (say) u_{100}, the hundredth term of this sequence, then you would first need to know each of the preceding 99 terms. It is preferable, then, to have sequences given in the second way, with each term defined as a function of n, its position in the sequence.

Example

One of the most famous sequences of all is the Fibonacci sequence $\{F_n\}$ which is defined by

$$F_1 = 1, \quad F_2 = 1 \text{ and } F_n = F_{n-1} + F_{n-2} \text{ for } n \geq 3.$$

This sequence begins

1, 1, 2, 3, 5, 8, 13, 21, ...

The general solution of sequences defined in this way is not within the scope of this course, but (for the interested reader) each term of the Fibonacci sequence is actually given by

$$F_n = \frac{1}{\sqrt{5}}\left\{ \left(\frac{1+\sqrt{5}}{2}\right)^n - \left(\frac{1-\sqrt{5}}{2}\right)^n \right\}$$

Activity 1

Check that the formula above for the Fibonacci sequence does, in fact, give the first three terms.

The activity above shows that an analytic approach is not always the most useful. It is much easier to find, say, F_{20} from adding the terms rather than by using the formula.

6.1 Arithmetic and geometric sequences and series

The sequence defined by

$$u_1 = a \text{ and } u_n = u_{n-1} + d \text{ for } n \geq 2$$

begins

$$a, \ a+d, \ a+2d, \ldots$$

and you should recognise this as the **arithmetic sequence** with first term a and common difference d.

The nth term (i.e. the solution) is given by $u_n = a + (n-1)d$.

The arithmetic series with n terms,

$$a + (a+d) + (a+2d) + \ldots + [a + (n-1)d],$$

has sum

$$\boxed{S_n = \frac{n}{2}[2a + (n-1)d]}$$

or

$$S_n = \frac{n}{2}(\text{first } + \text{ last})$$

and these results should be well known to you.

Example

An arithmetic series has the property that the sum of the first ten terms is half the sum of the **next** ten terms. Also its 100th term is 95. Find the first term and common difference.

Solution

Let the first term be a and the common difference be d. Then the sums of the first ten terms and the next ten terms are

$$\frac{10}{2}(a + (a+9d)) \text{ and } \frac{10}{2}((a+10d) + (a+19d))$$

Since the former is half the latter we deduce that

$$2a + 9d = \frac{1}{2}(2a + 29d)$$

or $\qquad 2a = 11d \qquad\qquad$ (1)

Also, as the 100th term is 95, we know that

$$a + 99d = 95 \qquad (2)$$

From (1) $99d = 18a$ and so in (2)

$$a + 18a = 19a = 95$$

Hence $\qquad a = 5$ and $d = \dfrac{10}{11}$.

Another important sequence defined by

$$u_1 = a \text{ and } u_n = ru_{n-1} \text{ for } n \geq 2,$$

begins

$$a, \quad ar, \quad ar^2, \ldots$$

This is the **geometric sequence** with first term a and common ratio r.

The nth term is given by $u_n = ar^{n-1}$.

The geometric series with n terms,

$$a + ar + ar^2 + \ldots + ar^{n-1}$$

has sum

$$\boxed{S_n = \frac{a(1-r^n)}{1-r} \text{ or } \frac{a(r^n-1)}{r-1}} \qquad \text{for } r \neq 1$$

Note that a **series** is the sum of a number of terms of a **sequence**. The terms 'arithmetic progression' (A.P.) and 'geometric progression' (G.P.) are not preferred here as the word 'progression' is used loosely in respect of both a sequence and a series. However, you should recognise the use of these terms and their abbreviations, since they are in common usage.

6.2 The sigma notation

When writing series, the shorthand Σ notation is used to represent the sum of a number of terms having a common form.

The series $f(1) + f(2) + \ldots + f(n-1) + f(n)$ would be written

$$\sum_{r=1}^{n} f(r).$$

What other way could the series be written using Σ notation?

The function f is the common form that each term of the series takes; r is called the **summation index**, being the variable quantity from term to term. The '$r=1$' below the sigma indicates the first value taken by r, and the 'n' above the sigma denotes the final term taken by r.

Note that, while it is customary to take $r=1$ for the first term, it is by no means essential. The above series would equally well be written as

$$\sum_{r=0}^{n-1} f(r+1)$$

In fact, later on in the chapter you will encounter series which, for convenience, will start with $r=0$.

Also, the choice of the letter 'r' is unimportant:

$$\sum_{r=1}^{n} f(r), \ \sum_{k=1}^{n} f(k) \text{ and } \sum_{i=1}^{n} f(i)$$

all represent the series $f(1)+f(2)+...+f(n)$.

You should know the following results relating to the Σ notation:

(1) $\displaystyle\sum_{r=1}^{n}\{f(r)+g(r)\}=\{f(1)+g(1)\}+\{f(2)+g(2)\}+...+\{f(n)+g(n)\}$

$$=\{f(1)+f(2)+...+f(n)\}+\{g(1)+g(2)+...+g(n)\}$$

$$=\sum_{r=1}^{n} f(r)+\sum_{r=1}^{n} g(r)$$

(2) $\displaystyle\sum_{r=1}^{n} af(r)=af(1)+af(2)+...+af(n)$ where a is some constant

$$=a\{f(1)+f(2)+...+f(n)\}$$

$$=a\sum_{r=1}^{n} f(r)$$

Note that $\displaystyle\sum_{r=1}^{n} nf(r)=n\sum_{r=1}^{n} f(r)$ also, since n is a fixed quantity, not a variable, in the summation.

(3) (a) $$\sum_{r=1}^{n} r = \frac{n(n+1)}{2}$$

(b) $$\sum_{r=1}^{n} r^2 = \frac{n}{6}(n+1)(2n+1)$$

(c) $$\sum_{r=1}^{n} r^3 = \frac{n^2}{4}(n+1)^2 \quad \text{or} \quad \left[\frac{n(n+1)}{2}\right]^2$$

(d) $$\sum_{r=1}^{n} 1 = \underset{\leftarrow \ n \ \text{times} \ \rightarrow}{(1+1+...+1)} = n$$

Since a '1' is wanted for each of $r = 1, 2, ..., n$

This result is easily overlooked, and often incorrectly written as

$$\sum_{r=1}^{n} 1 = 1$$

Example

Show that $$\sum_{r=1}^{n}\left(6r^2 + 4r - 1\right) = n(n+2)(2n+1).$$

Solution

$$\sum_{r=1}^{n}\left(6r^2 + 4r - 1\right) = \sum_{r=1}^{n} 6r^2 + \sum_{r=1}^{n} 4r - \sum_{r=1}^{n} 1 \qquad \text{by result (1)}$$

$$= 6\sum_{r=1}^{n} r^2 + 4\sum_{r=1}^{n} r - \sum_{r=1}^{n} 1 \qquad \text{by result (2)}$$

$$= 6.\frac{n}{6}(n+1)(2n+1) + 4.\frac{n}{2}(n+1) - n \quad \text{by result (3)}$$

$$= n(n+1)(2n+1) + 2n(n+1) - n$$

$$= n\left(2n^2 + 3n + 1 + 2n + 2 - 1\right)$$

$$= n\left(2n^2 + 5n + 2\right)$$

$$= n(n+2)(2n+1)$$

Exercise 6A

1. A geometric series has first term 4 and second term 7. Giving your answer to three significant figures, find the sum of the first twenty terms of the series. **(AEB)**

2. The first term of an arithmetic series is –13 and the last term is 99. The sum of the series is 1419. Find the number of terms and the common difference. Find also the sum of all the positive terms of the series. **(AEB)**

3. An arithmetic series has first term 7 and second term 11.

   (a) Find the 17th term.

   (b) Show that the sum of the first 35 terms is equal to the sum of the next 15 terms. **(AEB)**

4. The first three terms of a geometric series are $2x, x-8$ and $2x+5$ respectively. Find the possible values of x. **(AEB)**

5. An arithmetic series has first term $\ln 2$ and common difference $\ln 4$. Show that the sum S_n of the first n terms is $n^2 \ln 2$.

   Find the least value of n for which S_n is greater than fifty times the nth term. **(AEB)**

6. A geometric series has first term 4 and common ratio r, where $0 < r < 1$. Given that the first, second and fourth terms of this geometric series form three successive terms of an arithmetic series, show that $r^3 - 2r + 1 = 0$. Find the value of r. **(AEB)**

7. Given that $S(n) = n^2 + 4n$, write down an expression for $S(n-1)$ and simplify $S(n) - S(n-1)$.

By considering the result above, show that the sequence is arithmetic and state the first term and the common difference.
Determine the least number of terms required for the sum of this arithmetic series to exceed 10 000. **(AEB)**

8. Show that $\displaystyle\sum_{r=1}^{n} r(r+1) = \frac{n}{3}(n+1)(n+2)$.

9. Use the formulae for $\displaystyle\sum_{r=1}^{n} r$, $\displaystyle\sum_{r=1}^{n} r^2$ and $\displaystyle\sum_{r=1}^{n} r^3$ to

   show that $\displaystyle\sum_{r=1}^{n} \left(4r^3 - 3r^2 + r\right) = An^3(n+1)$, for some constant A to be found.

10. Express the kth term of the series
    $$S = 1.3.4 + 2.5.7 + 3.7.10 + 4.9.13 + \dots$$
    as a function of k. Hence show that the sum of the first n terms of S is
    $$\frac{n}{6}(n+1)\left(9n^2 + 19n + 8\right)$$

11. Find the formula for the sum of n terms of the series $4^2 + 7^2 + 10^2 + 13^2 + \dots$

12. The rth term of a finite series is u_r, and the sum of n terms is denoted by S_n, so that $S_n = \displaystyle\sum_{r=1}^{n} u_r$.

    If $S_n = 3n^2 + 5n$, express u_r as a function of r and find $\displaystyle\sum_{r=n}^{2n} u_r$.

6.3 Proof by induction

An inventor builds a climbing 'robot' which is designed to be able to climb any ladder which has equally spaced rungs, no matter how long it may be. (Being solar-powered, it can continue indefinitely if necessary.) The inventor tests it on a variety of ladders: on some of them, the robot succeeds; on others it does not.

Given any ladder, what conditions need to be satisfied for the robot to be able to climb the ladder?

You will see that there are, in fact, just two:

(a) In the first instance, the robot needs to be able to get on the ladder (presumably at the first rung); and

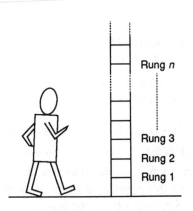

(b) if the robot is on any given rung (say rung k – as rungs are equally spaced, it does not matter where rung k is on the ladder), then it has to be able to get on to the next rung after this (rung $k+1$).

If the robot's programming and construction enable it to satisfy both these conditions, then it can climb as far up the ladder (ad infinitum if necessary) as its inventor could wish for; since by condition (a) the robot can get on the ladder (at rung 1). Then, by condition (b) it can get on to rung 2. By (b) again, it can get to rung 3, hence to rung 4, hence to rung 5, etc., etc. Thus the robot can reach rung n for **any** positive integer n.

No, the authors have not gone senile! The above is actually an illustration of a very powerful technique called **proof by induction**. The method is a cunning means of proving the truth of some statement, or formula, that is found by experimental means (for instance) but which, without a general proof, is only **known** to be true for certain values of the variable concerned.

For instance, the result

$$\sum_{r=1}^{n} r = 1 + 2 + \dots + n = \frac{n(n+1)}{2}$$

arises from the sum to n terms of an arithmetic series, and has already been proved.

What about the result $\displaystyle\sum_{r=1}^{n} r^2 = \frac{n}{6}(n+1)(2n+1)$?

Where did that come from?

One way, is to first note that the formula for $\displaystyle\sum_{r=1}^{n} r$ is a quadratic

in n, and so assume that the formula for $\displaystyle\sum_{r=1}^{n} r^2$ is a cubic in n, say

$$an^3 + bn^2 + cn + d$$

Then use the values found in the cases when $n = 1, 2, 3$ and 4 to set up and solve a system of four simultaneous equations in the four unknowns a, b, c, d (which turn out to be $\frac{1}{3}, \frac{1}{2}, \frac{1}{6}$ and 0 respectively).

However, this only **proves** that such an expression fits the bill in these four cases: namely $n = 1, 2, 3$ and 4. You could try it out for $n = 5, 6, 7, \dots$, as far as you liked. You could convince yourself that this expression for the sum of the squares of the first n positive integers just has to be true for every positive integer n; but you would have proved it in only a few (or even many) particular cases.

Try the robot approach:

when $n=1$, $\displaystyle\sum_{r=1}^{n} r^2 = 1^2 = 1$,

while the formula with $n=1$ gives

$$\tfrac{1}{6}(1)(1+1)(2\times1+1) = \tfrac{1}{6}\times1\times2\times3 = 1$$

also.

Hence the formula is true when $n=1$. (The robot is on the ladder at rung 1.)

Next, **assume** that

$$\sum_{r=1}^{k} r^2 = \frac{k}{6}(k+1)(2k+1)$$

(That is, the robot is on the ladder (somewhere) at rung k. Now what about rung $k+1$?)

Then it follows that

$$\sum_{r=1}^{k+1} r^2 = \sum_{r=1}^{k} r^2 + (k+1)^2$$

$$= \frac{k}{6}(k+1)(2k+1) + (k+1)^2 \qquad \text{(the first term was assumed above)}$$

$$= \frac{k}{6}(k+1)(2k+1) + \frac{6}{6}(k+1)^2 \qquad \text{(common denominator)}$$

$$= \frac{(k+1)}{6}\left\{k(2k+1) + 6(k+1)\right\} \qquad \text{(factorising)}$$

$$= \frac{(k+1)}{6}\left(2k^2 + 7k + 6\right)$$

$$= \frac{(k+1)}{6}(k+2)(2k+3)$$

Now notice that this expression is

$$\frac{1}{6}(k+1)([k+1]+1)(2[k+1]+1),$$

which is precisely the formula expected, but with $n = k+1$.

So **if** the formula assumed when $n = k$ is true **then**, by adding on the $(k+1)$th term, it must also be true when $n = k+1$, whatever k is. (The robot can get from rung k to rung $k+1$.)

In itself, this step of the process is a big IF. But the formula **is** true when $n=1$, so this 'stepping up' bit proves it must be true when $n=2$ also. Since it is true for $n=2$ (which it now is known to be) then it must be true for $n=3$ as well; and then for $n=4$, $n=5$,... and for all positive integers n.

Remember that the 'stepping up' part of the proof relies on an assumption (called the **induction hypothesis**) and it is important, therefore, to use the word 'assume' (or 'suppose') otherwise there is a large amount of written explanation to do at the end of this proof in order to finalise matters conclusively. The proof is clinched by showing that the whole process starts in the first place.

Example

Use mathematical induction to prove that, for all positive integers n,

$$2.2 + 3.2^2 + \ldots + (n+1).2^n = n.2^{n+1}$$

Solution

When $n=1$, LHS $= 2.2 = 4$

and $\qquad$ RHS $= 1.2^{1+1} = 1.4 = 4$

and the statement is true when $n=1$. $\qquad$ (starting step)

Assume that the formula is true for $n=k$; that is

$$2.2 + 3.2^2 + \ldots + (k+1).2^k = k.2^{k+1} \qquad \text{(induction hypothesis)}$$

Then, when $n=k+1$,

$$2.2 + 3.2^2 + \ldots + (k+1).2^k + (k+2).2^{k+1}$$

$$= \underbrace{\left\{2.2 + 3.2^2 + \ldots + (k+1).2^k\right\}} + (k+2).2^{k+1} \qquad ((k+1)\text{ term added})$$

$$= \qquad k.2^{k+1} \qquad\qquad + (k+2).2^{k+1} \qquad \text{(by the hypothesis)}$$

$$= 2^{k+1}(k+k+2)$$

$$= 2^{k+1}(2k+2)$$

$$= 2^{k+1}.2(k+1)$$

$$= (k+1).2^{k+2}$$

which is the required formula with k replaced by $k+1$. Hence if the statement is true for $n=k$, then it is also true for $n=k+1$.

By induction $2.2+3.2^2+\ldots+(n+1).2^n = n.2^{n+1}$ is true for all positive integers n.

Note: because it is easy to decide what the final expression ('the formula for $n=k$ with k replaced by $k+1$') should be in advance, many students 'fiddle' it into existence, or simply write it straight down, without showing the necessary working to demonstrate that it does indeed arise as a result of adding on the $(k+1)$th term to the assumed sum-to-k-terms. Be careful to show your working!

The following example illustrates the minimal amount of working that needs to be put down in order to clinch an inductive proof.

Example

Prove by induction that

$$\sum_{r=1}^{n}\frac{1}{r(r+1)(r+2)} = \frac{1}{4} - \frac{1}{2(n+1)(n+2)}$$

for all positive integers n.

Solution

For $n=1$,   LHS $= \displaystyle\sum_{r=1}^{1}\frac{1}{r(r+1)(r+2)} = \frac{1}{1\times2\times3} = \frac{1}{6}$,

while   RHS $= \dfrac{1}{4} - \dfrac{1}{2\times2\times3} = \dfrac{1}{4} - \dfrac{1}{12} = \dfrac{1}{6}$ also.

Now assume that

$$\sum_{r=1}^{k}\frac{1}{r(r+1)(r+2)} = \frac{1}{4} - \frac{1}{2(k+1)(k+2)}$$

Then

$$\sum_{r=1}^{k+1}\frac{1}{r(r+1)(r+2)} = \sum_{r=1}^{k}\frac{1}{r(r+1)(r+2)} + \frac{1}{(k+1)(k+2)(k+3)}$$

$$= \frac{1}{4} - \frac{1}{2(k+1)(k+2)} + \frac{1}{(k+1)(k+2)(k+3)}$$

$$= \frac{1}{4} - \frac{1}{(k+1)(k+2)}\left\{\frac{1}{2} - \frac{1}{k+3}\right\}$$

$$= \frac{1}{4} - \frac{1}{(k+1)(k+2)} \left\{ \frac{k+3-2}{2(k+3)} \right\}$$

$$= \frac{1}{4} - \frac{(k+1)}{2(k+1)(k+2)(k+3)}$$

$$= \frac{1}{4} - \frac{1}{2([k+1]+1)([k+1]+2)}, \text{ as required.}$$

Proof follows by induction.

Exercise 6B

Use mathematical induction to prove the following results for all positive integers n:

1. $\displaystyle\sum_{r=1}^{n} r^3 = \frac{1}{4}n^2(n+1)^2$

2. $\displaystyle\sum_{r=1}^{n} r(r+3) = \frac{1}{3}n(n+1)(n+5)$

3. $\displaystyle\sum_{r=1}^{n}(2r-1)(2r+1) = \frac{1}{2} + \frac{1}{6}(2n-1)(2n+1)(2n+3)$

4. $\displaystyle\sum_{r=1}^{n} \frac{2}{(r+1)(r+2)(r+3)} = \frac{1}{6} - \frac{1}{(n+2)(n+3)}$

5. $\displaystyle\sum_{r=1}^{n} r \times r! = (n+1)! - 1$

6. $\displaystyle\sum_{r=1}^{n} r \times 2^{r-1} = (n-1) \times 2^n + 1$

* 7. $\cos x + \cos 3x + \cos 5x + \ldots + \cos(2n-1)x = \dfrac{\sin 2nx}{2\sin x}$

8. $\displaystyle\sum_{r=1}^{n} r(r+1)\left(\frac{1}{2}\right)^{r-1} = 16 - (n^2+5n+8)\left(\frac{1}{2}\right)^{n-1}$

9. $\displaystyle\sum_{r=1}^{n}(-1)^{r+1}r^2 = (-1)^{n+1} \times \frac{n(n+1)}{2}$

6.4 The difference method

The process of proof by induction, whilst being a powerful mathematical tool, has the disadvantage that, in order to employ it, you really need to have the answer (or something you strongly suspect to be the answer) to begin with.

There are, however, direct methods of proof available in most cases. One of these is known as the method of differences, or the **difference method**.

The following example illustrates the method of differences. Although the working appears initially to be going nowhere, it will eventually lead to a direct proof that

$$\sum_{r=1}^{n} r^2 = \frac{1}{6}n(n+1)(2n+1)$$

During the proof it will be assumed that $\displaystyle\sum_{r=1}^{n} r = \frac{1}{2}n(n+1)$, which has been established previously as the sum of an arithmetic series.

Consider the following identity:

$$n^3 - (n-1)^3 \equiv n^3 - \left(n^3 - 3n^2 + 3n - 1\right)$$

i.e. $\qquad n^3 - (n-1)^3 \equiv 3n^2 - 3n + 1.$ $\qquad$ (1)

From this, the similar identity

$$(n-1)^3 - (n-2)^3 \equiv 3(n-1)^2 - 3(n-1) + 1$$

can be deduced by replacing n by $n-1$.

Also, replacing n by $n-2$ in equation (1) gives

$$(n-2)^3 - (n-3)^3 \equiv 3(n-2)^2 - 3(n-2) + 1, \text{ etc.}$$

Writing this sequence of results in a column form:

$$n^3 - (n-1)^3 = 3n^2 - 3n + 1$$

$$(n-1)^3 - (n-2)^3 = 3(n-1)^2 - 3(n-1) + 1$$

$$(n-2)^3 - (n-3)^3 = 3(n-2)^2 - 3(n-2) + 1$$

$$(n-3)^3 - (n-4)^3 = 3(n-3)^2 - 3(n-3) + 1$$

$$\vdots \qquad \vdots \qquad \vdots \qquad \vdots$$

$$3^3 - 2^3 = 3(3)^2 - 3(3) + 1$$

$$2^3 - 1^3 = 3(2)^2 - 3(2) + 1$$

$$1^3 - 0^3 = 3(1)^2 - 3(1) + 1$$

Now add up all the terms on the LHS: you get $n^3 - 0^3$, since all other terms appear once positively and once negatively, cancelling out. Adding up the RHS in three columns gives

$$3 \sum_{r=1}^{n} r^2 - 3 \sum_{r=1}^{n} r + n$$

Thus $\qquad n^3 = 3 \sum_{r=1}^{n} r^2 - 3 \sum_{r=1}^{n} r + n \qquad$ [using $\sum_{r=1}^{n} r = \frac{1}{2} n(n+1)$]

$$\Rightarrow \qquad 3 \sum_{r=1}^{n} r^2 = \left(n^3 - n\right) + 3 \times \frac{1}{2} n(n+1)$$

$$= n\left(n^2 - 1\right) + \frac{3}{2}n(n+1)$$

$$= \frac{2n}{2}(n-1)(n+1) + \frac{3}{2}n(n+1)$$

$$= \frac{n(n+1)}{2}\{2(n-1) + 3\}$$

$$= \frac{1}{2}n(n+1)(2n+1)$$

Finally, dividing by 3 gives the required result,

$$\sum_{r=1}^{n} r^2 = \frac{1}{6}n(n+1)(2n+1)$$

Example

By considering $n^5 - (n-1)^5$ and similar expressions, find the formula for $\displaystyle\sum_{r=1}^{n} r^4$ in terms of n, assuming the results for

$$\sum_{r=1}^{n} r, \sum_{r=1}^{n} r^2 \text{ and } \sum_{r=1}^{n} r^3.$$

Solution

$$n^5 - (n-1)^5 = 5n^4 - 10n^3 + 10n^2 - 5n + 1$$

$$(n-1)^5 - (n-2)^5 = 5(n-1)^4 - 10(n-1)^3 + 10(n-1)^2 - 5(n-1) + 1$$

$$(n-2)^5 - (n-3)^5 = 5(n-2)^4 - 10(n-2)^3 + 10(n-2)^2 - 5(n-2) + 1$$

$$\vdots \quad \vdots \qquad \vdots \qquad \vdots \qquad \vdots \qquad \vdots \qquad \vdots \quad \vdots$$

$$3^5 - 2^5 = 5(3)^4 - 10(3)^3 + 10(3)^2 - 5(3) + 1$$

$$2^5 - 1^5 = 5(2)^4 - 10(2)^3 + 10(2)^2 - 5(2) + 1$$

$$1^5 - 0^5 = 5(1)^4 - 10(1)^3 + 10(1)^2 - 5(1) + 1$$

Adding: $\displaystyle n^5 - 0^5 = 5\sum_{r=1}^{n} r^4 - 10\sum_{r=1}^{n} r^3 + 10\sum_{r=1}^{n} r^2 - 5\sum_{r=1}^{n} r + n$

Rearranging, and using the three standard results:

$$5\sum_{r=1}^{n} r^4 = \left(n^5 - n\right) + 10\frac{n^2}{4}(n+1)^2 - 10\frac{n}{6}(n+1)(2n+1) + 5\frac{n}{2}(n+1)$$

$$= \frac{6}{6}n(n-1)(n+1)\left(n^2+1\right) + \frac{15}{6}n^2(n+1)^2 - 10\frac{n}{6}(n+1)(2n+1) + \frac{15}{6}n(n+1)$$

$$= \frac{1}{6}n(n+1)\left\{6(n-1)\left(n^2+1\right) + 15n(n+1) - 10(2n+1) + 15\right\}$$

$$= \frac{1}{6}n(n+1)\left\{6n^3 - 6n^2 + 6n - 6 + 15n^2 + 15n - 20n - 10 + 15\right\}$$

$$= \frac{1}{6}n(n+1)\left(6n^3 + 9n^2 + n - 1\right)$$

$$= \frac{1}{6}n(n+1)(2n+1)\left(3n^2 + 3n - 1\right)$$

so that

$$\sum_{r=1}^{n} r^4 = \frac{1}{30}n(n+1)(2n+1)\left(3n^2 + 3n - 1\right),$$

admittedly not a very appealing result! You will note, however, that the method of differences consists of adding two sides of a set of identities of a common form, where one side is expressed as a difference of successive terms. In this way, almost all terms cancel on this side in the summation.

The difference method can be employed in other circumstances also.

Example
Prove that

$$\sum_{r=1}^{n} \frac{r}{(r+1)!} = 1 - \frac{1}{(n+1)!}$$

Solution
Some ingenuity is needed here to turn the one term in the summation on the LHS into two terms. Note that

$$\frac{r}{(r+1)!} = \frac{r+1-1}{(r+1)!} = \frac{r+1}{(r+1)!} - \frac{1}{(r+1)!} = \frac{1}{r!} - \frac{1}{(r+1)!}$$

so that

$$\sum_{r=1}^{n} \frac{r}{(r+1)!} = \sum_{r=1}^{n}\left(\frac{1}{r!} - \frac{1}{(r+1)!}\right)$$

$$= \left(\frac{1}{1!} - \frac{1}{2!}\right) + \left(\frac{1}{2!} - \frac{1}{3!}\right) + \left(\frac{1}{3!} - \frac{1}{4!}\right) + \dots$$

$$+ \left(\frac{1}{n-1!} - \frac{1}{n!}\right) + \left(\frac{1}{n!} - \frac{1}{(n+1)!}\right)$$

$$= \frac{1}{1!} - \frac{1}{(n+1)!} \qquad \text{[since all other terms cancel]}$$

$$= 1 - \frac{1}{(n+1)!}$$

The difference method can be summarised by the following, which has been described as the fundamental theorem of summation:

$$\boxed{\sum_{r=1}^{n} \{f(r) - f(r-1)\} = f(n) - f(0)}$$

where f is any function suitably defined on the non-negative integers.

As an example take $f(r) = \sin\left(ar + \dfrac{a}{2}\right)$ for some constant

a (not equal to a multiple of 2π). Then

$$\sin\left(ar + \frac{a}{2}\right) - \sin\left(a[r-1] + \frac{a}{2}\right)$$

$$= \sin\left(ar + \frac{a}{2}\right) - \sin\left(ar - \frac{a}{2}\right)$$

$$= 2\cos\left(\frac{ar + \dfrac{a}{2} + ar - \dfrac{a}{2}}{2}\right) \sin\left(\frac{ar + \dfrac{a}{2} - ar - \dfrac{a}{2}}{2}\right)$$

$$= 2\cos(ar)\sin\frac{a}{2}$$

and

$$\sum_{r=1}^{n} 2\cos(ar)\sin\frac{a}{2} = f(n) - f(0) = \sin\left(an + \frac{a}{2}\right) - \sin\left(\frac{a}{2}\right)$$

by the difference method; leading to the result

$$\sum_{r=1}^{n} \cos(ar) = \frac{1}{2}\left\{\frac{\sin\left(an + \dfrac{a}{2}\right)}{\sin\dfrac{a}{2}} - 1\right\}$$

or, since

$$\sin\left(an + \frac{a}{2}\right) - \sin\left(\frac{a}{2}\right) = 2\cos\left[\frac{a(n+1)}{2}\right]\sin\left(\frac{an}{2}\right),$$

$$\sum_{r=1}^{n}\cos(ar) = \frac{\cos\left[\dfrac{a(n+1)}{2}\right]\sin\left(\dfrac{an}{2}\right)}{\sin\dfrac{a}{2}}$$

If you find this approach a little confusing, it only enables you to save a line or two of working. In tricky cases, resorting to writing out the series in question and seeing the terms which cancel will prove much simpler to handle correctly.

Example

Express $\dfrac{1}{x(x+1)}$ in terms of partial fractions.

Hence show that $\displaystyle\sum_{r=1}^{n}\frac{1}{r(r+1)} = \frac{n}{n+1}$ for all positive integers n.

Solution

Assume $\qquad \dfrac{1}{x(x+1)} \equiv \dfrac{A}{x} + \dfrac{B}{x+1}.$

By the cover–up method (or multiplying through by $x(x+1)$ and comparing coefficients or substituting values), $A = 1$ and $B = -1$.

Then $\qquad \displaystyle\sum_{r=1}^{n}\frac{1}{r(r+1)} = \sum_{r=1}^{n}\left(\frac{1}{r} - \frac{1}{r+1}\right)$

$$= \left(\frac{1}{1} - \frac{1}{2}\right) + \left(\frac{1}{2} - \frac{1}{3}\right) + \left(\frac{1}{3} - \frac{1}{4}\right) + \dots$$

$$+ \left(\frac{1}{n-1} - \frac{1}{n}\right) + \left(\frac{1}{n} - \frac{1}{n+1}\right)$$

$$= \frac{1}{1} - \frac{1}{n+1} = \frac{n+1}{n+1} - \frac{1}{n+1}$$

$$= \frac{n}{n+1}, \text{ as required.}$$

Alternatively, note that this is $\displaystyle\sum_{r=1}^{n}\{f(r) - f(r-1)\}$ with

$f(r) = -\dfrac{1}{r+1}$. The sum is then

$$f(n) - f(0) = -\frac{1}{n+1} - \left(-\frac{1}{0+1}\right) = 1 - \frac{1}{n+1}, \text{ etc. as before.}$$

Exercise 6C

1. Show that $3r(r+1)=r(r+1)(r+2)-r(r-1)(r+1)$

   and deduce that $\displaystyle\sum_{r=1}^{n}r(r+1)=\frac{1}{3}n(n+1)(n+2)$.

2. Express $\dfrac{1}{r(r+2)}$ in partial fractions, and hence

   show that $\displaystyle\sum_{r=1}^{n}\frac{1}{r(r+2)}=\frac{3}{4}-\frac{2n+3}{2(n+1)(n+2)}$

3. Simplify the expression $(r+1)!-r!$ and hence

   prove that $\displaystyle\sum_{r=1}^{n}r\times r!=(n+1)!-1$.

4. Simplify the expression $\left(\sqrt{r}+\sqrt{r-1}\right)\left(\sqrt{r}-\sqrt{r-1}\right)$.

   Hence prove that $\displaystyle\sum_{r=1}^{n}\frac{1}{\sqrt{r}+\sqrt{r-1}}=\sqrt{n}$ for all

   positive integers n.

5. Given that r is a positive integer and $f(r)=\dfrac{1}{r^2}$,

   find a single expression for $f(r)-f(r+1)$. Hence

   prove that $\displaystyle\sum_{r=1}^{4n}\left(\frac{2r+1}{r^2(r+1)^2}\right)=\frac{(3n+1)(5n+1)}{n^2(4n+1)^2}$

6. Prove the identity

   $$\frac{2r+3}{r(r+1)}-\frac{2r+5}{(r+1)(r+2)}\equiv\frac{2(r+3)}{r(r+1)(r+2)}.$$

   Hence, or otherwise, find the sum of the series

   $$S_n=\frac{8}{1\times2\times3}+\frac{10}{2\times3\times4}+...+\frac{2(n+3)}{n(n+1)(n+2)}$$

7. Use the method of differences to find

   $$\sum_{r=1}^{n}\frac{1}{(n+r-1)(n+r)}$$ in terms of n.

8. Prove that $\displaystyle\sum_{r=1}^{n}\frac{r^2+r+1}{r^2+r}=n+1-\frac{1}{n+1}$.

9. Prove the identity
   $$\cos(A-B)-\cos(A+B)=2\sin A\sin B.$$
   Hence prove that
   $$\sin\theta\{\sin\theta+\sin3\theta+\sin5\theta+...+\sin(2n-1)\theta\}=\sin^2 n\theta$$

*10. Express $\dfrac{1}{r(r+1)(r+2)}$ in partial fractions. Hence

   prove the result

   $$\sum_{r=1}^{n}\frac{1}{r(r+1)(r+2)}=\frac{1}{4}-\frac{1}{2(n+1)(n+2)}$$

*11. By considering $\dfrac{1}{1+a^{n-1}}-\dfrac{1}{1+a^n}$, show that

   $$\sum_{r=1}^{N}\frac{a^{n-1}}{\left(1+a^{n-1}\right)\left(1+a^n\right)}=\frac{a^N-1}{2(a-1)\left(a^N+1\right)},$$

   where a is positive and $a\neq1$. Deduce that

   $$\sum_{r=1}^{N}\frac{2^n}{\left(1+2^{n-1}\right)\left(1+2^n\right)}<1. \qquad\text{(Cambridge)}$$

*12. Use the difference method to show that

   $$\sum_{k=1}^{n}\frac{1}{(k+1)\sqrt{k}+k\sqrt{k+1}}=1-\frac{1}{\sqrt{n+1}}$$

6.5 Infinite series

Thus far in this chapter you have studied only finite series. You have, however, already encountered at least one example of a series which can be 'summed-to-infinity' without simply obtaining an 'infinitely large number', namely the geometric series

$$a+ar+ar^2+...+ar^{n-1}+...,$$

provided that $-1<r<1$.

The sum to n terms of a geometric series can be expressed as

$$S_n=\frac{a(1-r^n)}{1-r} \qquad (r\neq1)$$

which can be split up as

$$\frac{a}{1-r} - \frac{ar^n}{1-r}.$$

For $|r| < 1$, $r^n \to 0$ as $n \to \infty$ (said 'r^n tends to zero as n tends to infinity'), in which case the second term $\to 0$ also. This is written

$$\lim_{n \to \infty} \left(\frac{ar^n}{1-r} \right) = 0$$

and said 'the limit as n tends to infinity of $\left(\dfrac{ar^n}{1-r} \right)$ is zero'. The infinite geometric series converges in this case to the number

$$\lim_{n \to \infty} \{S_n\} = \frac{a}{1-r},$$

or $\qquad S_\infty = \dfrac{a}{1-r}$ for short.

When $|r| > 1$, $\dfrac{ar^n}{1-r} \not\to 0$, and the geometric series 'diverges', having no limit.

The sum-to-infinity of any convergent series is defined in the following way: given S_n, the sum to n terms of a series,

$$S_\infty = \lim_{n \to \infty} (S_n)$$

Example

From an earlier example, $\displaystyle\sum_{r=1}^{n} \frac{r}{(r+1)!} = 1 - \frac{1}{(n+1)!} = S_n$.

Then

$$S_\infty = \lim_{n \to \infty} \left(1 - \frac{1}{(n+1)!} \right) = 1$$

since $\qquad \dfrac{1}{(n+1)!} \to 0$ as $n \to \infty$;

i.e. the sum of the infinite series

$$\frac{1}{2!} + \frac{2}{3!} + \frac{3}{4!} + \dots \text{ is } 1.$$

Example

Given that $S_n = \dfrac{2n^2 + 3n + 1}{3n^2 + 5n - 7}$, find $\lim\limits_{n \to \infty}(S_n)$.

Solution

By dividing the numerator and denominator of S_n by n^2, S_n can be written in the form

$$S_n = \frac{\left(2 + \dfrac{3}{n} + \dfrac{1}{n^2}\right)}{\left(3 + \dfrac{5}{n} - \dfrac{7}{n^2}\right)}$$

Now, as $n \to \infty$, $\dfrac{1}{n} \to 0$ and $\dfrac{1}{n^2} \to 0$ so that $S_n \to \dfrac{2}{3}$.

Thus $S_\infty = \dfrac{2}{3}$.

Another way of deducing this is to observe that, for n 'large', the numerator is $\approx 2n^2$; the '$3n$' and the '1' paling into insignificance in comparison; while the denominator is $\approx 3n^2$ for similar reasons.

Then $S_n \approx \dfrac{2n^2}{3n^2} = \dfrac{2}{3}$.

Exercise 6D

1. The first term of a geometric series is 8 and the sum to infinity is 400. Find the common ratio.

2. The first, second and third terms of a geometric series are p, p^2 and q respectively, where $p < 0$. The first, second and third terms of an arithmetic series are p, q, p^2 respectively.

   (a) Show that $p = -\frac{1}{2}$ and find the value of q.

   (b) Find the sum-to-infinity of the geometric series.

3. Given S_n, deduce the value of S_∞ in each of the following cases:

   (a) $S_n = \dfrac{n}{2n+1}$

   (b) $S_n = \dfrac{1}{4} - \dfrac{1}{2(n+1)(n+2)}$

   (c) $S_n = \dfrac{(3n+1)(5n+1)}{(4n+1)^2}$

   (d) $S_n = \dfrac{(2n+3)(n+1)}{n(n+2)(n+4)}$

   (e) $S_n = \dfrac{n(2n+5)}{(n+1)(n+2)}$

   (f) $S_n = \dfrac{5n+11}{2(n+1)(n+2)}$

   (g) $S_n = \dfrac{3}{4} - \dfrac{2n+3}{2(n+1)(n+2)}$

4. Given $S(n) = n \times 2^{n+1}$, find $\lim\limits_{n \to \infty}\left(\dfrac{S(n+1)}{S(n)}\right)$.

5. Assuming the results $\displaystyle\sum_{r=1}^{n} r = \frac{1}{2}n(n+1)$

and $\displaystyle\sum_{r=1}^{n} r^2 = \frac{1}{6}n(n+1)(2n+1)$, find an expression

for $\displaystyle\sum_{r=1}^{n} r(r+1)$ in terms of n. Hence determine

$$\lim_{n \to \infty} \frac{\displaystyle\sum_{r=1}^{n} r(r+1)}{\left(\displaystyle\sum_{r=1}^{n} r\right)^{\frac{3}{2}}}$$

6. A geometric series is given by

$$e^{3x} + 3e^x + 9e^{-x} + \ldots$$

(a) Find the value of the sum-to-infinity in the case when $x = \ln 2$.

(b) Determine the ranges of values of x for which a sum-to-infinity exists.

6.6 Infinite binomial series

In *Pure Mathematics* you will have encountered the **binomial theorem** for positive integers n; that is, the (finite) series expansions for $(a+b)^n$ in terms of a, b and n when $n = 1, 2, 3, \ldots$

Remember, $(a+b)^n = \binom{n}{0}a^n + \binom{n}{1}a^{n-1}b + \binom{n}{2}a^{n-2}b^2 + \ldots + \binom{n}{n}b^n$

$$= \sum_{r=0}^{n} \binom{n}{r}a^{n-r}b^r,$$

where $\displaystyle\binom{n}{r} = \frac{n!}{(n-r)!r!} = \frac{n(n-1)(n-2)\ldots(n-r+1)}{r!}$ (for $0 \le r \le n$)

are called the **binomial coefficients**.

From this, the result

$$(1+x)^n = 1 + nx + \frac{n(n-1)}{2!}x^2 + \frac{n(n-1)(n-2)}{3!}x^3 + \ldots \quad (2)$$

can be deduced, and this series terminates (i.e. is finite) in the cases when n is a positive integer, since the factor $(n-n)$ appears in all the coefficients of powers of x from x^{n+1} onwards.

What happens: when n is not a positive integer?

when n is a negative integer such as $n = -3$?

when n is a rational such as $\frac{1}{2}$?

In these cases, the factor of zero no longer appears at any stage in the expansion and the series continues indefinitely. Although the binomial coefficient $\binom{n}{r}$ or ^nC_r is only defined for non-negative integers n and r, (note that $\binom{n}{r}$ is defined to be zero when $r > n$), the coefficients still take the form given in equation (2). The proof of this result forms part of an activity later in the chapter.

Example

Expand $(1+x)^{-3}$ in ascending powers of x, up to and including the term in x^3.

Solution

Using the given expansion in the form

$$(1+x)^n = 1 + nx + \frac{n(n-1)}{2!}x^2 + \frac{n(n-1)(n-2)}{3!}x^3 + \dots$$

gives

$$(1+x)^{-3} = 1 + (-3)x + \frac{(-3)(-4)}{2}x^2 + \frac{(-3)(-4)(-5)}{6}x^3 + \dots$$

$$= 1 - 3x + 6x^2 - 10x^3 + \dots$$

Example

Expand $(1-6x)^{\frac{1}{2}}$ up to the term in x^3.

Solution

$$(1-6x)^{\frac{1}{2}} = (1+[-6x])^{\frac{1}{2}}$$

$$= 1 + \tfrac{1}{2}(-6x) + \frac{(\frac{1}{2})(-\frac{1}{2})}{2!}(-6x)^2 + \frac{(\frac{1}{2})(-\frac{1}{2})(-\frac{3}{2})}{3!}(-6x)^3 + \dots$$

| 'x' is now $-6x$ |

| $(-6x)^2 = (-6x)(-6x)$ |
| $= 36x^2$ |

$$= 1 - 3x - \frac{9}{2}x^2 - \frac{27}{2}x^3 \dots$$

Example

Expand $(4+3x)^{-\frac{1}{2}}$ up to the term in x^3.

Solution

Now the form of the general binomial expansion given is for $(1+\text{'something'})^{\text{power}}$, while this example is $(4+\text{'something'})^{\text{power}}$.

Although it is quite possible to adapt back to the form $(a+b)^n$, you are strongly advised to begin each binomial expansion (of the infinite variety) with $(1 + ...)$

This is easily done here in the following way:

$$4+3x = 4\left(1+\frac{3}{4}x\right)$$

so that

$$(4+3x)^{-\frac{1}{2}} = \left[4\left(1+\frac{3}{4}x\right)\right]^{-\frac{1}{2}}$$

$$= 4^{-\frac{1}{2}}\left(1+\frac{3}{4}x\right)^{-\frac{1}{2}} \qquad [\textit{Not } 4\left(1+\frac{3}{4}x\right)^{-\frac{1}{2}}]$$

$$= \frac{1}{2}\left(1+\frac{3}{4}x\right)^{-\frac{1}{2}}$$

To demonstrate this simple algebraic technique has taken four lines of working, as this is an example. It can be performed automatically in your working provided you do not make the mistake highlighted in the bracket above, which is a very common error indeed.

To continue,

$$(4+3x)^{-\frac{1}{2}} = \frac{1}{2}\left(1+\frac{3}{4}x\right)^{-\frac{1}{2}}$$

$$= \frac{1}{2}\left\{1+\left(-\frac{1}{2}\right)\left(\frac{3}{4}x\right)+\frac{\left(-\frac{1}{2}\right)\left(-\frac{3}{2}\right)}{2!}\left(\frac{3}{4}x\right)^2+\frac{\left(-\frac{1}{2}\right)\left(-\frac{3}{2}\right)\left(-\frac{5}{2}\right)}{3!}\left(\frac{3}{4}x\right)^3+...\right\}$$

$$= \frac{1}{2}\left\{1-\frac{3}{8}x+\frac{27}{128}x^2-\frac{135}{1024}x^3+...\right\}$$

$$= \frac{1}{2}-\frac{3}{16}x+\frac{27}{256}x^2-\frac{135}{2048}x^3+...$$

6.7 Conditions for convergence of the binomial series

The infinite geometric series

$$1 + x + x^2 + x^3 + \ldots + x^n + \ldots$$

has
$$S_\infty = \frac{1}{1-x} = (1-x)^{-1}.$$

This familiar result is therefore an example of an infinite binomial expansion, and you have already seen that this series **converges** only if $-1 < x < 1$.

When n is a positive integer, or zero, the binomial series for $(1+x)^n$ converges for all values of x, since the expansion is finite. This is not the case, however, when n is not a positive integer, as already noted.

*Activity 2

By writing $(1+x)^n$ as $\displaystyle\sum_{r=0}^{\infty} u_r$, with

$$u_r = \frac{n(n-1)(n-2)\ldots(n-r+1)}{1 \times 2 \times 3 \ldots r} x^r,$$

the sequence $\{u_r\}$ can be defined by

$$u_1 = 1 \text{ and } u_r = \frac{(n-r+1)}{r} x \times u_{r-1} \text{ for } r \geq 2.$$

Write a program to find the partial sums of $(1+X)^N$ as follows

(i)   Choose suitable input values of N and X.

(ii) Define variables S, M, R and U with initial values
      $S = 1$, $M = N$, $R = 0$, $U = 1$. (S is the sum so far; M will be the additional factor of $(N - R + 1)$ at each stage; R is the number of terms added after the 1; and U is the last term added to the sum.)

(iii) Repeat the steps   Print R and S at this point

                                       Now increase R by 1;

                                       U becomes $\dfrac{(U \times M \times X)}{R}$;

                                       S becomes $S + U$;

                                       decrease M by 1.

This could be done on a programmable calculator. You need to be able to repeat the step once each time you press (for instance) the 'EXECUTE' button.

The purpose of the investigation is to choose values of N and X and discover which values of X lead to the convergence of $(1+X)^N$ for the various possible values of N. The convergence/divergence of the geometric series suggests the investigation of the cases

$$X < -1, \ X = -1, \ -1 < X < 1, \ X = 1, \ X > 1$$

for various possible values of N.

The conclusions you should have reached from the Activity above are as follows.

When n is not a positive integer (or zero), the series expansion of $(1+x)^n$ is convergent

(i) for $-1 < x < 1$ when $n \leq -1$,

(ii) for $-1 < x \leq 1$ when $-1 < n < 0$,

(iii) for $-1 \leq x \leq 1$ when $n > 0$.

The above results are not widely acknowledged and you are not required to know them in this detail. However, you will be expected to be able to quote the following, simplified rule:

> For n not a positive integer, or zero, the series expansion of $(1+x)^n$ is convergent for $-1 < x < 1$ in general.

Example

State the values of x for which the following series expansions converge:

(a) $(2-x)^{-7}$ (b) $(1+4x)^{\frac{3}{4}}$ (c) $\dfrac{1}{\sqrt[3]{3+2x}}$

Solution

(a) $(2-x)^{-7} = 2^{-7}\left(1 - \dfrac{x}{2}\right)^{-7}$, which converges for $-1 < -\dfrac{x}{2} < 1$,

i.e. for $-2 < x < 2$.

(b) $(1+4x)^{\frac{3}{4}}$ converges for $-1 < 4x < 1$, i.e. for $-\dfrac{1}{4} < x < \dfrac{1}{4}$

(In fact $-\dfrac{1}{4} \leq x \leq \dfrac{1}{4}$)

(c) $\dfrac{1}{\sqrt[3]{3+2x}} = (3+2x)^{-\frac{1}{3}} = 3^{-\frac{1}{3}}\left(1+\dfrac{2x}{3}\right)^{-\frac{1}{3}}$, converging for

$$-1 < \dfrac{2x}{3} < 1 \Rightarrow -\dfrac{3}{2} < x < \dfrac{3}{2}. \quad \text{(In fact, } -\dfrac{3}{2} < x \le \dfrac{3}{2}\text{)}$$

Example

Write down the expansion of $(1-2x)^{\frac{1}{2}}$ up to and including the term in x^3. By setting $x = \dfrac{1}{100}$, use this expansion to find an approximation to $\sqrt{2}$ to eight places of decimals.

Solution

$$(1-2x)^{\frac{1}{2}} = 1 + \frac{1}{2}(-2x) + \frac{\left(\frac{1}{2}\right)\left(-\frac{1}{2}\right)}{2!}(-2x)^2 + \frac{\left(\frac{1}{2}\right)\left(-\frac{1}{2}\right)\left(-\frac{3}{2}\right)}{3!}(-2x)^3 + \ldots$$

$$= 1 - x - \frac{1}{2}x^2 - \frac{1}{2}x^3 \ldots$$

Setting $\quad x = \dfrac{1}{100} \quad \Rightarrow \quad (1-0.02)^{\frac{1}{2}} = 1 - \dfrac{1}{100} - \dfrac{1}{2}\left(\dfrac{1}{100}\right)^2 - \dfrac{1}{2}\left(\dfrac{1}{100}\right)^3 \ldots$

$$\Rightarrow \quad \sqrt{0.98} = 1 - 0.01 - 0.00005 - 0.0000005 \ldots$$

Now $\qquad 0.98 = \dfrac{98}{100} = \dfrac{49}{100} \times 2$ so that

$$\sqrt{0.98} = \frac{7}{10}\sqrt{2}$$

Then $\qquad \dfrac{7}{10}\sqrt{2} \approx 0.9899495$

and $\qquad \sqrt{2} \approx \dfrac{10 \times 0.9899495}{7} = 1.41421357$ (to 8 d.p.)

All this working can easily be done without a calculator, and to 8 d.p. $\sqrt{2} = 1.41421356$.

Example

Given that $-1 < x < 1$, find the expansion of $\dfrac{3-2x}{(1+x)(4+x^2)}$ in ascending powers of x, up to and including the term in x^3.

Solution

$$\frac{3-2x}{(1+x)(4+x^2)} = (3-2x)(1+x)^{-1}(4+x^2)^{-1}$$

$$= (3-2x)(1+x)^{-1}\frac{1}{4}\left(1+\frac{x^2}{4}\right)^{-1}$$

$$= \frac{1}{4}(3-2x)\left(1-x+x^2-x^3+...\right)\left(1-\frac{x^2}{4}+...\right)$$

$$= \frac{1}{4}(3-2x)\left(1-x+\frac{3}{4}x^2-\frac{3}{4}x^3...\right)$$

$$= \frac{3}{4}-\frac{5}{4}x+\frac{17}{16}x^2-\frac{15}{16}x^3...$$

Alternatively, you could write $\dfrac{3-2x}{(1+x)(4+x^2)}$ in partial fractions:

$$\frac{1}{1+x}-\frac{x+1}{4+x^2} = (1+x)^{-1}-(1+x)\frac{1}{4}\left(1+\frac{x^2}{4}\right)^{-1} \text{ etc.,}$$

as before.

Exercise 6E

1. Write down the first four terms in the binomial expansions of

   (a) $(1+3x)^{\frac{1}{3}}$ (b) $(2+x)^{-1}$ (c) $\sqrt{1+\frac{x}{2}}$

   (d) $(5-3x)^{-2}$ (e) $\frac{1+x}{1-x}$ (f) $\frac{1-x}{\sqrt{1+x^2}}$

   For each part above, state the (simplified) range of values of x for which the expansion is valid.

2. Find, in simplified form, the first three non-zero terms in ascending powers of x of the series expansions of

   (a) $\dfrac{1+3x}{(1-2x)^4}$ for $|x|<\frac{1}{2}$

   (b) $(2+x)\sqrt{1-x}$ for $|x|<1$

3. Expand $\dfrac{3+x}{(1+x^2)(1+2x)}$ in ascending powers of x,

   up to and including the term in x^3.

   State the range of values of x for which this expansion is valid.

4. Obtain the expansion of $(16+y)^{\frac{1}{2}}$ in ascending powers of y up to and including the term in y^2.

   Hence show that if k^3 and higher powers of k are neglected, $\sqrt{16+4k+k^2} \approx 4+\frac{k}{2}+\frac{3k^2}{32}$.

5. Obtain the expansion in ascending powers of x, up to and including the term in x^3, of

   $$\frac{1+5x}{(1+2x)^{\frac{1}{2}}} \text{ for } |x|<\frac{1}{2}.$$

   By putting $x=0.04$ deduce an approximate value of $\dfrac{1}{\sqrt{3}}$, giving your answer to three decimal places.

6. Expand $\dfrac{x}{(1-2x)^2(1-3x)}$ up to the term in x^3.

   For what range of values of x is the expansion valid?

7. Write down the binomial series for $\sqrt{\dfrac{1-x^2}{1+x^2}}$ up to and including the term in x^4.

8. Determine the series expansion of $(1-x)^{-\frac{1}{2}}$ up to and including the term in x^3. By setting $x=\dfrac{1}{10}$ determine, without the aid of a calculator, an approximate value of $\sqrt{10}$, giving your answer to 7 decimal places.

9. Use the binomial theorem to show that

$$\frac{x^2}{\sqrt{4-x^2}}=\frac{1}{2}x^2+\frac{1}{16}x^4+kx^6+...\left(|x|<2\right)$$

   for some constant k, and state its value.

   Hence show by integrating these first three terms of the series, that the value of the integral

$$I=\int_0^1\frac{x^2\,dx}{\sqrt{4-x^2}}$$

   is approximately 0.1808.

6.8 Maclaurin expansions

Along with infinite geometric series and the general binomial series, many other functions can also be represented as **power series** (which can be thought of as polynomials of infinite degree). For such a power series to exist, the function in question needs to be infinitely differentiable, with each derivative,

$f^{(n)}(x)\ \ (n=1,2,3,...)$, capable of being evaluated at $x=0$ and in some range of values of x containing 0. Consider, for example, $f(x)=e^x$. One way of defining this exponential function is by choosing the base number e in such a way that $f'(x)=e^x$ also; that is, the function is its own derivative. Hence $f^{(n)}(x)=e^x$ for $n=1,2,3,....$ Maclaurin's theorem can now be illustrated in this case.

Writing $e^x=a_0+a_1x+a_2x^2+a_3x^3+a_4x^4+...$, where a_r is the coefficient of x^r for $0\le r<\infty$, repeated differentiation gives

$$e^x=a_1+2a_2x+3a_3x^2+4a_4x^3+...$$

and $\quad e^x=\quad\ 2a_2+3\times2\times a_3x+4\times3a_4x^2+...$

and $\quad e^x=\quad\quad\quad 3\times2a_3+4\times3\times2a_4x+...$

and $\quad e^x=\quad\quad\quad\quad\quad 4\times3\times2a_4+...\quad\quad$ etc.

Since $e^0=1$, substituting $x=0$ in each line gives

$$1=a_0,\quad 1=a_1,\quad 1=2a_2,\quad 1=3\times2a_3,\quad 1=4\times3\times2a_4\ ...$$

In general, it is easily seen that the nth derivative evaluated at $x = 0$, $f^{(n)}(0)$, gives

$$1 = n(n-1)(n-2)...3 \times 2a_n,$$

so that $\quad a_n = \dfrac{1}{n!}$

The power series for e^x is then

$$e^x = 1 + x + \frac{x^2}{2!} + \frac{x^3}{3!} + ... + \frac{x^n}{n!} + ...$$

$$= \sum_{r=0}^{\infty} \frac{x^r}{r!}$$

and this is called the Maclaurin series, or Maclaurin expansion, of e^x.

How can you find the series for e^{-x}?

To obtain the power series for e^{-x} it is not necessary to repeat the above process: simply replacing x by $-x$ in the series for e^x gives

$$e^{-x} = 1 - x + \frac{x^2}{2!} - \frac{x^3}{3!} + ... = \sum_{r=0}^{\infty} \frac{(-1)^r x^r}{r!}$$

(Note that $(-1)^r = -1$ when r is odd, and $(-1)^r = +1$ when r is even.)

For a general function $f(x)$, satisfying the relevant conditions, Maclaurin's theorem gives the expansion

$$f(x) = f(0) + f'(0)x + f''(0)\frac{x^2}{2!} + f'''(0)\frac{x^3}{3!} + ...$$

i.e. $\quad f(x) = \sum_{r=0}^{\infty} f^{(r)}(0)\frac{x^r}{r!}$

Activity 3

Using the results $\dfrac{d}{dx}(\sin x) = \cos x$ and $\dfrac{d}{dx}(\cos x) = -\sin x$, find the Maclaurin series for $\sin x$. Without repeating the whole process, deduce the series for $\cos x$.

Activity 4

Use Maclaurin's theorem to prove that

$$(1+x)^n = 1 + nx + \frac{n(n-1)}{2!}x^2 + \frac{n(n-1)(n-2)}{3!}x^3 + \ldots$$

Example

Determine the Maclaurin series for $\tanh x$ up to and including the term in x^3.

Solution

$$f(x) \quad = \tanh x$$

$$f'(x) \quad = \mathrm{sech}^2 x$$

$$f''(x) = 2\mathrm{sech}x\left(-\mathrm{sech}x\,\tanh x\right)$$

$$\quad = -2\mathrm{sech}^2 x \tanh x$$

$$f'''(x) = -2\mathrm{sech}^2 x \times \mathrm{sech}^2 x - 2\tanh x\left(-2\mathrm{sech}^2 x \tanh x\right)$$

$$\quad = -2\mathrm{sech}^4 x + 4\mathrm{sech}^2 x \tanh^2 x$$

This gives

$$f(0) \quad = 0 \quad (\text{since } \tanh 0 = 0)$$

$$f'(0) \quad = 1 \quad (\text{since } \mathrm{sech}\,0 = 1)$$

$$f''(0) \quad = -2 \times 1^2 \times 0 = 0$$

$$f'''(0) = -2 \times 1^4 + 4 \times 1^2 \times 0^2 = -2$$

So $\quad \tanh x = 0 + 1 \times x + 0 \times \dfrac{x^2}{2} + (-2)\dfrac{x^3}{6} + \ldots$

$$= x - \frac{x^3}{3} + \ldots$$

The following alternative approach is quite useful.

Write $y = \tanh x$. Then $\dfrac{dy}{dx} = \text{sech}^2 x = 1 - \tanh^2 x = 1 - y^2$. Next,

differentiate $\left\{\dfrac{dy}{dx} = 1 - y^2\right\}$ with respect to x implicitly, to give

$$\frac{d^2 y}{dx^2} = -2y\frac{dy}{dx}$$

and $\qquad \dfrac{d^3 y}{dx^3} = -2y\left(\dfrac{d^2 y}{dx^2}\right) - 2\dfrac{dy}{dx}\left(\dfrac{dy}{dx}\right)$ (using the Product Rule)

$$= -2y\frac{d^2 y}{dx^2} - 2\left(\frac{dy}{dx}\right)^2 \text{ etc.}$$

Then, when $x = 0$, $y = 0$, $\dfrac{dy}{dx} = 1 - 0^2 = 1$, $\dfrac{d^2 y}{dx^2} = -2 \times 0 \times 1 = 0$,

$\dfrac{d^3 y}{dx^3} = -2 \times 0 \times 0 - 2 \times 1^2 = -2, \dots$

Activity 5

1. Determine the Maclaurin expansions of the following functions, up to and including the term in x^3:

   (a) $\dfrac{1}{1-x}$

   (b) $\ln(1+x)$ (Why is it not possible to find a power series for $\ln x$?)

   (c) $\ln(1-x)$

   Describe how the series for (c) can be found

   (i) using the answer to (b);

   (ii) using the answer to (a).

2. Use the results $\dfrac{d}{dx}(\sinh x) = \cosh x$ and $\dfrac{d}{dx}(\cosh x) = \sinh x$ to find the Maclaurin series for $\sinh x$ and $\cosh x$.

3. Prove Euler's relationship $e^{i\theta} = \cos\theta + i\sin\theta$.

4. Use the Maclaurin series for $\sin x, \cos x, \sinh x$ and $\cosh x$ to show that $\sin ix = i\sinh x$ and $\cos ix = \cosh x$, where $i^2 = -1$

Example

Given that the first non-zero term in the series expansion of $e^{-px} - (1+2x)^{-q}$ in ascending powers of x is $-4x^2$, find the value of p and the value of q.

Solution

$$e^{-px} = 1 - (px) + \frac{(px)^2}{2!} - \dots$$
$$= 1 - px + \frac{1}{2}p^2x^2 + \dots$$

and $(1+2x)^{-q} = 1 + (-q)(2x) + \frac{(-q)(-q-1)}{2!}(2x)^2 + \dots$

$$= 1 - 2qx + 2q(q+1)x^2 + \dots$$

Subtracting

$$e^{-px} - (1+2x)^{-q} = (2q-p)x + \left(\frac{1}{2}p^2 - 2q^2 - 2q\right)x^2 + \dots$$

It is given that the coefficient of x is zero. Thus $p = 2q$. The coefficient of x^2 is then $\frac{1}{2}(2q)^2 - 2q^2 - 2q$. As this is equal to -4, it follows that $q = 2$ and $p = 4$.

Validity

The series expansions for e^x, e^{-x}, $\sin x$, $\cos x$, $\sinh x$ and $\cosh x$ (also for $\tan x$ and $\tanh x$, although these are not very straightforward and so cannot easily be remembered) are valid for all real x.

However, the series for $\ln(1+x)$ is valid for $-1 < x \leq 1$ only, while the series for $\ln(1-x)$ is valid for $-1 \leq x < 1$.

It is not within the scope of this course formally to establish these results, but you should learn them and you may be expected to use them.

Exercise 6F

1. Write down the first four terms in the series expansions of

   (a) e^{-2x} (b) $\ln\left(1+\dfrac{x}{2}\right)$ (c) $\sin 3x$

   (d) $\cos\dfrac{1}{2}x$ (e) $\ln\left(\dfrac{1+x}{1-x}\right)$ (f) $\sin 2x - \cos 4x$

   (g) $\dfrac{e^{-x}}{2+x}$ (h) $\left(1+e^{-x}\right)\left(1-2e^{-x}\right)$

2. Use Maclaurin's theorem to determine the series expansions of the following functions, up to and including the term in x^3:

   (a) $f(x) = \sin^{-1} x$ (b) $f(x) = \sqrt{\cos x}$

   (c) $f(x) = \tan^{-1}\left\{\sinh(x+\ln 2)\right\}$

   (d) $f(x) = 2^x$

   (For (d): $\dfrac{d}{dx}\left(a^x\right) = \dfrac{d}{dx}\left(e^{x\ln a}\right) = \ln a.e^{x\ln a} = a^x \ln a$)

3. The series expansion, in ascending powers of θ, of $4\cos 2\theta - \cos 4\theta$ begins $A + B\theta^4$, where A and B are integers. Find the values of A and B.

4. Use the Maclaurin series for $\cos x$ and $\ln(1+y)$ to show that $\ln(\cos x) = Ax^2 + Bx^4$ when terms in x^5 and higher powers of x can be neglected.

   State the values of the constants A and B.

5. Given that $y = \tan x$, show that $\dfrac{dy}{dx} = 1+y^2$ and

   $\dfrac{d^2y}{dx^2} = 2y\left(1+y^2\right)$. Obtain an expression for $\dfrac{d^3y}{dx^3}$ in terms of y. Evaluate these derivatives at $x=0$ and hence write down the Maclaurin series of $\tan x$, including the term in x^3.

6. Given that $0 < x < 1$, write down the sum of the infinite series $x + \dfrac{x^2}{2} + \dfrac{x^3}{3} + \ldots + \dfrac{x^r}{r} + \ldots$. By integrating this series term by term, show that

   $\dfrac{x^2}{1\times 2} + \dfrac{x^3}{2\times 3} + \dfrac{x^4}{3\times 4} + \ldots + \dfrac{x^{r+1}}{r(r+1)} + \ldots$

   $= x + (1-x)\ln(1-x)$

   Hence, or otherwise, find the sum of the infinite series

   $\dfrac{1}{1\times 2} + \dfrac{1}{2\times 3}\left(\dfrac{1}{2}\right) + \dfrac{1}{3\times 4}\left(\dfrac{1}{2}\right)^2 + \ldots + \dfrac{1}{r(r+1)}\left(\dfrac{1}{2}\right)^{r-1} + \ldots$

7. The function $y = f(x)$ satisfies the differential equation $\dfrac{d^2y}{dx^2} + 6\dfrac{dy}{dx} + 9y = 36\sin 3x$, and is such that $f(0) = 2$ and $f'(0) = -4$. Write down the value of $f''(0)$ and obtain the value of $f'''(0)$. Hence obtain the Maclaurin expansion of $f(x)$ in ascending powers of x up to and including the term in x^3.

8. Given $f(x) = \dfrac{3}{1+x} + \dfrac{1}{1-2x} + \dfrac{2}{(1-2x)^2}$, show that

   $\ln\{f(x)\} = \ln 6 + Ax + Bx^2$, provided that terms in x^3 and higher terms of x can be neglected. Find the value of A and the value of B.

9. Write down the expansion of e^{2x} in ascending powers of x up to and including the term in x^3.

   Show that the series expansion of $\dfrac{e^{2x}}{1+x}$ is

   $1 + x + x^2 + \ldots$ ($|x| < 1$) and find the coefficient of x^3 in this expansion. Use these four terms of the expansion to find an approximation to $\displaystyle\int_0^{\frac{1}{4}} \dfrac{e^{2x}}{1+x}\,dx$, giving your answer to 3 decimal places.

10. Show that when θ is small enough for θ^2 and higher powers of θ to be neglected, $(2-\tan\theta)(1+\sin 2\theta) = 2+3\theta$. Hence find an approximation for $\displaystyle\int_0^{0.02}(2-\tan\theta)(1+\sin 2\theta)\,d\theta$, giving your answer to 4 decimal places.

11. Given that $-\dfrac{\pi}{2} < x < \dfrac{\pi}{2}$ and that $y = (\sec x + \tan x)^{\frac{1}{2}}$, prove that

    (a) $2\dfrac{dy}{dx} = y\sec x$, and

    (b) $4\dfrac{d^2y}{dx^2} = y\sec x(\sec x + 2\tan x)$.

    Use these results to find the values of y, $\dfrac{dy}{dx}$ and $\dfrac{d^2y}{dx^2}$ when $x=0$. Find the value of $\dfrac{d^3y}{dx^3}$ when $x=0$. Find a cubic polynomial approximation for $(\sec x + \tan x)^{\frac{1}{2}}$ when x is small and hence deduce an estimate to 5 decimal places for the integral $\displaystyle\int_0^{0.1}(\sec x + \tan x)^{\frac{1}{2}}\,dx$.

12. Given that $y = \ln(1+\sin x)$, find $\dfrac{dy}{dx}$ and show that

$(1+\sin x)\dfrac{d^2 y}{dx^2} + 1 = 0$. Find the fourth-degree

polynomial approximation to $y = \ln(1+\sin\theta)$.

Hence show that if x^5 and higher powers of x are neglected,

$$\ln\left(\frac{1+\sin x}{1+x}\right) = k\left(x^4 - x^3\right)$$

where k is a constant. State the value of k.

6.9 General terms

In some cases, you have already seen and worked with the general terms of a number of the series expansions encountered in this chapter. For instance, the general term of the binomial series for $(1+x)^n$ is

$$\frac{n(n-1)(n-2)\dots(n-r+1)}{r!}x^r$$

Note: 'n' has a specific value here and should not therefore be used as a variable.

In most cases it will be the term in x^n that will be required. The series

$$e^x = 1 + x + \frac{x^2}{2!} + \frac{x^3}{3!} + \dots$$

has general term $\dfrac{x^n}{n!}$, as has already been seen. With finite series, n was usually taken as the last term in the summation and r used as the summation index, but with infinite series there is no last term and n is often used. As long as you do not get confused, or use n as a variable when it is also being used as a fixed value at the same time, then there is no problem. The general term is the one which represents the form of each term of the series.

Thus $\qquad \displaystyle\sum_{n=0}^{\infty} \frac{x^n}{n!} = e^x.$

In some cases, such as the series for $\sin x$,

$$\boxed{\sin x = x - \frac{x^3}{3!} + \frac{x^5}{5!} - \frac{x^7}{7!} + \dots}$$

only some powers of x are non-zero; here, the odd ones – the coefficient of x^n is zero when x is even. This is easily dealt with

$$\boxed{\sin x = \sum_{n=1}^{\infty} (-1)^{n+1}\frac{x^{2n-1}}{(2n-1)!}}$$

(Check that this gives the correct terms with the correct signs.)

Activity 6

Write down the general terms in the series expansions of

$$e^{-x}, \quad \cos x, \quad \ln(1+x), \quad \ln(1-x), \quad \frac{1}{1-x}, \quad \sinh x, \quad \cosh x$$

Example

Prove that the coefficient of x^k in the binomial expansion of

$\dfrac{1}{(1-x)^2}$ is $k+1$.

Method 1

Using the expansion $\dfrac{1}{1-x} = 1 + x + x^2 + x^3 + \dots + x^k + x^{k+1} + \dots,$

for which all the coefficients are 1 (remember this is the infinite geometric series), and differentiating:

$$\frac{1}{(1-x)^2} = 0 + 1 + 2x + 3x^2 + \dots + kx^{k-1} + (k+1)x^k + \dots$$

and the coefficient of x^k is seen to be $(k+1)$, as required.

Method 2

Using the general term of the binomial series,

$$\frac{n(n-1)(n-2)\dots(n-k+1)}{k!}x^k,$$

with $n = -2$ and $'x' = -x$, gives the general term

$$\frac{(-2)(-3)(-4)\dots(-2-k+1)}{k!}(-x)^k$$

$$= (-1)^k \frac{2 \times 3 \times 4 \dots (k+1)}{k!}(-1)^k x^k \qquad \text{(taking out the factor of } -1 \text{ from each of the } k \text{ terms in the numerator)}$$

$$= (-1)^{2k}\frac{(k+1)!}{k!}x^k$$

$$= 1(k+1)x^k \qquad \text{(since } 2k \text{ is even)}$$

$$= (k+1)x^k$$

So that x^k has coefficient $(k+1)$.

Exercise 6G

1. Find the coefficient of x^n in the series expansions of

   (a) e^{3x}　　　(b) $\ln(1+4x)$　(c) $\cos 2x$

   (d) $\sin^2 x$　　(e) e^{1-x}　　(f) $\sinh\dfrac{x}{2}$

2. Express $f(x) = \dfrac{1}{(2-x)(1+x)}$ in partial fractions.

   Hence show that the coefficient of $x^n (n \geq 0)$ in the series expansion of $f(x)$ is $\dfrac{1}{3}\left\{\dfrac{1}{2^{n+1}} + (-1)^n\right\}$.

3. Find the values of the constants A, B and C for which $\dfrac{x}{(1-2x)^2(1-3x)} \equiv \dfrac{A}{1-3x} + \dfrac{B}{1-2x} + \dfrac{C}{(1-2x)^2}$.

   Hence write down the series expansion of

   $\dfrac{x}{(1-2x)^2(1-3x)}$ in ascending powers of x, up to

   and including the term in x^3. For what range of values of x is this expansion valid? Determine, in terms of n, the coefficient of x^n in this expansion.

4. Show that the coefficient of x^n in the binomial

   expansion of $(1-x)^{-4}$ is $\dbinom{n+3}{3}$.

5. Determine an expression for the coefficient of $x^n (n \geq 2)$ in the series expansion of $\dfrac{x^2+3}{x+1}$, where $|x| < 1$.

6. Find the general term in the series expansion of $\dfrac{1+3x}{(1-2x)^4}$ for $|x| < \frac{1}{2}$.

7. For $n \geq 1$, prove that the coefficient of x^n in the power series expansion of $\dfrac{1+x+x^2}{(1-x)^2}$ is $3n$.

8. Given that, $f(x) = \ln\left\{\dfrac{(1-3x)^2}{1+2x}\right\}$

   (a) determine the Maclaurin series of $f(x)$ up to and including the term in x^3;

   (b) state the range of values of x for which the series in (a) is valid;

   (c) find the coefficient of x^n in this expansion.

6.10 Miscellaneous Exercises

1. Mr Brown invests £350 a year at the beginning of every year in a savings scheme. At the end of each year, interest of 7% of the total so far invested is added to the scheme. Show that, if no money is withdrawn, there will be £S in the scheme at the end of the nth year, where

   $S = 350\left(1.07 + 1.07^2 + ... + 1.07^n\right)$. By using the sum of a geometric series, find the least number of years necessary for the total in the scheme to exceed £25 000.

2. Express $u_r = \dfrac{1}{(2r-1)2r(2r+1)}$ in partial fractions.

   Denoting $\displaystyle\sum_{r=1}^{n} u_r$ by S_n, prove that

   $S_n = \dfrac{1}{2(2n+1)} + \dfrac{1}{3} - \dfrac{1}{4} + \dfrac{1}{5} - ... + \dfrac{1}{2n-1} - \dfrac{1}{2n}$.

   By considering the Maclaurin series for

   $\ln(1+x)$, or otherwise, find $\displaystyle\lim_{n \to \infty} S_n$.

3. Write down and simplify the first three terms in

   the series expansion of $\left(1 + \dfrac{x}{3}\right)^{-\frac{1}{2}}$ in ascending

   powers of x. State the set of values of x for which the series is valid.

   Given that x is so small that terms in x^3 and higher powers of x may be neglected, show that

   $e^{-x}\left(1 + \dfrac{x}{2}\right)^{-\frac{1}{2}} = 1 - \dfrac{7}{6}x + \dfrac{17}{24}x^2$.

4. Prove by mathematical induction that, for all positive integers n,

$$\sum_{r=1}^{n}\frac{3r+2}{r(r+1)(r+2)}=\frac{n(2n+3)}{(n+1)(n+2)}.$$

Hence, or otherwise, find the sum of the infinite series

$$\frac{8}{2\times3\times4}+\frac{11}{3\times4\times5}+\frac{14}{4\times5\times6}+...+\frac{3k+2}{k(k+1)(k+2)}+...$$

5. (a) Show that $(2k+1)^4-(2k-1)^4\equiv64k^3+16k$.
   Using this identity, prove that

$$\sum_{k=1}^{n}\left(64k^3+16k\right)=(2n+1)^4-1.$$

   (b) Assuming the result $\sum_{k=1}^{n}k=\frac{1}{2}n(n+1)$, use the result in (a) to prove that $\sum_{k=1}^{n}k^3=\frac{1}{4}n^2(n+1)^2$.

(Oxford)

6. A geometric series has first term 1 and common ratio $\frac{1}{2}\sin2\theta$.

   (a) Find the sum of the first 10 terms in the case when $\theta=\frac{\pi}{4}$, giving your answer to 3 decimal places.

   (b) Given that the sum-to-infinity is $\frac{4}{3}$, find the general solution for θ in radians.

7. (a) Use the formulae for $\sum_{r=1}^{n}r$ and $\sum_{r=1}^{n}r^2$ to show that $\sum_{r=0}^{n}(r+1)(r+2)=\frac{1}{3}(n+1)(n+2)(n+3)$.

   (b) Using partial fractions, or otherwise, find the sum of the series $S_n=\sum_{r=0}^{n}\frac{1}{(r+1)(r+2)}$.

   Deduce the value of $\lim_{n\to\infty}S_n$.

8. Given that $e^y=e^x+e^{-x}$, show that $\frac{d^2y}{dx^2}+\left(\frac{dy}{dx}\right)^2-1=0$. Find the values of y, $\frac{dy}{dx}$ and $\frac{d^2y}{dx^2}$ when $x=0$. Hence determine the Maclaurin series for y in ascending powers of x up to and including the term in x^4.

9. All the terms of a certain geometric progression are positive. The first term is a and the second term is a^2-a. Find the set of values of a for which the series converges.

   Given that $a=\frac{5}{3}$:

   (a) find the sum of the first 10 terms of the series, giving your answer to 2 decimal places;

   (b) show that the sum-to-infinity of the series is 5;

   (c) find the least number of terms of the series required to make their sum exceed 4.999.

10. Use induction to prove that

$$\sum_{r=1}^{n}r^2=\frac{1}{6}n(n+1)(2n+1)$$

   Hence find $\sum_{r=1}^{n}(n+r-1)(n+r)$, giving your answer in terms of n.

11. (a) Write down in ascending powers of x the series for $\ln(1-x)$, where $|x|<1$. Hence find $\sum_{r=1}^{\infty}\frac{1}{r\times2^r}$, giving your answer in the form $\ln p$, for some number p.

   (b) Find $\sum_{r=1}^{\infty}\frac{1}{(r+1)!2^r}$.

12. Given that $|x|<\sqrt{3}$, determine the expansion of $f(x)=\frac{16-x}{(2-x)(3+x^2)}$ in ascending powers of x up to and including the x^3 term. Hence find, correct to four decimal places, an approximation to

$$\int_0^1\frac{16-x}{(2-x)(3+x^2)}dx$$

13. By considering $\sum_{n=1}^{N}\left[\cos\left(n-\frac{1}{2}\right)x-\cos\left(n+\frac{1}{2}\right)x\right]$, or otherwise, show that

$$\sum_{n=1}^{N}\sin nx=\csc\frac{1}{2}x\times\sin\left[\frac{1}{2}(N+1)x\right]\times\sin\left(\frac{1}{2}Nx\right),$$

   provided that $\sin\frac{1}{2}x\neq0$. Deduce that

$$\sum_{n=1}^{N-1}\sin\frac{n\pi}{N}<\csc\frac{\pi}{2N}\text{ for all }N\geq2.\quad\text{(Cambridge)}$$

14. (a) Write down and simplify binomial series in ascending powers of x up to and including the terms in x^3 for $(1+x)^{-1}$, $(1-2x)^{-1}$ and $(1-2x)^{-2}$.

(b) Express $\dfrac{6-11x+10x^2}{(1+x)(1-2x)^2}$ in partial fractions.

(c) Using the series from (a), expand $\dfrac{6-11x+10x^2}{(1+x)(1-2x)^2}$ in ascending powers of x up to and including the term in x^3.

15. Prove by induction that $\displaystyle\sum_{r=1}^{n} r(3r+1) = n(n+1)^2$ for all positive integers n.   (Cambridge)

16. Show that the sum of the first 50 terms of the geometric series with first term 1 and common ratio $r = 2^{\frac{1}{50}}$ is $\dfrac{1}{r-1}$. Hence, by using the trapezium rule with 50 intervals of equal width, show that $\displaystyle\int_0^1 2^x dx$ is approximately $\dfrac{r+1}{100(r-1)}$, where $r = 2^{\frac{1}{50}}$. Evaluate this expression to 3 decimal places.

17. Write down the expansions of

(i) $\ln(1+2x)$, (ii) $\ln(1+3x)$, (iii) $(1-2x)^{-3}$ in ascending powers of x up to and including the term in x^3. Given that x is small enough for x^4 and higher powers of x to be ignored, show that

(a) $\ln\left\{\dfrac{(1+2x)^3}{(1+3x)^2}\right\} = 3x^2 - 10x^3$

(b) $(1-2x)^{-3} - e^{6x} - 2\ln\left\{\dfrac{(1+2x)^3}{(1+3x)^2}\right\} = kx^3$ for some constant k, stating the value of k.

18. (a) By considering the expansion of $\ln(1-x)$ find the sum of the infinite series $\displaystyle\sum_{r=1}^{\infty} \dfrac{1}{r \times 2^{r-1}}$.

(b) Write down the first four terms and the general term of the expansion in ascending powers of x of $(1-x)^{-1}$. Hence, by differentiation, obtain the first 3 terms and the general term in the expansion of $(1-x)^{-2}$, and find the sum of the infinite series

$$\sum_{r=1}^{\infty} \dfrac{r}{2^{r-1}}.$$

19. Assuming the series expansions for $\cos x$, $\ln(1+x)$ and $(1+x)^{-1}$, show that the series expansions of $\cos[\ln(1+x)]$ and $\sec[\ln(1+x)]$ are given respectively by $1 - \dfrac{1}{2}x^2 + \dfrac{1}{2}x^3 - \dfrac{5}{12}x^4 + \ldots$

and $1 + \dfrac{1}{2}x^2 - \dfrac{1}{2}x^3 + \dfrac{2}{3}x^4 + \ldots$

Show by differentiating the series for $\cos[\ln(1+x)]$ that the series for $\sin[\ln(1+x)]$ is

$x - \dfrac{1}{2}x^2 + \dfrac{1}{6}x^3 + \ldots$ and use this together with the series for $\sec[\ln(1+x)]$ to find a series expansion for $\tan[\ln(1+x)]$ as far as the x^3 term.

20. Let $\phi(j) = \dfrac{4^{j+1}(j-1)}{3(j+2)}$

(a) Show that $\phi(j) - \phi(j-1) = \dfrac{j^2 4^j}{(j+1)(j+2)}$

(b) Hence find, in terms of n, the sum of the series $\displaystyle\sum_{j=1}^{n} \dfrac{j^2 4^j}{(j+1)(j+2)}$ (Cambridge)

21. Given that $f(x) = (2x-1)(2x+1)$,

(a) express $\displaystyle\sum_{r=1}^{n} f(r)$ as a cubic in n

(b) show that $\displaystyle\sum_{r=1}^{n} \dfrac{1}{f(r)} = \dfrac{n}{2n+1}$

(c) evaluate $\displaystyle\lim_{n \to \infty} \sum_{r=1}^{n} \dfrac{1}{f(r)}$

(d) find the coefficient of x^n when $\dfrac{1}{f(x)}$ is expanded in ascending powers of x, distinguishing between the cases n odd and n even. State the set of values of x for which this expansion is valid.

7 PROPERTIES OF CURVES

Objectives

After studying this chapter you should

- have been reminded of the graphs of all the standard functions;
- understand how to find the important points on a graph;
- be able to find the vertical, horizontal and oblique asymptotes to a given curve, where appropriate;
- be able to identify restricted regions of the plane;
- be able to sketch the curves of functions related to a given function;
- be able to work with the curves of functions given in parametric form;
- understand how to derive the equations of chords, tangents and normals of a given curve;
- be able to apply standard elimination techniques to curves defined parametrically in order to determine their cartesian equations.

7.0   Introduction

Note on graphics calculators

During the work in this chapter you will be expected to have access to graph-plotting software or a graphics calculator. You are encouraged to use these facilities not only to confirm answers gained analytically, but also to help guide you in your line of attack to many of the problems. More importantly, you should be willing to experiment: the use of such aids as a companion to intelligent mathematical thought could boost your understanding of functions and their graphs enormously. Used as a substitute for intelligent mathematical thought, they will merely prove to be little more than expensive toys.

You should note that, when questions are set on examination papers, working must be shown which supports any answers which you have arrived at. It is, therefore, important that you develop the necessary analytical skills outlined here.

Activity 1

(a)   Copy and complete the following table of coordinates for the

function $y = \dfrac{1}{36} x^3 \left(x^2 - 7 \right)^2$:

x	–3	–2	–1	0	1	2	3
y							

Now plot these points on a piece of graph paper, taking 1 cm
to 1 unit on each of the coordinate axes, and join them up.

(b)   Comment on the graph you have just drawn in relation to its
equation.

(c)   Plot the graph of $y = \dfrac{1}{36} x^3 \left(x^2 - 7 \right)^2$ on a graph-plotter/

graphics calculator for x from –3 to 3. Compare this with your
graph and discuss the results in your class or group.

The above activity was really a warning about the difficulties that
could arise by plotting points without doing any detailed analysis.

The function $y = \dfrac{1}{36} x^3 \left(x^2 - 7 \right)^2$ is a polynomial of degree 7

(presumably called a heptic rather than a septic!), and as such
could have up to 7 crossing points on the x-axis, and up to 6
turning points. The purpose of part (a) was to get you to draw a
straight line – the alarm bells should have been ringing, loudly.

Another problem with accurate scale-drawings is that they might
miss out on the key features. If this sounds stupid, think of the

graph of $y = e^x$, which is shown opposite, and should be very
familiar to you.

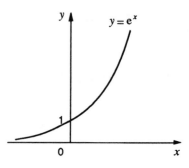

Such a diagram gives the general impression of exponential
growth. It is, however, remarkably inaccurate! Try it on your
graph plotter, and see if you can scale it so that the part of the
graph for $x > 0$ stays on the screen while the other part of the graph
for $x < 0$ does not simply become the negative x-axis.

Consider taking 1 cm to 1 unit on each axis and **plotting** points for
$x = 0, 1, 2, 3, ...$ When you get to $x = 64$ (64 cm is approximately
2 feet from the origin), the y-coordinate is

$$e^{64} \approx 6 \times 10^{27} \, \text{cm} = 6 \times 10^{25} \text{m}.$$

Now the radius of the observable universe is only about $3 \times 10^{26} \, \text{m}$,
so your diagram of accurately plotted points would be halfway
across the universe by now. The point of all this is that the
exponential function not only outgrows all finite polynomials

(sooner or later), but that it cannot be drawn both accurately **and** realistically.

You will see now why it is important not to let the graph-plotters do all your thinking for you. At best, they only work with a limited number of points on the screen, and what they draw for you is only an approximation to a continuous line, straight or curved. The purpose of this chapter is to enable you to handle a wide range of functions, given in a number of ways and **justify** the key features of their graphs analytically.

7.1 Graphs of standard functions

Activity 2

Try to sketch as many of the graphs of the following functions without the aid of a graph-plotter in the first instance. If you get stuck, or wish to experiment a little, then use whatever facilities you have to continue with.

In the relevant cases, try different sets of values of the constants involved $(a, b, c, ...)$; in particular, consider the cases $a < 0$ and $a > 0$.

1. (a) $y = ax^2 + bx + c$

    (b) $y = ax^3 + bx^2 + cx + d$

    How many different 'sorts' of quadratics/cubics are there?

2. (a) $y = ae^x$

    (b) $y = e^{ax}$

    (c) $y = \ln(ax)\ (x > 0)$

    (d) $y = a\ln x\ \ (x > 0)$

    (e) $y = a\sin x$

    (f) $y = a\cos x$

    (g) $y = a\tan x$

    (h) $y = a\sinh x$

    (i) $y = a\cosh x$

    (j) $y = a\tanh x$

3. (a) $y = \dfrac{a}{x}$ (b) $y = \dfrac{a}{x^2}$

4. In each case in Questions 1, 2 and 3, comment on any symmetric properties possessed by the graphs of these functions (e.g. reflection, rotation, translation, ...).

7.2 Important points

While there are some features of functions which are best looked at generally, there are a number of points on a curve which must be determined exactly. These are

(a)   the crossing points on the axes;

(b)   the turning points (T.P.) of the curve;

(c)   points of inflexion (P. of I.).

Reminders: Given a curve with equation $y = f(x)$:

(a)   the crossing points on the axes occur when $x = 0$ (on the y-axis) and when $y = 0$ (on the x-axis). These crossing points then have coordinates $(0, f(0))$ and $(a_1, 0), (a_2, 0), ..., (a_n, 0)$ where the a_i's $(i = 1$ to $n)$ are the n solutions to the equation $f(x) = 0$.

(b)   the stationary values (i.e. the turning points and horizontal points of inflexion) occur when $\dfrac{dy}{dx} = 0$, having coordinates

$$\left(b_1, f(b_1)\right), \left(b_2, f(b_2)\right), ..., \left(b_k, f(b_k)\right),$$

where the b_i's $(i = 1$ to $k)$ are the k solutions to the equation $f'(x) = 0$.

If $f''(b_i) < 0$ then $\left(b_i, f(b_i)\right)$ is a **maximum** point, while if $f''(b_i) > 0$ then $\left(b_i, f(b_i)\right)$ is a **minimum** point.

(c)   points of inflexion, in general, occur when $\dfrac{d^2y}{dx^2} = 0$. It is not necessary that $\dfrac{dy}{dx} = 0$. Unfortunately, it is not always the case that $\dfrac{d^2y}{dx^2} = 0 \Rightarrow$ inflexion. [Think of the graph of $y = x^4$: when $x = 0$, $y = 0$, $\dfrac{dy}{dx} = 0$, $\dfrac{d^2y}{dx^2} = 0$, $\dfrac{d^3y}{dx^3} = 0$ but $\dfrac{d^4y}{dx^4} = 24$. The point $(0, 0)$ is in fact, a minimum turning point.]

As a general rule, however, complications are kept to a minimum at A Level, and as you are not required to work beyond the second derivative $\dfrac{d^2y}{dx^2}$, or $f''(x)$, in this context, it will generally be assumed that $\dfrac{d^2y}{dx^2} = 0$ implies a point of inflexion.

Example

For $x > 0$, a curve has equation $y = \dfrac{\ln x}{x}$.

(a) State the coordinates of the point A where the curve crosses the x-axis.

(b) Calculate, in terms of e, the coordinates of B, the turning point of the curve, and the value of $\dfrac{d^2 y}{dx^2}$ at B. Describe the nature of B.

(c) Find the coordinates of C, the point of inflexion of the curve.

(d) Sketch the curve.

Solution

(a) When $y = 0$, $\ln x = 0 \Rightarrow x = 1$ so $A = (1, 0)$.

(b)
$$\frac{dy}{dx} = \frac{x.\dfrac{1}{x} - (\ln x).1}{x^2} \quad \text{by the Quotient Rule}$$

$$= \frac{1 - \ln x}{x^2}$$

For a T.P., $\dfrac{dy}{dx} = 0 \Rightarrow \ln x = 1 \Rightarrow x = e$ and $B = \left(e, \dfrac{1}{e}\right)$.

$$\frac{d^2 y}{dx^2} = \frac{x^2\left(-\dfrac{1}{x}\right) - (1 - \ln x)2x}{x^4} \quad \text{by the Quotient Rule}$$

$$= \frac{2 \ln x - 3}{x^3}$$

When $x = e$ (at B), $\dfrac{d^2 y}{dx^2} = -\dfrac{1}{e^3} < 0$, and B is a maximum point.

(c) For a P. of I., $\dfrac{d^2 y}{dx^2} = 0 \Rightarrow \ln x = \dfrac{3}{2} \Rightarrow x = e^{\frac{3}{2}}$ and

$$C = \left(e^{\frac{3}{2}}, \frac{3}{2e^{\frac{3}{2}}}\right).$$

(d) Now $\dfrac{\ln x}{x} > 0$ for all $x > 1$, but as e^x grows more quickly than any polynomial in x, so $\ln x$ grows more slowly than any polynomial, including a linear one (in this case, just x).

Thus $\dfrac{\ln x}{x} \to 0$ as $x \to \infty$.

For $0 < x < 1$, the reverse is true: $\ln x \to -\infty$ as $x \to 0$; also $\dfrac{1}{x} \to \infty$ as $x \to 0$, so that $\ln x.\dfrac{1}{x} \to -\infty$.

The results are summarised below.

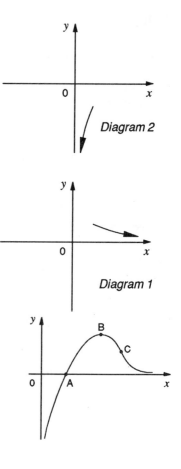

As $x \to 0_+$ (i.e. from the positive side), $y \to -\infty$ (diagram 1) and as $x \to \infty$, $y \to 0_+$ (diagram 2).

The curve crosses the x-axis at $A(1, 0)$, has a single turning point at

$$B\left(e, \frac{1}{e}\right) \approx (2.72, 0.368)$$

and a (non-horizontal) point of inflexion at

$$C\left(e^{\frac{3}{2}}, \frac{3}{2e^{\frac{3}{2}}}\right) \approx (4.48, 0.335).$$

The sketch of the curve then looks like the one opposite.

Notice that no attempt has been made to impose a scale on the graph, yet all essential features have been incorporated **and fully justified**. This is what curve-sketching is all about.

Exercise 7A

1. Find the coordinates of the point of inflexion of the curve with equation $y = x^3 - x^2 - x - 15$.

2. A curve has equation $y = x - 1 + \dfrac{1}{x+1}$. Calculate the coordinates of the turning points of the curve and determine their nature.

3. Determine the coordinates of the points of inflexion of the curve with equation $y = \operatorname{sech} x$. Sketch the curve $y = \operatorname{sech} x$.

4. A curve has equation $y = x^3 - 6x^2 + 3x + 10$.

   (a) Find the coordinates of the points at which this curve meets the coordinate axes.

   (b) Find also the coordinates of the point of inflexion of the curve. Sketch the curve.

5. Find the coordinates of the turning points of the curve with equation $y = x^2 e^{-3x}$, and determine their nature. Sketch the curve.

6. The diagram below shows the shape of the graph of the function f, where $f: x \to xe^x$ for real x.

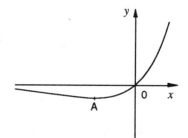

   Determine the coordinates of the stationary point A and hence write down the range of f.

7. A curve has equation $y = \dfrac{x-1}{\sqrt{x^2 + 2}}$. Find $\dfrac{dy}{dx}$ and hence find the coordinates of the turning point of the curve. Determine whether this turning point is a maximum or a minimum.

8. Determine the coordinates and nature of the turning point of the curve $y = 5\cosh x + \sinh x$. Sketch the curve.

7.3   Asymptotes

In the example in Section 7.2, the crossing point, turning point and point of inflexion were found and yet it was still not possible to do more than guess about the complete behaviour of the curve of the function $\dfrac{\ln x}{x}$.

In order to complete the picture, it was necessary to see what happened near $x = 0$ (on the positive side) and for very large values of x. The 'limiting behaviour' of the function for such values of x was made clear without having to resort to plotting individual points. Such 'limiting behaviour' is called the asymptotic behaviour of the function, or of its curve, as it approaches, but in practice never quite reaches, a steady state: usually a straight line which is call an **asymptote** of the curve.

The graph of $y = \tan x$ has vertical asymptotes at regular intervals of π radians, occurring when

$$x = \ldots, -\frac{\pi}{2}, \frac{\pi}{2}, 3\frac{\pi}{2}, \ldots \text{ (diagram 1 opposite).}$$

The graph of $y = \tanh x$ has horizontal asymptotes at

$$y = \pm 1 \text{ (diagram 2).}$$

The graph of $y = \dfrac{1}{x}$ has one horizontal asymptote, $y = 0$, and one vertical asymptote, $x = 0$ (diagram 3).

Unless the asymptote approached by the curve coincides with one of the coordinate axes, it should be drawn as a broken line. It is important to mark asymptotes on diagrams, if for no other reason than to prevent your diagram going where it should not.

Vertical asymptotes are more easily spotted than others since they are usually associated with values of x which cannot be input in the given function, since it would become undefined.

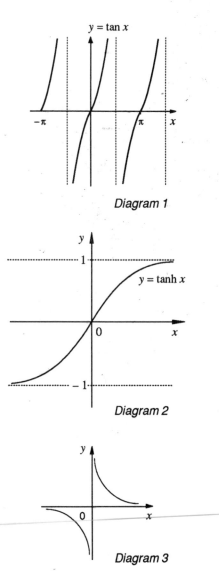

Diagram 1

Diagram 2

Diagram 3

Example

Sketch the graphs of the following functions, and state the equations of any asymptotes.

(a) $y = \ln(x - 1)$ $(x > 1)$

(b) $y = \dfrac{3}{x - 2}$ $(x \neq 2)$

(c) $y = \dfrac{1}{(x-1)(x-4)}$ $(x \neq 1, x \neq 4)$

Solution

(a) As $x \rightarrow 1_+$ (x approaches 1 from the positive side, i.e. from above), $\ln(x-1) \rightarrow -\infty$

For $x \leq 1$, $\ln(x-1)$ is undefined.

Then $x = 1$ is a vertical asymptote, and the graph is simply a translation of $y = \ln x$.

The crossing point occurs when $x = 2$, since $\ln(2-1) = 0$.

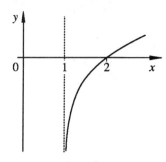

(b) $y = \dfrac{3}{x-2}$ is not defined for $x = 2$, since division by zero is not permissible: the vertical asymptote is thus $x = 2$.

Also, when $x = 0$, $y = -\dfrac{3}{2}$, but $y = 0$ gives no values of x, so the curve does not cross or touch the x-axis. However, as $x \rightarrow \infty$, $y \rightarrow 0_+$ and as $x \rightarrow -\infty$, $y \rightarrow 0-$, so the x-axis is also an asymptote of the curve.

In fact, although this example is a simple case, it is not always clear which side of the asymptote the curve is.

Here, as $x \rightarrow 2_+$ (x approaches 2 from above), $y \rightarrow +\infty$, and as $x \rightarrow 2-$, $y \rightarrow -\infty$.

[It is easy to check these results using any calculator by choosing, say, $x = 2.001$ and $x = 1.999$ in turn.]

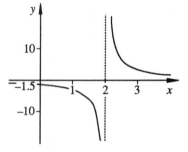

(c) $y = \dfrac{1}{(x-1)(x-4)} \quad \left(= \dfrac{1}{x^2 - 5x + 4} \right)$

When $x = 0$, $y = \dfrac{1}{4}$ so $\left(0, \tfrac{1}{4}\right)$ is the only crossing point here.

As $x \rightarrow +\infty$, $y \rightarrow 0_+$ and as $x \rightarrow -\infty$, $y \rightarrow 0_+$.

[Note that when x is very large (positively or negatively), the '$-5x$' and the '4' become insignificant in comparison to the x^2 and the curve is approximately $\dfrac{1}{x^2}$ for large $|x|$.] Thus $y = 0$ is a horizontal asymptote.

$x = 1$ and $x = 4$ are vertical asymptotes, and

$$\text{as } x \rightarrow 4_+, \quad y \rightarrow +\infty;$$
$$\text{as } x \rightarrow 4_-, \quad y \rightarrow -\infty;$$
$$\text{as } x \rightarrow 1_+, \quad y \rightarrow -\infty;$$
$$\text{as } x \rightarrow 1_-, \quad y \rightarrow +\infty.$$

A preliminary sketch might look something like the diagram opposite.

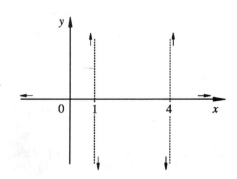

It is clear that, since the curve does not cross the x-axis between $x = 1$ and $x = 4$, there is a maximum point somewhere in this interval. For the present, there is no suggestion that finding the coordinates of this maximum is necessary (under exam conditions never do more than is asked of you – there isn't time!) but a little calculus would do the trick.

An alternative is to complete the square of $x^2 - 5x + 4$ by writing it as $\left(x - \dfrac{5}{2}\right)^2 - \dfrac{9}{4}$ which has a minimum at $\left(\dfrac{5}{2}, -\dfrac{9}{4}\right)$ so that its reciprocal has a maximum at $\left(\dfrac{5}{2}, -\dfrac{4}{9}\right)$.

The completed graph is shown opposite.

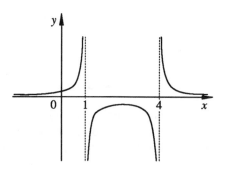

Example

Determine the equations of all the asymptotes of the curve with equation

$$y = \frac{x^2 - x - 6}{1 - x^2}$$

Find all the crossing points of the curve with the coordinate axes, and sketch the curve.

Solution

The function $\dfrac{x^2 - x - 6}{1 - x^2}$ is called a rational function, being the quotient of two polynomials. Such a 'fraction' is considered proper if the numerator is of lower degree than the denominator. In this example, the 'fraction' is improper (i.e. top heavy) and long division can be undertaken as follows:

$$\frac{x^2 - x - 6}{1 - x^2} = \frac{-\left(1 - x^2\right) - x - 5}{1 - x^2} = -1 - \frac{x + 5}{1 - x^2}$$

$$\left(\text{or } -1 - \frac{x + 5}{(1 - x)(1 + x)}\right)$$

Now, clearly, $x = 1$ and $x = -1$ are vertical asymptotes of the curve.

As $x \to 1_+$, $y \to +\infty$ and as $x \to 1_-$, $y \to -\infty$

As $x \to -1_+$, $y \to -\infty$ and as $x \to -1_-$, $y \to +\infty$.

Also, for large $|x|$, $\dfrac{x + 5}{1 - x^2} \approx \dfrac{x}{-x^2} = -\dfrac{1}{x}$ so that $\dfrac{x^2 - x - 6}{1 - x^2} \approx -1 + \dfrac{1}{x}$ for large values of $|x|$.

Then, as $x \to +\infty, y \to -1_+$

and as $x \to -\infty, y \to -1_-$

and $y = -1$ is a horizontal asymptote.

Next, when $x = 0,\ y = -6$;

and when $y = 0,\ x^2 - x - 6 = 0$

$\Rightarrow$ $(x - 3)(x + 2) = 0$

$\Rightarrow$ $x = -2, 3$

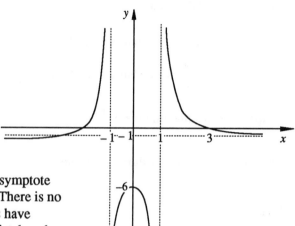

The curve looks like the one shown opposite.

Notice that the curve actually crosses the horizontal asymptote before turning and approaching it again as $x \to -\infty$. There is no reason why this should not happen, but some students have difficulty with the idea and think they have made a mistake where the 'as $x \to -\infty, y \to -1_-$' is concerned.

The other point to note is that the curve is clearly not symmetric in any vertical axis: the point (0, –6) may well not be the turning point. Calculus would be needed to determine the positions of the maximum and minimum points sketched here.

Oblique asymptotes

Consider the curve with equation $y = \dfrac{x^2 - 5x + 11}{x + 2}$. This is definitely a 'top heavy' algebraic fraction. Long division would give

$$\frac{x^2 - 5x + 11}{x + 2} \equiv Ax + B + \frac{C}{x + 2}$$

for some constants A, B and C.

A is clearly 1 since the LHS here is essentially $\dfrac{x^2}{x} = 1.x$ and C could be deduced by the Cover-up Method. This standard 'multiplying-through-and-substituting-values/composing-coefficients' method can be used as an alternative to long-division. Another alternative is the algebraic 'long-division' manipulation method used in the last example:

$$\frac{x^2 - 5x + 11}{x + 2} \equiv \frac{x(x + 2) - 7x + 11}{x + 2}$$

$$\equiv \frac{x(x+2)-7(x+2)+25}{x+2}$$

$$\equiv x-7+\frac{25}{x+2}$$

The curve here has vertical asymptote $x=-2$ (as $x\rightarrow-2_{+}$, $y\rightarrow+\infty$ and as $x\rightarrow-2_{-}$, $y\rightarrow-\infty$).

Now as $\quad x\rightarrow+\infty$, $\dfrac{25}{x+2}\rightarrow0_{+}$ and $y\approx(x-7)_{+}$,

while as $\quad x\rightarrow-\infty$, $\dfrac{25}{x+2}\rightarrow0_{-}$ and $y\approx(x-7)_{-}$.

Thus the curve has no horizontal asymptote, but has the line $y=x-7$. Such an asymptote is called **oblique**.

When $\quad x=0$, $y=\dfrac{11}{2}$,

and when $\quad y=0$, $x^{2}-5x+11=0$

$$\Rightarrow \quad x=\frac{5\pm\sqrt{-19}}{2}$$

and there are no crossing points on the x-axis.

The curve looks like the one shown opposite.

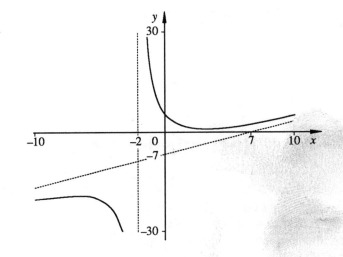

Exercise 7B

1. For each of the following curves find the coordinates of any crossing points of the curve with the coordinate axes, and obtain the equations of the asymptotes.

   (a) $y=\dfrac{x^{2}+2x-3}{x+2}\,(x\neq-2)$

   (b) $y=\dfrac{x-3}{x^{2}+2x-3}\,(x\neq-3, x\neq1)$

   (c) $y=x+\dfrac{4}{x^{2}}\,(x\neq0)$

   (d) $y=\dfrac{x^{2}}{x^{2}+1}$

2. Find the constants A, B and C such that

   $$\frac{x^{2}-5}{x-2}\equiv Ax+B+\frac{C}{x-2}$$

   Determine the equations of the two asymptotes of the curve

   $$y=\frac{x^{2}-5}{x-2}$$

   and show that the curve has no real turning points. Sketch the graph of the curve.

3. For $x \neq 1$, a curve is defined by the equation $y = \dfrac{x+2}{(x-1)^2}$. Find

   (a) the coordinates of the crossing points of this curve with the axes;

   (b) the coordinates of any turning points of the curve;

   (c) the equations of the asymptotes of the curve.

4. The curve C has equation $y = \dfrac{x^2 + ax - 2a^2}{x+2}$ where a is a constant such that $a \neq 1$ and $a \neq -2$.

   (a) Find $\dfrac{dy}{dx}$ and deduce that if C has stationary points then $-2 < a < 1$.

   (b) Find the equations of the asymptotes of C.

   (c) Draw a sketch of C for the case where $0 < a < 1$.

   (d) Draw a sketch of C for the case where $1 < a < 2$.   (Cambridge)

5. A curve has equation $y = \dfrac{x^2 + x}{x-3}$. Find the coordinates of any crossing points of the curve with the coordinate axes, and any turning points of the curve. Determine also the equations of the curve's asymptotes and sketch this curve.

6. Given that the curve $y = \dfrac{4 - ax^2}{b+x}$ has asymptotes $x = -1$ and $y = 1 - x$, find the values of a and b.

   Show that, at all points of the curve, $\dfrac{dy}{dx}$ is negative. Sketch the curve.   (Cambridge)

7. A curve has equation $y = -\ln\left|1 - x^2\right|$, $x \neq \pm 1$. Determine

   (a) the coordinates of the points where the curve crosses the axes;

   (b) the equations of the asymptotes of the curve.

7.4   Restricted regions

In an equation of the form $y = f(x)$, there are very often either individual values of x, or whole ranges of values of x, which cannot be used. Usually these are either immediately obvious, or in most cases, explicitly excluded in the question, and present little difficulty.

However, looking back at the final three curves in the examples of Section 7.3, you will note that there are ranges of values of y which cannot be obtained as output values from the function concerned. They are restricted regions of the plane, or 'forbidden areas', where the function cannot go.

Take the example $y = \dfrac{x^2 - 5x + 11}{x+2}$: in the region above the maximum point and below the minimum point, there are no values of y obtained by the function. One way to find this range of values would involve sketching a graph of the whole curve; noting that such a restricted region exists; then using calculus to determine the positions of the two turning points.

In cases like this, however, there is an alternative approach that can be used to begin with which is based on the observations relating to the solution of quadratic equations which led to the study of complex numbers in Chapter 3.

The quadratic equation $ax^2 + bx + c = 0$ has solutions

$$x = \frac{-b \pm \sqrt{b^2 - 4ac}}{2a}$$

If these values of x are to be real, then the **discriminant**, '$b^2 - 4ac$', must be greater than or equal to 0.

Now

$$y = \frac{x^2 - 5x + 11}{x + 2}$$

$$\Rightarrow \quad (x+2)y = x^2 - 5x + 11$$

$$\Rightarrow \quad 0 = x^2 - (5+y)x + (11 - 2y)$$

For real values of x,

$$(5+y)^2 - 4.1.(11 - 2y) \geq 0 \quad (a = 1, \ b = -(5+y), \ c = 11 - 2y)$$

$$\Rightarrow \quad y^2 + 10y + 25 - 44 + 8y \geq 0$$

$$\Rightarrow \quad y^2 + 18y - 19 \geq 0$$

$$\Rightarrow \quad (y+19)(y-1) \geq 0$$

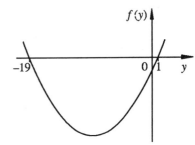

$$\Rightarrow \text{(see graph)} \ y \leq -19 \text{ or } y \geq 1$$

Hence, the restricted region in this case is $-19 < y < 1$, and the curve in question does not enter this mathematical 'no-go area'.

A bonus of this method is that -19 and 1 must be coordinates of the turning points of the curve.

$$y = -19 \Rightarrow 0 = x^2 + 14x + 49 = (x+7)^2 \Rightarrow x = -7.$$

$$y = 1 \Rightarrow 0 = x^2 - 6x + 9 = (x-3)^2 \Rightarrow x = 3.$$

The curve then has a maximum point at $(-7, -19)$ and a minimum point at $(3, 1)$, and there are no values of y between -19 and 1.

In both cases above, the value of y gave rise to a quadratic equation in x which had double roots. Explain why this is so.

Example

For the curve whose equation is

$$y = \frac{4}{(x-4)} - \frac{1}{x-1}$$

find the equations of the three asymptotes. Determine the set of values of y for which no part of the curve exists and deduce the coordinates of the turning points of the curve. Sketch the curve.

Solution

Note, first, that $y = \dfrac{4}{x-4} - \dfrac{1}{x-1} = \dfrac{3x}{(x-4)(x-1)}$ or $\dfrac{3x}{x^2 - 5x + 4}$

The vertical asymptotes are $x = 1$ and $x = 4$.

[As $x \to 1_+$, $y \to -\infty$; $x \to 1_-$, $y \to +\infty$. As $x \to 4_+$, $y \to +\infty$; as $x \to 4_-$, $y \to -\infty$.]

Next, as $x \to \infty$, $y \to 0_+$ and as $x \to -\infty$, $y \to 0_-$ so that $y = 0$ is a horizontal asymptote.

$$y = \frac{3x}{x^2 - 5x + 4} \Rightarrow \left(x^2 - 5x + 4\right)y = 3x \Rightarrow yx^2 - (5y + 3)x + 4y = 0$$

For real values of x,

$$(5y + 3)^2 - 4.y.4y \geq 0 \Rightarrow 25y^2 + 30y + 9 - 16y^2 \geq 0$$

$$\Rightarrow \qquad 3y^2 + 10y + 3 \geq 0$$

$$\Rightarrow \qquad (3y + 1)(y + 3) \geq 0$$

$$\Rightarrow y \leq -3, \, y \geq -\frac{1}{3}$$

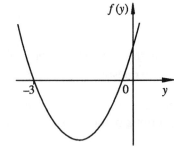

and the curve takes no values of y such that $-3 < y < -\dfrac{1}{3}$.

When $y = -3$, $-3x^2 + 12x - 12 = 0 \Rightarrow x^2 - 4x + 4 = 0 \Rightarrow (x-2)^2 = 0 \Rightarrow x = 2$

When $y = -\dfrac{1}{3}$, $-\dfrac{1}{3}x^2 - \dfrac{4}{3}x - \dfrac{4}{3} = 0 \Rightarrow x^2 + 4x + 4 = 0 \Rightarrow (x+2)^2 = 0 \Rightarrow x = -2$

The turning points are then

a maximum at $(2, -3)$ and a minimum at $(-2, -\frac{1}{3})$.

When $x = 0$, $y = 0$ and vice versa, so there is only one crossing point.

The curve looks like the one opposite.

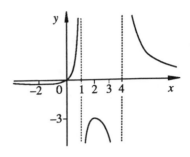

Exercise 7C

1. A curve has equation $y = \dfrac{(x-1)^2}{x+2}$. Show that there are no values of x for which $-12 < y < 0$.

2. Given that $y = \dfrac{2+10x-x^2}{1+x^2}$, find the range(s) of possible values of y.

3. Find the set of values of k for which the equation $2x^2 + 4x + 5 = kx$ has no real roots.

4. Determine the possible values of y in the following cases:

   (a) $y = \dfrac{3-x^2}{x+2}$ (b) $y = \dfrac{x+2}{3-x^2}$

5. Given that x is real, show that $-4 \le \dfrac{4x-3}{x^2+1} \le 1$

   Sketch the curve with equation $y = \dfrac{4x-3}{x^2+1}$,

   showing clearly on your sketch

   (a) the coordinates of the points where the curve crosses the coordinate axes;

   (b) the coordinates of the maximum and minimum point;

   (c) the shape of the curve for large values of $|x|$.

6. A curve has equation $y = \dfrac{x^2+3x+9}{x^2-2x+2}$. Find the range of values of y which exist for real x. Deduce the coordinates of the turning points of the curve and sketch the curve.

7. Given that x is real and $y = \dfrac{(x-2)^2}{x^2+4}$, show that $0 \le y \le 2$. Hence write down the coordinates of the two stationary points on the curve with

   equation $y = \dfrac{(x-2)^2}{x^2+4}$. Sketch the curve showing clearly how the curve approaches its asymptote. With the aid of your sketch, explain why the equation $x(x^2+4) = (x-2)^2$ has only one real root.

7.5   Symmetry

In Chapter 4 of *Pure Mathematics*, you encountered a number of transformational symmetries using functions.

The results you should be aware of are as follows:

Given the graph of function $y = f(x)$, and a non-zero constant a,

  (i)   the graph of $y = f(x) + a$ is a translation of $y = f(x)$,

   parallel to the *y*-axis of $\begin{pmatrix} 0 \\ a \end{pmatrix}$;

  (ii) the graph of $y = f(x+a)$ is a translation of $y = f(x)$

   parallel to the *x*-axis of $\begin{pmatrix} -a \\ 0 \end{pmatrix}$;

(iii) the graph of $y = af(x)$ is a stretch of $y = f(x)$, parallel to the y-axis, by a scale factor of a;

(iv) the graph of $y = f(ax)$ is a stretch of $y = f(x)$, parallel to the x-axis, by a scale factor of $\dfrac{1}{a}$.

Two results, in particular, were noted:

$y = f(-x)$ is a reflection of $y = f(x)$ in the y-axis

and $y = -f(x)$ is a reflection of $y = f(x)$ in the x-axis.

It is these final two results which will be developed further in this section.

Activity 3

Using a graph-plotting facility, draw the graphs of $y = f(x)$ in each of the following cases. For each example, plot on the same diagram the graph of $y = f(-x)$, and comment on the type of symmetry (if any) relating $f(x)$ to $f(-x)$.

1. $f(x) = x^2$
2. $f(x) = 2x^3$
3. $f(x) = x^5 - 4x$

4. $f(x) = x^4 + 2x^2 - 1$
5. $f(x) = x - \dfrac{7}{x}$
6. $f(x) = 2\sin 3x$

7. $f(x) = 2\cos 2x + 1$
8. $f(x) = \tan 2x$
9. $f(x) = \cosh \tfrac{1}{2}x$

10. $f(x) = \tanh x$
11. $f(x) = x^2 + \sin x$

12. $f(x) = \sec x + \tan x$

In Activity 3, you should have noted that the functions in 1, 4, 7, 9 exhibited reflection symmetry in the y-axis; while those in 2, 3, 5, 6, 8 and 10 exhibited two-fold, (i.e.180°) rotational symmetry about the origin.

Use the series from Chapter 6, if necessary, to explain why the above results turned out to be as they did.

Check your ideas for the functions in 11 and 12, which failed to exhibit either type of symmetry.

Odd and even functions

A function f is said to be an **even function** if and only if

$$\boxed{f(-x) = f(x)}$$

for all x in the domain of f. Such a function has reflection symmetry in the y-axis.

A function f is said to be an **odd function** if and only if

$$\boxed{f(-x)=-f(x)}$$

for all x in the domain of f. Such a function has (two-fold) rotational symmetry about the origin.

Example

Determine whether the following functions are odd, even or neither:

(a) $f(x)=\sin x\cos x$; (b) $g(x)=\sin x\cos x+1$

(c) $h(x)=x^2-\dfrac{1}{x}+4$; (d) $i(x)=x\tan x$

Solution

(a) $f(-x)=\sin(-x)\cos(-x)$

$\quad\quad\quad=-\sin x.\cos x$ $[\sin(-x)=-\sin x$ and $\cos(-x)=\cos x\,]$

$\quad\quad\quad=-(\sin x\cos x)$

$\quad\quad\quad=-f(x)$

and f is an odd function.

Alternatively: $f(x)=\tfrac{1}{2}\sin 2x$ so

$f(-x)=\tfrac{1}{2}\sin(-2x)=-\tfrac{1}{2}\sin 2x=-f(x)$.

(b) $g(-x)=-\sin x\cos x+1$, and g is neither odd nor even.

(c) $h(-x)=(-x)^2-\dfrac{1}{(-x)}+4=x^2+\dfrac{1}{x}+4$, and h is neither odd

nor even.

(d) $i(-x)=(-x)\tan(-x)=-x.-\tan x=x\tan x=i(x)$, and i is an even function.

Two immediate consequences

For an even function f, $\displaystyle\int_{-a}^{a}f(x)\,dx=2\int_{0}^{a}f(x)\,dx$ since the area under the curve (and above the x-axis) from $-a$ to 0 is equal to the area under the curve from 0 to a.

For an odd function f, $\displaystyle\int_{-a}^{a}f(x)\,dx=0$ since the area on one side of the y-axis has area of equal magnitude to that on the other side, but of opposite sign.

Exercise 7D

1. Determine whether the following functions are odd or even or neither:

   (a) $f(x) = 2x^2 - 3$

   (b) $f(x) = \sin^2 x$

   (c) $f(x) = \dfrac{\tan x}{x}$ $(x \neq 0)$ (d) $f(x) = \sinh x - x \cosh x$

   (e) $f(x) = |x|$

   (f) $f(x) = \cos(x^3)$

   (g) $f(x) = \sqrt[5]{x}$

   (h) $f(x) = \dfrac{|x|}{x}$ $(x \neq 0)$

   (i) $f(x) = \ln|x|$ $(x \neq 0)$.

2. For $x \geq 0$, find the coordinates of the stationary point, the point of inflexion and any crossing point on the axes of the curve of $y = \dfrac{x}{1+x^2}$.

   Show that $\dfrac{x}{1+x^2}$ is an odd function, and hence sketch the graph of this curve for all real values of x.

3. The function g is given by $g(x) = \dfrac{\sin x}{x}$. By considering the Maclaurin series of $\sin x$, or otherwise, show that $\lim\limits_{x \to 0} \{g(x)\} = 1$. Prove that the graph of $y = g(x)$ is symmetric in the y-axis. Sketch the graph of $y = g(x)$ for $-3\pi \leq x \leq 3\pi$.

4. The function f is a polynomial of degree four (quartic). Functions g and h are defined by

   $$g(x) = f(x) + f(-x), \quad h(x) = f(x) - f(-x).$$

   Show that g is an even function and h is an odd function.

7.6 Associated graphs

Activity 4

You will need to use a graph-plotting facility in this activity.

Choose a function; call it $y = f(x)$. Draw the graph of this function.

What do you think the graphs of

(a) $y = \dfrac{1}{f(x)}$
(b) $y = |f(x)|$
(c) $y^2 = f(x)$

will look like? Try and decide before you draw them.

Now try a linear function, a quadratic function, a rational function, log functions, exponential functions, trigonometric or hyperbolic functions; a function of your own devising.

Decide how you would answer the following questions:

what happens to the zeros of a function?

what happens to asymptotes?

what about restricted regions?

Write out your conclusions in detail.

Example

Sketch the curve of $y = \dfrac{x(4-x)}{4+x}$

Hence draw the curve of $y^2 = \dfrac{x(4-x)}{4+x}$

Solution

$$\frac{x(4-x)}{4+x} \equiv \frac{-x(x+4)+8x}{x+4} \equiv \frac{-x(x+4)+8(x+4)-32}{x+4}$$

$$\equiv -x+8-\frac{32}{x+4}$$

Then $y = \dfrac{x(4-x)}{4+x}$ has a vertical asymptote $x = -4$ and an oblique

asymptote $y = -x+8$.

When $x = 0$, $y = 0$ and when $y = 0$, $x = 0$ or 4, so there are crossing points at $(0, 0)$ and $(4, 0)$.

The graph of $y = \dfrac{x(4-x)}{4+x}$ is shown opposite.

What about the graph of $y^2 = \dfrac{x(4-x)}{4+x}$**?**

Firstly, $y^2 \ge 0$ for real values of y, so that

$$\frac{x(4-x)}{4+x} \ge 0.$$

From the above graph, it can be seen that $\dfrac{x(4-x)}{4+x}$ is only ≥ 0 for $x < -4$ and $0 \le x \le 4$.

The regions of the plane represented by $-4 \le x < 0$ and $x \ge 4$ are thus restricted regions.

Also, for those values of x for which real values of y exist, $y = \pm\sqrt{\dfrac{x(4-x)}{4+x}}$, and the curve is necessarily symmetric in the x-axis.

Finally, the curve looks like the one shown opposite.

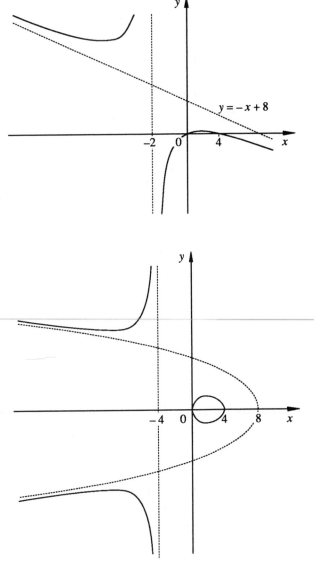

It is worth noting that vertical asymptotes remain unchanged; horizontal asymptotes would become pairs of horizontal asymptotes such that, for example, the asymptote

$y = a$ for $y = f(x)$ would give rise to $y = \pm\sqrt{a}$ for $y^2 = f(x)$ provided that $a \geq 0$. An oblique asymptote such as $y = 8 - x$ here would give rise to a curved asymptote $y^2 = 8 - x$, which is the parabola indicated on the diagram.

Another minor, but common, oversight amongst students is to draw the closed curve portion for $0 \leq x \leq 4$ with 'pointed' end points on the x-axis, as shown in the diagrams opposite.

instead of

In the next chapter you will learn how to differentiate functions such as $y^2 = \dfrac{x(4-x)}{4+x}$ implicitly to get (in this instance)

$$2y \frac{dy}{dx} = \frac{16 - 8x - x^2}{(4+x)^2}$$

so that

$$\frac{dy}{dx} = \frac{16 - 8x - x^2}{2y(4+x)^2}$$

where $y = 0$ gives an infinite gradient.

Example

Sketch the graph of $y = f(x)$, where $f(x) = (2x-1)(2x+1)$.

Hence draw, on separate axes, the graphs of $y = |f(x)|$, $y^2 = f(x)$

and $y = \dfrac{1}{f(x)}$.

Solution

The first part is easy: $f(x)$ is a quadratic with crossing points on the axes at $\left(\frac{1}{2}, 0\right), \left(-\frac{1}{2}, 0\right)$ and $(0, -1)$ with the graph shown opposite.

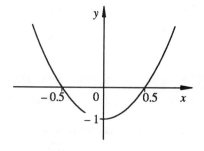

Now the modulus function $|x|$ changes only the sign of x if it is negative, and leaves x unchanged if $x \geq 0$.

The graph of $y = |f(x)|$ then simply converts any negative part of the graph into its positive reflection.

Thus $y = |(2x-1)(2x+1)|$ looks like diagram 1 opposite.

Note here (for example) that at $x = -\frac{1}{2}$, the 'turning point' is not a smooth one ($\frac{dy}{dx} \neq 0$ for instance), so do not be tempted to round it off as shown in diagram 2.

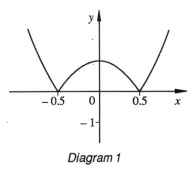

Diagram 1

For $y^2 = (2x-1)(2x+1)$, the key points are

(i)   the graph is symmetric in the x-axis;

(ii) no values of x can be taken for which $y^2 < 0$;

(iii) the curve crosses the x-axis vertically.

Diagram 2

The gradient of the curve of $y^2 = f(x)$ will in general differ from that of $y = f(x)$ at corresponding points of the curves, but a sketch is not intended to display such fine detail.

For $y = \dfrac{1}{f(x)}$ compared to $y = f(x)$, it should be obvious that

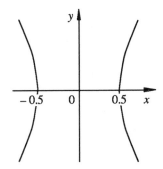

as $y \to +\infty$ in $y = f(x)$, $y \to 0_+$ in $y = \dfrac{1}{f(x)}$;

as $y \to -\infty$ in $y = f(x)$, $y \to 0_-$ in $y = \dfrac{1}{f(x)}$;

as $y \to 0_+$ in $y = f(x)$, $y \to +\infty$ in $y = \dfrac{1}{f(x)}$; and

as $y \to 0_-$ in $y = f(x)$, $y \to -\infty$ in $y = \dfrac{1}{f(x)}$.

Thus vertical asymptotes of $f(x)$ become zeros of $\dfrac{1}{f(x)}$, and

zeros of $f(x)$ give rise to vertical asymptotes of $\dfrac{1}{f(x)}$.

Then $y = \dfrac{1}{(2x-1)(2x+1)}$ has the graph as shown on the right.

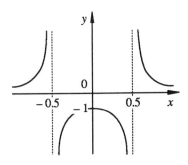

Exercise 7E

In Questions 1–4 you are given the graph of $y = f(x)$. In each case draw the graph of the associated function(s) stated.

1.

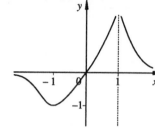

Draw the graph of $y^2 = f(x)$.

2.

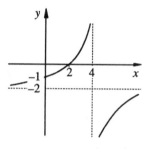

Draw the graph of $y = |f(x)|$.

3.

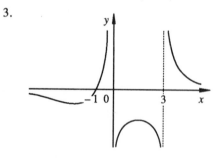

Draw the graphs of

(a) $y = |f(x)|$ (b) $y^2 = f(x)$.

4.

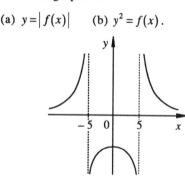

Draw the graphs of

(a) $y = |f(x)|$ (b) $y^2 = f(x)$

(c) $y = \dfrac{1}{f(x)}$.

5. The diagram shows the graph of $y = g(x)$ where

$g(x) = \dfrac{x-2}{x}$. Draw the graphs of

(a) $y = \dfrac{x^2-4}{x^2}$

(b) $y = \left|\dfrac{x-2}{x}\right|$

(c) $y = \left|\dfrac{x^2-4}{x^2}\right|$.

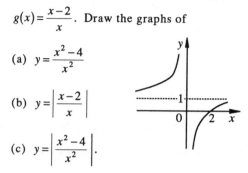

6. Show that $f(x) = \dfrac{x}{1+x^2}$ is an odd function. Determine the coordinates of the turning points on the graph of $y = f(x)$. Sketch the curves of $y = f(x)$ and $y^2 = f(x)$.

7. For $-2\pi \le x \le 2\pi$, sketch the graph of $y = \cos x$. Hence draw the graph of $y = \sec x$.

8. Sketch the graphs of the curves with equations

(a) $y = x^4(1-x)$ (b) $y^2 = x^4(1-x)$

(c) $y = \left|x^4(1-x)\right|$.

Find the coordinates of the turning points of the curve (b).

9. Sketch the graph of the curve with equation $y = f(x)$, where $f(x) = x^3 - x$. Hence draw the graphs of

(a) $y = \dfrac{1}{f(x)}$ (b) $y = |f(x)|$.

10. Sketch the graph of $y = (x+1)(3x+1)$. Sketch also the graph of $y^2 = (x+1)(3x+1)$ and state the equations of its asymptotes.

11. The graph of the function $y = \dfrac{x+2}{x+5}$ is given.

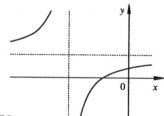

Determine

(a) the equations of the asymptotes of this curve;

(b) the coordinates of the crossing points with the axes.

Sketch the curve of $y^2 = \dfrac{x+2}{x+5}$.

12. Sketch the graph of the curve with equation

$y = x(x-4)^2$. Determine the coordinates of that turning point of the curve which does not lie on the x-axis. Sketch the graph of $y^2 = x(x-4)^2$ and deduce the range of values of the real number k such that $x(x-4)^2 = k^2$ has exactly one real root.

7.7 Parametric forms

In many cases, the variables x and y are both dependent upon a third variable or parameter. If you have done any Mechanics, you will know that this extra variable is very often time. In other instances the parameter may be some angle, θ(say). In this way, a function may not appear in the form $y = f(x)$; but rather each of the x– and y– components are given as functions of the parameter;

e.g. $\qquad x = f(t), y = g(t)$

Note: t does not have to indicate time.

Elimination

If you are asked to draw the curve of a function given parametrically (in terms of t, say) the most natural thing to do is to get back to an equation involving only x's and y's; its cartesian equation. This process, not unsurprisingly, is called **elimination**.

Example

A curve is defined parametrically by the equations

$$x = t^2, y = \frac{1}{t} \quad (t \neq 0).$$

Sketch the curve.

Solution

Now $y = \dfrac{1}{t} \Rightarrow t = \dfrac{1}{y} \Rightarrow x = \left(\dfrac{1}{y^2}\right)$ or $y^2 = \dfrac{1}{x}$.

The graph of $y = \dfrac{1}{x}$ (shown opposite) is well known.

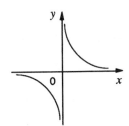

and the graph of $y^2 = \dfrac{1}{x}$ can then be deduced as shown.

However, there are difficulties that could arise, as you will see in the example below. You should be aware of these problems.

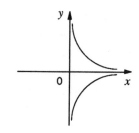

Example

A curve is defined parametrically by the equations $x = 2t^2$, $y = t^4$, where t is a parameter. Determine the cartesian equation of this curve. Sketch the curve.

Solution

$$x = 2t^2 \Rightarrow x^2 = 4t^4 \Rightarrow x^2 = 4y,$$

so that the cartesian equation is

$$y = \frac{x^2}{4}.$$

This is a parabola, with graph shown opposite.

But wait! $t = 0 \Rightarrow x = 0$ and $y = 0$.

Otherwise, $x > 0$ and $y > 0$ so the graph should be only the right-hand 'half' of the one drawn above.

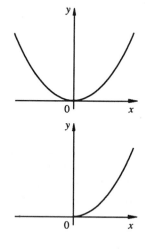

The elimination process is not always as straightforward as this.

Example

The parametric representation of a curve C is

$$x = 3\cos\theta + \cos 3\theta, \quad y = 3\sin\theta - \sin 3\theta.$$

Determine the cartesian equation of C.

Solution

The identities $\cos 3\theta \equiv 4\cos^3\theta - 3\cos\theta$ and $\sin 3\theta \equiv 3\sin\theta - 4\sin^3\theta$ are easily established. Thus

$$x = 4\cos^3\theta \quad \text{and} \quad y = 4\sin^3\theta$$

or $\qquad \cos\theta = \left(\dfrac{x}{4}\right)^{\frac{1}{3}} \quad \text{and} \quad \sin\theta = \left(\dfrac{y}{4}\right)^{\frac{1}{3}}.$

To eliminate θ, use the well known identity $\cos^2\theta + \sin^2\theta = 1$ to get

$$\left(\frac{x}{4}\right)^{\frac{2}{3}} + \left(\frac{y}{4}\right)^{\frac{2}{3}} = 1$$

Exercise 7F

Eliminate the parameter in each of the following sets of parametric equations in order to find the cartesian equation of the curve they represent.

1. $x = 2t^{\frac{3}{2}}$, $y = 3t$ $(t \geq 0)$

2. $x = \dfrac{t}{1+t^3}$, $y = \dfrac{t^2}{1+t^3}$

   [Hint: $\dfrac{y}{x}$]

3. $x = \cosh\theta$, $y = \sinh\theta$

4. $x = \cos t$, $y = \tan t$

5. $x = t^3 - 3t + 2$, $y = 3(t^2 - 1)$

   [Hint: $x = t(t^2 - 3) + 2$ and $t^2 = \dots$]

6. $x = \dfrac{2}{\cosh t}$, $y = 3e^t$

7. $x = 2t^2$, $y = t(1 - t^2)$

8. $x = a\sin\theta\cos^2\theta$, $y = a\sin^2\theta\cos\theta$

   [Hint: $\dfrac{y}{x}$ and xy]

9. $x = a\left(\dfrac{1+t^2}{1-t^2}\right)$, $y = \dfrac{2bt}{1-t^2}$

   [Hint: $t = \tan\frac{1}{2}\theta$]

10. $x = 2\cos\theta + 3\cos 2\theta$,

    $y = 2\sin\theta + 3\sin 2\theta$

    [Hint: simultaneous equations]

A perfectly natural question to ask

If it is possible to eliminate the parameter and derive the cartesian equation of a curve, why have curves defined parametrically in the first place? To put it another way,

what extra information can you deduce from the parametric form of an equation that cannot be found in the cartesian equation?

Note: it is not always possible to eliminate the parameter. Even when it is, as you will have seen in Exercise 7F, the cartesian equation may be of a form that does not easily lend itself to analysis.

It is easy, conceptually, to think of the parameter t as representing time: then, for any value of t, the parametric equations give the coordinates (x, y) of a point which is in motion as t varies. The parametric equations then indicate **how** that point is moving along the curve in question.

Consider the parametric equations

$$x = \cos t, \quad y = \sin t \quad \text{for } 0 \leq t < 2\pi.$$

Using the identity $\cos^2 t + \sin^2 t = 1$, the curve is seen to be

$$x^2 + y^2 = 1,$$

which is a circle, centre the origin and radius 1.

Next, consider the equations

$$x = \sin t, \quad y = \cos t \quad \text{for } 0 \le t < 2\pi.$$

Again, $\sin^2 t + \cos^2 t = 1$ gives the circle $x^2 + y^2 = 1$.

What is the difference?

As t increases from 0 to 2π, choose some easy values of t to work with.

	$t = 0$	$t = \dfrac{\pi}{2}$	$t = \pi$	$t = \dfrac{3\pi}{2}$	....
$x = \cos t, \quad y = \sin t$	(1, 0)	(0, 1)	(−1, 0)	(0, −1)	...
$x = \sin t, \quad y = \cos t$	(0, 1)	(1, 0)	(0, −1)	(−1, 0)	...

In the first case you will see that as t increases from 0 to 2π, the point (x, y) moves around the circle in an anticlockwise direction, starting from the point $(1, 0)$.

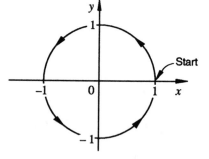

In the second case, however, the same circle is traversed, but this time in a clockwise direction, starting from $(0, 1)$.

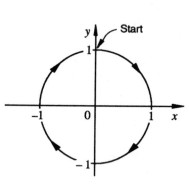

Although it is helpful for you to be aware of this aspect of parametrisation, it is most unlikely that you will be required to employ such notions in a Pure Mathematics examination.

7.8 $\dfrac{dy}{dx}$ and $\dfrac{d^2y}{dx^2}$ from the parametric form

When a curve is given in the explicit form $y = f(x)$, it is easy to find $\dfrac{dy}{dx}$ and $\dfrac{d^2y}{dx^2}$ by direct differentiation. At your disposal you have the product rule, the quotient rule and the **Chain Rule** for complicated functions, f. Do not worry if you have not heard the term 'Chain Rule' before, it is simply a statement of the rule for differentiating composite functions, and it is summed up by

$$\frac{dy}{dx} = \frac{dy}{dt} \cdot \frac{dt}{dx} \quad \text{or} \quad \frac{dy}{dt} \bigg/ \frac{dx}{dt}$$

Although dx, dy, dt, du, dv, dz, ... do not actually make sense by themselves, they do behave in the same way algebraically as genuinely finite variables, and can be thought of as cancelling: so

$$\frac{dy}{dx} = \frac{dy}{d\!\!\!/t} \cdot \frac{d\!\!\!/t}{dx} \quad \text{because the } dt\text{'s 'cancel'.}$$

[Note that higher derivatives **do not** cancel in this way:

$$\frac{d^2y}{dx^2} \neq \frac{d^2y}{dt^2} \cdot \frac{d^2t}{dx^2}$$

Indeed one reson for writing the '2' in different places in the numerator and denominator of the higher-order derivatives is to avoid the temptation to cancel in this way.]

Given a curve in parametric form

$$x = f(t), \quad y = g(t),$$

the Chain Rule gives

$$\frac{dy}{dx} = \frac{dy}{dt} \bigg/ \frac{dx}{dt} = \frac{g'(t)}{f'(t)}$$

which, in general, will be a function of t and **not** of x. This is crucial in finding $\dfrac{d^2y}{dx^2}$ in any form.

Example

Given the curve with parametric representation

$$x = 4\cos^3 t , \quad y = 4\sin^3 t$$

find $\dfrac{dy}{dx}$ in terms of t and show that $\dfrac{d^2y}{dx^2} = \dfrac{1}{12}\operatorname{cosec} t \sec^4 t .$

Solution

$$\frac{dx}{dt} = 4.3\cos^2 t.(-\sin t) = -12\sin t\cos^2 t$$

and
$$\frac{dy}{dt} = 4.3\sin^2 t.\cos t = 12\sin^2 t\cos t.$$

Then

$$\frac{dy}{dx} = \frac{dy}{dt}\Big/\frac{dx}{dt} = \frac{12\sin^2 t\cos t}{-12\sin t\cos^2 t} = -\tan t$$

Now, as $\dfrac{dy}{dx}$ is a function of t, it is no good trying to differentiate it

as if it were a function of x, since $\dfrac{d^2y}{dx^2} = \dfrac{d}{dx}\left(\dfrac{dy}{dx}\right).$ The next part

is easier to understand if $\dfrac{dy}{dx}$ is assigned a label, say m.

Then $\dfrac{d^2y}{dx^2} = \dfrac{dm}{dx} = \dfrac{dm}{dt}.\dfrac{dt}{dx}$ or $\dfrac{dm}{dt}\Big/\dfrac{dx}{dt}$ by the Chain Rule.

Since $m\left(=\dfrac{dy}{dx}\right)$ is a function of t, $\dfrac{dm}{dt}$ presents no problem (in

principle, that is) and $\dfrac{dx}{dt}$ has already been found.

To continue:

$$\frac{d^2y}{dx^2} = \frac{d}{dx}\left(\frac{dy}{dx}\right) = \frac{d}{dt}\left(\frac{dy}{dx}\right).\frac{dt}{dx}$$

$$= \frac{d}{dt}(-\tan t) . \frac{1}{-12\sin t\cos^2 t}$$

$$= -\sec^2 t . \frac{1}{-12\sin t\cos^2 t}$$

$$= \frac{1}{12}\operatorname{cosec} t \sec^4 t$$

Example

The curve C has parametric form

$$x = t^3 - 3t + 2, \quad y = 3(t^2 - 1).$$

Find $\dfrac{dy}{dx}$ and $\dfrac{d^2y}{dx^2}$ as functions of t. Hence show that C has a turning point at the point $(2, -3)$ and determine its nature.

[Look back at your answer to Exercise 7F, Question 5, for the equivalent cartesian form of C. After working through Chapter 8 you should be able to differentiate this equation implicitly, but for now the parametric approach is a big advantage in this respect.]

Solution

Firstly, the point $(2, -3)$ occurs when $t = 0$.

$$\frac{dx}{dt} = 3t^2 - 3 \text{ and } \frac{dy}{dt} = 6t$$

so that

$$\frac{dy}{dx} = \frac{6t}{3t^2 - 3} = \frac{2t}{t^2 - 1}$$

When $t = 0$, $\dfrac{dy}{dx} = 0$ so the curve C has a stationary value at $(2, -3)$.

Next,

$$\frac{d^2y}{dx^2} = \frac{d}{dt}\left(\frac{dy}{dx}\right) \cdot \frac{dt}{dx} = \left\{\frac{(t^2-1).2 - 2t.2t}{(t^2-1)^2}\right\} \cdot \frac{1}{3(t^2-1)} = \frac{-2(1+t^2)}{3(t^2-1)^3}$$

and when $t = 0$, $\dfrac{d^2y}{dx^2} = \dfrac{2}{3} > 0$ and $(2, -3)$ is a minimum point.

7.9 Conic sections

There is a family or curves which are known collectively as **conic sections**.

[The interested reader might like to find out why.]

These are the circle, the ellipse, the parabola and the hyperbola. Although a general treatment of these, and the coordinate geometry associated with them, is not required here, they are worth looking at in some detail as their parametric forms are easy to work with and widely used.

The circle

The circle, centre the origin and radius r has cartesian equation

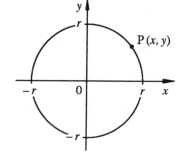

$$x^2 + y^2 = r^2$$

and parametric representation

$$x = r\cos\theta, \quad y = r\sin\theta$$

The circle, centre (a, b) and radius r has cartesian equation

$$(x-a)^2 + (y-b)^2 = r^2$$

and parametric representation

$$x = a + r\cos\theta, \quad y = b + r\sin\theta$$

The ellipse

An ellipse can be considered as a circle, stretched parallel to its two axes by different scale factors, say by a parallel to the x-axis, and by b parallel to the y-axis.

The cartesian equation is then

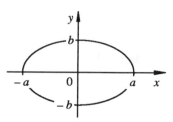

$$\frac{x^2}{a^2} + \frac{y^2}{b^2} = 1$$

(compare with $\dfrac{x^2}{r^2} + \dfrac{y^2}{r^2} = 1$ for the circle when $a = b = r$), and the parametric representation is

$$x = a\cos\theta, \quad y = b\sin\theta.$$

The parabola

The parabola for which the x-axis is the central axis has cartesian equation

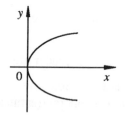

$$y^2 = 4ax \ (a > 0)$$

and parametric form

$$x = at^2, \quad y = 2at$$

The hyperbola

The hyperbola has cartesian equation

$$\frac{x^2}{a^2} - \frac{y^2}{b^2} = 1$$

and parametric representation

$$x = a\cosh\theta, \quad y = b\sinh\theta.$$

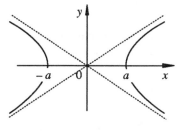

Note that, for large $|x|$ and $|y|$, $\frac{x^2}{a^2} \approx \frac{y^2}{b^2}$ so the hyperbola has a pair of oblique asymptotes

$$y = \pm\frac{b}{a}x.$$

The rectangular hyperbola

When the two asymptotes of the hyperbola ar

e perpendicular to each other, the curve is called a rectangular hyperbola. An example which you have encountered before is the curve of

$$y = \frac{c^2}{x} \quad (c \neq 0)$$

which has the parametric form

$$x = ct, \quad y = \frac{c}{t} \quad \text{for } t \neq 0.$$

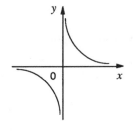

A rotation of the axis about the origin will transform this graph into a standard hyperbola.

Exercise 7G

1. Sketch the curve defined parametrically by
   $$x = t^2 - 2, \quad y = t.$$

2. In each of the following cases, determine

   $\dfrac{dy}{dx}$ and $\dfrac{d^2y}{dx^2}$ as functions of t.

   Simplify your answers as much as possible.

   (a) $x = 2t^{\frac{3}{2}}, \quad y = 3t \quad (t \geq 0)$

   (b) $x = \dfrac{t}{1+t^3}, \quad y = \dfrac{t}{1+t^3} \quad (t \neq -1)$

   (c) $x = \sqrt{1+t^2}, \quad y = \sinh^{-1}t$

   (d) $x = a\cosh\theta, \quad y = b\sinh\theta$

3. Given
   $$x = \theta + \sin\theta, \quad y = 1 - \cos\theta \quad (0 \leq \theta < 2\pi)$$
   show that
   $$\frac{dy}{dx} = \tan\frac{1}{2}\theta.$$

   Sketch the curve represented by these parametric equations and state the line of symmetry.

4. By completing the square, determine the coordinates of the centre, and the radius, of each of the circles with equations

   (a) $x^2 + y^2 + 4x - 6y = 12$

   (b) $x^2 + y^2 + 2x - 6y - 26 = 0$

5. Show that the parametric equations

$$x^2 - y^2 = 4. \; x = t + \frac{1}{t}, \; y = t - \frac{1}{t} \quad (t \neq 0)$$

are a representation of the hyperbola with cartesian equation

$$x^2 - y^2 = 4.$$

7.10 Applications

In Chapter 8 of *Pure Mathematics*, you worked with the following results relating to a curve with equation $y = f(x)$.

The derived function, or derivative, $\frac{dy}{dx} = f'(x)$, gives the gradient of the curve at any point, and also the gradient of the tangent to the curve at each point.

The normal to a curve at any point is the line through that point which is perpendicular to the curve (and hence also perpendicular to its tangent).

You will do some further work in these areas.

Another application of the work on parameters (in particular) is in finding the locus of points (i.e. the curves traced out by these points) under certain controlling conditions.

The final area of application is in noting the existence, or number, of roots to a given equation $f(x) = 0$, say. If this equation is rewritten as

$$g(x) = h(x) \qquad \text{for two functions } g \text{ and } h,$$

and the graphs of $y = g(x)$ and $y = h(x)$ are drawn, then the points of intersection represent the roots of $f(x) = 0$. This method will only be used in simple cases.

Example

Show that the parametric form

$$x = 5\cos\theta, \; y = 4\sin\theta$$

is a representation of the ellipse with equation

$$16x^2 + 25y^2 = 400.$$

Sketch the ellipse and mark on it the coordinates of the points where the ellipse crosses the coordinate axes.

The point $P\left(3, \dfrac{16}{5}\right)$ lies on the ellipse. Find the equation of both the tangent and the normal to the ellipse at P.

This tangent meets the x-axis at A and the y-axis at B, while the normal meets the x-axis at C and the y-axis at D. Determine the coordinates of A, B, C and D.

Solution

$$16x^2 + 25y^2 = 16\left(25\cos^2\theta\right) + 25\left(16\sin^2\theta\right) = 400\left(\cos^2\theta + \sin^2\theta\right) = 400$$

since $\cos^2\theta + \sin^2\theta = 1$. Thus $x = 5\cos\theta, \ y = 4\sin\theta$ parametrises the ellipse.

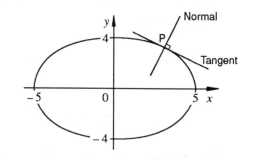

When $\cos\theta = \dfrac{3}{5}, \ \sin\theta = \dfrac{4}{5}$ (i.e. $\tan\theta = \dfrac{4}{3}, \ \theta \approx 53.13°$)

$$x = 5\cos\theta, \ y = 4\sin\theta \ \text{gives the point } P\left(3, \dfrac{16}{5}\right).$$

Now $\dfrac{dx}{d\theta} = -5\sin\theta \ $ and $ \ \dfrac{dy}{d\theta} = 4\cos\theta,$

so $\dfrac{dy}{dx} = -\dfrac{4\cos\theta}{5\sin\theta}$

$$= -\dfrac{4 . \cancel{\tfrac{3}{5}}}{5 . \cancel{\tfrac{4}{5}}}$$

$$= -\dfrac{3}{5} \quad \text{at the point P.}$$

The gradient of the tangent at P is $-\dfrac{3}{5}$ and the gradient of the normal is $\dfrac{5}{3}$ (since their product is −1).

The equation of the tangent is then

$$y - \dfrac{16}{5} = -\dfrac{3}{5}(x-3)$$

or $\qquad 5y + 3x = 25$

and the equation of the normal is

$$y - \dfrac{16}{5} = \dfrac{5}{3}(x-3)$$

or $\qquad 15y = 25x - 27$

This tangent cuts the coordinate axes at $A\left(\dfrac{25}{3},\ 0\right)$ and $B(0,\ 5)$

while the normal cuts the coordinate axes at

$C\left(\dfrac{27}{25},\ 0\right)$ and $D\left(0,\ -\dfrac{9}{5}\right)$.

Example

A rod of length a is initially at rest standing vertically on the y-axis, with its lower end at the origin. The rod is then moved so that its top end remains on the y-axis, with the lower end moving along the positive x-axis, until it comes to rest horizontally (see diagrams below).

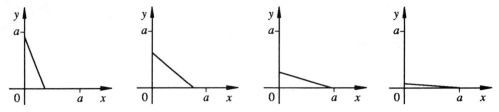

The midpoint of the rod is M. What path does M trace out (i.e. what is the locus of M) during this motion?

Solution

At any point of the motion, let the coordinates of the end on the x-axis be $(p,\ 0)$ and those of the end on the y-axis be $(0,\ q)$, where $0 \le p, q \le a$.

Then M has coordinates

$$\left(\frac{p}{2},\ \frac{q}{2}\right), \quad \text{i.e. } x = \frac{p}{2},\ y = \frac{q}{2}$$

By Pythagoras' theorem

$$p^2 + q^2 = a^2$$

$$\Rightarrow \quad (2x)^2 + (2y)^2 = a^2$$

$$\Rightarrow \quad x^2 + y^2 = \left(\frac{a}{2}\right)^2$$

which is the equation of a circle, centre the origin and radius $\dfrac{a}{2}$.

M traces out a quarter of this circle as this motion takes place.

Example

The point $P\left(ct, \dfrac{c}{t}\right)$ lies on the rectangular hypobola $xy = c^2$.

Show that the normal to the curve at P has equation

$$t^3 x - ty = c\left(t^4 - 1\right).$$

The tangent at P cuts the x-axis at X, and the normal at P cuts the y-axis at Y. Show that the locus of M, the midpoint of XY, has cartesian equation

$$y = \frac{c^4 - x^4}{2c^2 x}$$

Sketch the graph of this locus, stating clearly the coordinates of the points where it crosses the x-axis.

Solution

The parametric equations of the hyperbola are

$$x = ct \ , \ \ y = \frac{c}{t}$$

Thus

$$\frac{dx}{dt} = c \ \ \text{and} \ \ \frac{dy}{dt} = -\frac{c}{t^2} \ \ \Rightarrow \ \ \frac{dy}{dx} = -\frac{1}{t^2}$$

So the tangent has gradient $-\dfrac{1}{t^2}$, and the normal has gradient t^2.

The equation of the normal is

$$ct^4 - c = t^3 x - ty$$

$$\Rightarrow \qquad ct^4 - c = t^3 x - ty$$

$$\Rightarrow \qquad ct^4 - c = t^3 x - ty \ \ \text{i.e.} \ \ t^3 x - ty = c\left(t^4 - 1\right)$$

This normal cuts the y-axis when $x = 0 \Rightarrow Y = \left(0 \ , \ -\dfrac{c\left(t^4 - 1\right)}{t}\right)$

The equation of the tangent is

$$y - \frac{c}{t} = -\frac{1}{t^2}(x - ct)$$

$$\Rightarrow \quad t^2 y - ct = -(x - ct)$$

$$\Rightarrow \quad t^2 y + x = 2ct$$

which cuts the x-axis when $y = 0 \Rightarrow X = (2ct, 0)$

The midpoint of XY is M, with coordinates

$$\left(\frac{2ct + 0}{2}, \; \frac{0 + -\frac{c}{t}(t^4 - 1)}{2} \right)$$

$$= \left(ct, \; -\frac{c}{2t}(t^4 - 1) \right).$$

This is a parametric form for M with equations

$$x = ct, \; y = -\frac{c}{2t}(t^4 - 1)$$

$$t = \frac{x}{c} \;\Rightarrow\; y = -\frac{c}{2\left(\frac{x}{c}\right)}\left(\frac{x^4}{c^4} - 1\right)$$

$$\Rightarrow\; y = -\frac{c^2}{2x}\left(\frac{x^4 - c^4}{c^4}\right)$$

i.e. $\quad y = \dfrac{c^4 - x^4}{2c^2 x}, \quad$ as required.

For $y = \dfrac{c^4 - x^4}{2c^2 x}$, the line $x = 0$ (the y-axis) is a vertical asymptote, since,

$$x \to 0_+, \; y \to +\infty \text{ and as } x \to 0_-, \; y \to -\infty.$$

Also, as $x \to +\infty$, $y \to -\infty$ and as $x \to -\infty$, $y \to +\infty$

When $y = 0$,

$$c^4 - x^4 = 0 \;\Rightarrow\; (c^2 - x^2)(c^2 + x^2) = 0$$

$$\Rightarrow\; (c - x)(c + x)(c^2 + x^2) = 0$$

$$\Rightarrow\; x = c \text{ or } -c \qquad [x^2 \neq -c^2]$$

The graph then looks like the one opposite.

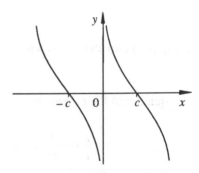

Exercise 7H

1. A curve has equation $y = (5 - 3x)^{-2}$. Find the equation of the tangent to the curve at the point $\left(1, \frac{1}{4}\right)$.

2. A curve has equation $y = \frac{2}{2-x} + \frac{3x-1}{x^2+1}$.
   Determine the equation of the normal to the curve at the point $(1, 3)$.

3. The points P and Q lie on the curve with equation $y = \frac{1}{1+x^2}$. At P, $x = 1$, and at Q, $x = 1 + h$.
   Prove that the chord PQ has gradient $\frac{-(2+h)}{2(2+2h+h^2)}$ and hence determine the equation of the tangent at P.

4. The tangent to the curve $y = \frac{3\tan x}{1+\sin x}$ at the point on the curve where $x = \frac{\pi}{6}$ cuts the x-axis at the point T.
   Prove that the distance $OT = \frac{1}{6}\left(2\sqrt{3} - \pi\right)$, where O is the origin.

5. Prove that the tangent at P(4, 4) to the curve $y = \frac{x^2}{4}$ has equation $2x - y - 4 = 0$.
   This tangent meets the line $4x + 3y - 12 = 0$ at the point Q. Calculate the coordinates of Q.
   The normal at P to $y = \frac{x^2}{4}$ meets $4x + 3y - 12 = 0$ at the point R. Calculate the coordinates of R.

6. A curve has parametric equations
   $$x = e^\theta \cos\theta, \quad y = e^\theta \sin\theta.$$
   Prove that the gradient at the point P with parameter θ is $\tan\left(\theta + \frac{\pi}{4}\right)$, and deduce that the tangent at P makes a fixed angle with OP, where O is the origin.

7. The curve with equation $y^2 = 4x$ has parametric representation $x = t^2$, $y = 2t$. Prove that the normal at $\left(t^2, 2t\right)$ to the curve has equation
   $$y + tx = 2t + t^3.$$
   The normals at $A\left(\frac{1}{4}, -1\right)$ and $B(4, 4)$ to the curve meet at the point N. Determine the coordinates of N.

8. Find the equation of the tangent to the ellipse $\frac{x^2}{16} + y^2 = 1$ at the point $(4\cos t, \sin t)$. This tangent cuts the coordinate axes at Q and R, and the midpoint of QR is M. Show that the locus of M has cartesian equation
   $$\frac{16}{x^2} + \frac{1}{y^2} = 4.$$

9. A parabola has parametric coordinates
   $$x = 3p^2, \quad y = 6p.$$
   Determine the cartesian equation of this curve. Show that the equation of the normal to this parabola at the point $P\left(3p^2, 6p\right)$ is
   $$y + px = 6p + 3p^3.$$
   Find the point of intersection R of the normal at P and the normal at $Q\left(3q^2, 6q\right)$. Given that the straight line through P and Q passes through the point $(-6, 0)$ show that $pq = 2$ and deduce that R lies on the parabola.

10. Sketch the curve defined parametrically by
    $$x = 2 + t^2, \quad y = 4t.$$
    Write down the equation of the straight line with gradient m passing through the point $(1, 0)$. Show that this line meets the curve when
    $$mt^2 - 4t + m = 0.$$
    Find the values of m for which this quadratic equation has equal roots. Hence determine the equations of the tangents to the curve which pass through the point $(1, 0)$.

7.11 Miscellaneous Exercises

1. Eliminate the parameter from each of the following pairs of equations

   (a) $x = 2 + t^2$, $y = t^3 - 1$

   (b) $x = a\cos^3\theta$, $y = a\sin^3\theta$

   (c) $x = 3e^t$, $y = \dfrac{5}{\sinh t}$

2. Find the values of R and α such that

   $$5\cosh x - 4\sinh x \equiv R\cosh(x - \alpha)$$

   Hence sketch the curve with equation

   $$y = 5\cosh x - 4\sinh x.$$

3. Sketch the graphs of $y = f(x)$ and $y = g(x)$ on the same diagram, where

   $$f(x) = \left|\frac{x+1}{x-1}\right| \ (x \neq 1) \ \text{ and } \ g(x) = |x+2|.$$

   Find the x-coordinates of the four points of intersection of the two graphs.

4. The points A and B lie on the curve with equation $y = \dfrac{1}{(x+1)^2}$, having x-coordinates $x = 1$ and $x = 1 + h$ respectively. Show that the gradient of the line AB is

   $$-\frac{(h+4)}{4(2+h)^2}$$

   and deduce the gradient of the tangent to the curve at A.

5. The diagram shows a sketch of the curve defined for $x > 0$ by the equation

   $$y = x^2 \ln x.$$

   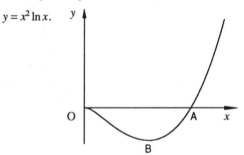

   The curve crosses the x-axis at A and has a local minimum at B.

   (a) State the coordinates of A and calculate the gradient of the curve at A.

   (b) Determine the coordinates of B and calculate the value of $\dfrac{d^2y}{dx^2}$ at B.

6. The curve C has equation $y = \dfrac{(x-3)^2}{x+1}$.

   (a) By considering the set of values of y for real x, show that no part of C exists in the interval $-16 < y < 0$.

   (b) Show that the line $y = x - 7$ is an asymptote to C and state the equation of the other asymptote.

   Sketch C, showing the coordinates of the points at which C meets the coordinate axes and the way in which C approaches the asymptotes.

7. A curve is defined for $-\dfrac{\pi}{6} < \theta < \dfrac{\pi}{6}$ by the parametric equations

   $$x = \sin 4\theta + 2\sin 2\theta, \ \ y = \cos 4\theta - 2\cos 2\theta.$$

   Prove that $\dfrac{dy}{dx} = -\tan\theta$. Find $\dfrac{d}{d\theta}\left(\dfrac{dy}{dx}\right)$ and show

   that $\dfrac{d^2y}{dx^2} = -\dfrac{1}{8}$ when $\theta = 0$.

8.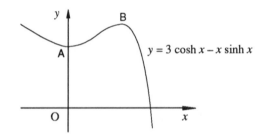

   The diagram shows a sketch of the curve with equation $y = 3\cosh x - x\sinh x$, which cuts the y-axis at the point A.

   Prove that, at A, y takes a minimum value and state this value.

   Given that $\dfrac{dy}{dx} = 0$ at B, show that the x-coordinate of B is the positive root of the equation

   $$x\cosh x - 2\sinh x = 0.$$

9. (a) Given that $\dfrac{2x^2 + 2x - 3}{x^2 - 4} = k$, show that

   $$(2-k)x^2 + 2x + (4k-3) = 0.$$

   Hence determine the values taken by k when x is real.

(b) A curve has equation $y = \dfrac{2x^2 + 2x - 3}{x^2 - 4}$.

    (i) State the equations of its three asymptotes.

    (ii) Find the coordinates of the turning points. (There is no need to establish whether they are maximum or minimum points.)

    (iii) Sketch the curve.

10. A curve is given by the equations

    $x = a(\cos 2t + 2\cos t)$, $y = a(2\sin t - \sin 2t)$, where t is a parameter and a is a positive constant.

    Prove that $\qquad \dfrac{dy}{dx} = -\tan\dfrac{1}{2}t$.

11. Find the values of the constants A, B, C for

    which $\dfrac{2x^2 + 3x + 1}{x - 1} \equiv Ax + B + \dfrac{C}{x - 1}$.

    Deduce the equations of the asymptotes of the

    curve with equation $y = \dfrac{2x^2 + 3x + 1}{x - 1}$.

    Find the coordinates of the turning points of this curve.

    Sketch the curve.

12. The diagram shows a sketch of the curve with

    equation $y = \dfrac{3\cos x}{2 - \sin x}$ for $0 \le x \le \pi$.

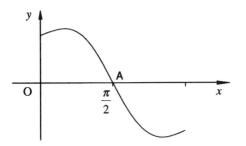

    (a) Find the values of x, in the interval $0 \le x \le \pi$,

    for which $\dfrac{dy}{dx} = 0$, giving your answers in radians.

    (b) Determine the range of values taken by y.

    (c) Determine the equation of the normal to the curve at the point $A\left(\dfrac{\pi}{2}, 0\right)$.

13. Write down the equations of the asymptotes of

    the curve $y = \dfrac{3x - 1}{x + 2}$. Sketch this curve. Hence draw the graphs of the curves

    (a) $y = \left|\dfrac{3x - 1}{x + 2}\right|$:
        (b) $y^2 = \dfrac{3x - 1}{x + 2}$.

14. The curve C has equation $y = \dfrac{x^2 + x - 2}{x + 1}$ $(x \ne -1)$.

    (a) Determine the equations of the asymptotes of C, and the coordinates of the points where C crosses the coordinate axes.

    (b) Show that $\dfrac{dy}{dx}$ is positive at all points of C.

    (c) Sketch the graph of C.

15. The curve C has equation $y = \dfrac{(x - 1)^2}{x + 1}$.

    (a) Obtain the equations of the asymptotes of C.

    (b) Show that C has two stationary points and find their coordinates.

    (c) Draw a sketch of C.

    (d) On the same diagram draw a sketch of the

    curve of $y = -\dfrac{1}{x^2}$ and deduce that the equation

    $x^2(x - 1)^2 + x + 1 = 0$

    has no real roots.   (Cambridge)

16. A curve is described parametrically by the

    equation $x = \dfrac{1 + t}{t}$, $\dfrac{1 + t^3}{t^2}$.

    Find the equation of the normal to the curve at the point where $t = 2$.

17. Given that t is a non-zero parameter, show that

    the point $P\left[2\left(t + \dfrac{1}{t}\right), \left(t - \dfrac{1}{t}\right)\right]$ always lies on the

    hyperbola $x^2 - 4y^2 = 16$.

    Show that the tangent at P to the hyperbola has equation

    $x(t^2 + 1) - 2y(t^2 + 1) = 8t$.

    Write down the equations of the two asymptotes of the hyperbola. The tangent to the hyperbola at P meets the two asymptotes at L and M. Find the coordinates of L and M in terms of t.

18. A curve is defined parametrically by

    $x = \dfrac{2t}{1 + t}$, $y = \dfrac{t^2}{1 + t}$.

    Prove that the normal to the curve at the point

    $\left(1, \dfrac{1}{2}\right)$ has equation $6y + 4x = 7$. Determine the coordinates of the other point of intersection of this normal with the curve.

    Find the cartesian equation of the curve.

19. The curve C_1 has equation

$$y = \frac{x+a}{x-a}$$

where a is a positive constant.

(a) Show that $\dfrac{dy}{dx} < 0$ at all points of C_1.

(b) Draw a sketch of C_1.

The curve C_2 has equation

$$y = \left(\frac{x+a}{x-a}\right)^2.$$

(c) Show by differentiation that C_2 has exactly one stationary point and find the coordinates of this point.

(d) On a separate diagram draw a sketch of C_2.

(e) Show by means of a graphical argument that there are values of m, which need not be specified, such that the equation

$$m(x-a)^3 - (x+a)^2 = 0$$

has three distinct real roots.   (Cambridge)

20. A curve is given in terms of the parameter t by the equations

$$x = a\cos^2 t, \quad y = a\sin^3 t \quad \left(0 < t < \frac{\pi}{2}\right),$$

where a is a positive constant. Find and simplify an expression for $\dfrac{dy}{dx}$ in terms of t.

The normal to the curve at the point where $t = \dfrac{\pi}{6}$ cuts the y-axis at the point N. Find the distance ON in terms of a, where O is the origin.

21. Let f be the function with domain $\{x \text{ is real, } x \neq -3, \, x \neq 1\}$ given by $f(x) = \dfrac{2x-3}{x^2+2x-3}$.

(a) Find the values of k for which the equation

$$\frac{2x-3}{x^2+2x-3} = k$$

has no real roots. Hence state the range of f.

(b) Find the coordinates of the stationary points of the graph of f.

(c) State the equations of the asymptotes of the graph of f. Sketch the graph of f, showing clearly the stationary points and where the graph crosses the axes.

22. A curve has equation $y = \dfrac{x^2-1}{3x-5}$.

(a) Prove that, for all real vaues of x, the value of y cannot lie between $\dfrac{2}{9}$ and 2.

(b) Find the coordinates of the turning points of the curve.

(c) Show that one asymptote to the curve has equation $9y = 3x+5$ and state the equation of the other asymptote.

(d) Sketch the curve, showing its asymptotes.

23. The curve C has equation

$$y = \frac{a}{x} + \frac{b}{x^2},$$

where a and b are constants, $a > 0$ and $b \neq 0$.

(a) Show that C has exactly one stationary point and find its coordinates in terms of a and b.

(b) On separate diagrams, draw a sketch of C for $b > 0$ and a sketch of C for $b < 0$, and in each case mark the coordinates of any intersections with the coordinate axes.

(c) Use your diagrams to show that there are positive values of m for which the equation

$$mx^3 - ax - b = 0$$

has three real roots.   (Cambridge)

24. (a)

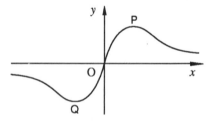

A sketch of the curve

$$y = \frac{ax^2+bx+c}{x^2+hx+k}$$

where a, b, c, h and k are constants, is shown above. The maximum point P is at $(1, 1)$ and the minimum point Q is at $(-1, -1)$. The curve passes through the origin, and the x-axis is an asymptote to the curve. Explain why $a = 0$, and find the values of b, c, h and k.

(b)

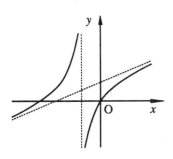

A sketch of the curve $y = \dfrac{Ax^2 + Bx}{x + C}$, where A, B and C are constants, is shown above. The lines $x = -1$ and $y = x + 4$, also shown in the diagram, are asymptotes to the curve. Find the values of A, B and C. (Cambridge)

25. The parametric equations of a curve $x = t - \tanh t$, $y = \operatorname{sech} t$ show that if $t \neq 0$ then

$$\frac{dy}{dx} = -\operatorname{cosech} t.$$

The point T has parameter t. Find the equation of the tangent to the curve at T. The tangent crosses the x-axis at U. Show that UT has constant length.

26. A curve is given by the parametric equations

$$x = \sec t + \tan t, \quad y = \operatorname{cosec} t + \cot t \quad \text{for } 0 < t < \frac{\pi}{2}.$$

Prove that $\dfrac{dy}{dx} = -\dfrac{1 - \sin t}{1 - \cos t}$.

Show that the normal to the curve at the point S, where $t = \tan^{-1}\left(\dfrac{3}{4}\right)$, has equation $x - 2y + 4 = 0$.

Find an equation of the normal to the curve at the point T, where $t = \tan^{-1}\left(\dfrac{4}{3}\right)$. These normals meet at the point N. Find the coordinates of N.

27. The parabola $y^2 = 4ax$ has parametric form $x = at^2$, $y = 2at$ for a constant a and real parameter t. Show that the normal to the parabola at the point $P\left(ap^2, 2ap\right)$ has equation $y + px = 2ap + ap^3$. This normal meets the parabola again at the point $Q\left(aq^2, 2aq\right)$.

Show that $q = -\left(p + \dfrac{2}{p}\right)$.

The tangent to the parabola at P meets the tangent to the parabola at Q at the point R. Determine the coordinates of R in terms of a and p, and find the cartesian equation of the locus of R.

28. Show that $x = a\cos\theta$, $y = b\sin\theta$ is a parametric representation of the ellipse with equation

$$\frac{x^2}{a^2} + \frac{y^2}{b^2} = 1.$$

Prove that the equation of the tangent to the ellipse at $P(a\cos\theta, b\sin\theta)$ has equation

$$ay\sin\theta + bx\cos\theta = ab.$$

This tangent meets the x-axis at A and the y-axis at B. M is the midpoint of AB. Find the coordinates of M and a cartesian equation of the locus of M as θ varies.

29. Find the equation of the chord joining the two points $P\left(cp, \dfrac{c}{p}\right)$ and $Q\left(cq, \dfrac{c}{q}\right)$ on the rectangular hyperbola $xy = c^2$. By considering a suitable limit, deduce that the tangent to the curve at the point P has equation

$$p^2 y + x = 2cp.$$

This tangent cuts the y-axis at R and M is the midpoint of PR. Determine a cartesian equation of the locus of M as p varies.

8 FURTHER CALCULUS

Objectives

After studying this chapter you should

- be able to differentiate expressions defined implicitly;
- be able to use approximate methods for integration such as the trapezium rule and Simpson's rule;
- understand how to calculate volumes of revolution;
- be able to find arc lengths and areas of surfaces of revolution;
- be able to derive and use simple reduction formulae in integration.

8.0 Introduction

You should have already covered the material in *Pure Mathematics,* Chapters 8, 11, 12, 14, 17 and 18 on calculus. This chapter will enable you to see applications of the ideas of integration you have already met and help you to find derivatives and values of integrals when previously you had no method available.

8.1 Implicit functions

When a curve is defined by a relation of the form $y = f(x)$ we say that y is an **explicit function** of x and we can usually apply one of the standard procedures to find $\dfrac{dy}{dx}$.

However, the expression $y^3 - 8xy + x^2 = 4$ is an **implicit function** of x. It also defines a curve, but because we cannot easily make y the subject we need to adopt a different strategy if we wish to find the gradient at a particular point. Let us consider a more simple curve first of all.

Activity 1

Sketch the circle with equation $x^2 + y^2 = 5$. The point P(1, 2) lies on the circle and O is the origin. Write down the gradient of OP. Deduce the gradient of the tangent to the circle at P.

Suppose $z = y^2$, then by the Chain Rule

$$\frac{dz}{dx} = \frac{dz}{dy} \times \frac{dy}{dx}$$

$$= 2y\frac{dy}{dx}$$

Activity 2

By differentiating each term with respect to x, show that when

$$x^2 + y^2 = 5, \quad \frac{dy}{dx} = -\frac{x}{y}.$$

Hence deduce the value of the gradient at the tangent to the circle $x^2 + y^2 = 5$ at the point (1, 2).

Check your answer with that from Activity 1.

Example

Find the gradient of the curve with equation $y^3 - 8xy + x^2 = 4$ at the point (1, 3).

Solution

By the product rule,

$$\frac{d}{dx}(xy) = y + x\frac{dy}{dx}$$

Also

$$\frac{d}{dx}(y^3) = 3y^2\frac{dy}{dx}$$

So differentiating $y^3 - 8xy + x^2 = 4$ with respect to x gives

$$3y^2\frac{dy}{dx} - 8y - 8x\frac{dy}{dx} + 2x = 0$$

When $x = 1$ and $y = 3$,

$$27\frac{dy}{dx} - 24 - 8\frac{dy}{dx} + 2 = 0$$

$$\Rightarrow \quad 19\frac{dy}{dx} - 22 = 0 \quad \Rightarrow \quad \frac{dy}{dx} = \frac{22}{19}$$

Example

A curve has equation $x^3 + xy + y^3 + 29 = 0$ and P is the point $(1, -3)$.

(a) Show that P lies on the curve.

(b) Show that the curve has a stationary point at P.

(c) Find the value of $\dfrac{d^2y}{dx^2}$ at P and hence determine whether the curve has a maximum or minimum point at P.

Solution

(a) Substituting $x = 1$, $y = -3$ into the right-hand side of the equation gives

$$1 - 3 - 27 + 29 = 0.$$

Hence P lies on the curve.

(b) Differentiating implicitly with respect to x gives

$$3x^2 + y + x\frac{dy}{dx} + 3y^2\frac{dy}{dx} = 0$$

Substituting $x = 1$, $y = -3$ gives

$$3 - 3 + \frac{dy}{dx} + 27\frac{dy}{dx} = 0$$

So $\dfrac{dy}{dx} = 0$ at the point P.

(c) You need to differentiate the first equation in the solution to (b) implicitly with respect to x. This gives

$$6x + \frac{dy}{dx} + \frac{dy}{dx} + x\frac{d^2y}{dx^2} + 6y\left(\frac{dy}{dx}\right)\left(\frac{dy}{dx}\right) + 3y^2\frac{d^2y}{dx^2} = 0$$

At P, $x = 1$, $y = -3$ and $\dfrac{dy}{dx} = 0$, so

$$6 + \frac{d^2y}{dx^2} + 27\frac{d^2y}{dx^2} = 0$$

$$\frac{d^2y}{dx^2} = -\frac{3}{14}$$

This negative value of $\dfrac{d^2y}{dx^2}$ at the stationary point P tells us we have a maximum point at P.

Exercise 8A

Find the gradient of the following curves at the points indicated in Questions 1 to 6.

1. $x^2 + y^2 = 3$ at $(2, -1)$

2. $2x^3 + 4xy - y^2 = 5$ at $(1, 3)$

3. $xy^2 + 3x^2 y = 6$ at $(-3, 2)$

4. $\cos(x + y) + xy = 0$ at $\left(\frac{1}{2}\pi, 0\right)$

5. $e^{3x-y} + y^2 = 10$ at $(1, 3)$

6. $\sqrt{x} + \sqrt{y} = 3$ at $(4, 1)$

7. Given that $e^y = e^x + e^{-x}$, show that

$$\frac{d^2 y}{dx^2} + \left(\frac{dy}{dx}\right)^2 - 1 = 0. \qquad \text{(AEB)}$$

8. Find the value of $\dfrac{dy}{dx}$ and the value of $\dfrac{d^2 y}{dx^2}$ at the point $(2, -1)$ on the curve with equation

$$x^2 - 3x^2 y + y^4 = 17.$$

8.2   Approximate integration – trapezium rule

Activity 3

Evaluate $\displaystyle\int_2^3 x^4 dx$.

Now consider the curve with equation $y = x^4$. The points A and B on the x-axis are where $x = 2$ and $x = 3$ respectively. The lines $x = 2$ and $x = 3$ cut the curve at D and C respectively. Write down the y-coordinates of D and C.

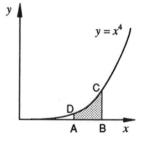

Find the area of the trapezium ABCD and compare your answer with the integral you evaluated.

Why is the approximation quite good?

Activity 4

Repeat the idea of Activity 3 for the integral $\displaystyle\int_1^2 x^4 dx$ and the corresponding trapezium.

Do you get a good approximation for the integral this time by considering a trapezium?

Can you explain why?

In general, when the graph of $y = f(x)$ is approximately linear for

$a \le x \le b$, the value of the integral $\int_a^b f(x) dx$ can be approximated

by the area of a trapezium. This can be seen easily from the
diagram opposite for the case when $f(x) \ge 0$ for $a \le x \le b$.

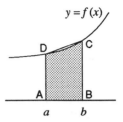

The area of the trapezium ABCD is

$$\frac{1}{2}(b-a)\{f(a)+f(b)\}$$

Hence
$$\int_a^b f(x) \approx \frac{(b-a)}{2}\{f(a)+f(b)\}$$

The curve can usually be approximated to a straight line if the
interval considered is very small. To obtain an approximation
over a larger interval, the interval is usually split into smaller ones.
For ease of computation, the interval of integration is usually
divided into strips of equal width.

Activity 5

By considering four strips of equal width and considering the
approximate area to be that of four trapezia, estimate the value of

$$\int_0^1 \cos\sqrt{x}\ dx,$$

working with four decimal places and giving your final answer to
three significant figures. (Remember to use a *radian* setting on
your calculator!)

How close were you to the exact value

$$2\cos 1 + 2\sin 1 - 2 \approx 0.763546?$$

In general, if you wish to find the approximate value of $\int_a^b f(x)dx$,

you divide the interval $a \le x \le b$ into n strips of equal width h. Let
$x_0(=a), x_1, x_2, \ldots, x_n(=b)$ be the equally spaced x-coordinates.
Then the values $f(x_0), f(x_1), \ldots, f(x_n)$ can be written more
conveniently as $f_0, f_1, f_2, \ldots, f_n$ and these values are called the
ordinates.

Activity 6

Given that $f(x) \geq 0$ for $a \leq x \leq b$, the integral $\int_a^b f(x)\,dx$ is an area. By considering the strips on the diagram opposite to be approximately trapezia, show that the value of the integral above is approximately

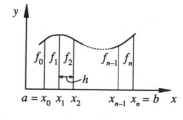

$$\frac{h}{2}(f_0 + f_1) + \frac{h}{2}(f_1 + f_2) + \ldots + \frac{h}{2}(f_{n-1} + f_n).$$

Hence show that

$$\int_a^b f(x)\,dx \approx \frac{h}{2}\left\{f_0 + 2(f_1 + f_2 + \ldots + f_{n-1}) + f_n\right\}$$

This result is known as the **trapezium rule**.

Sometimes an integral is very difficult or impossible to evaluate exactly and so an approximate method is used.

Example

Use the trapezium rule with 5 ordinates to find the approximate value of

$$\int_1^3 \frac{1}{\sqrt{(1+x^3)}}\,dx,$$

giving your answer to three decimal places.

Solution

We must remember that 5 ordinates means 4 strips (rather like 5 fence posts and 4 strips of fencing between them). In this case $x_0 (= a) = 1$ and $x_4 (= b) = 3$. Each strip is of width 0.5 and so $h = 0.5$; $x_1 = 1.5$; $x_2 = 2.0$; $x_3 = 2.5$. Therefore $f_0 \approx 0.7071$; $f_1 \approx 0.4781$; $f_2 \approx 0.3333$; $f_3 \approx 0.2453$; $f_4 \approx 0.1890$.

Using the trapezium rule,

$$\text{integral} \approx \frac{0.5}{2}\left\{f_0 + 2(f_1 + f_2 + f_3) + f_4\right\}$$

$$\approx 0.752$$

Activity 7

If you have a graphics calculator with the facility to graph and integrate, find the value given for

$$\int_1^3 \frac{1}{\sqrt{(1+x^3)}}dx$$

and compare your answer with that in the example above.

Suggest a way that a more accurate approximation to the integral in the above example could be found.

Write a computer program to find the approximate value of the integral using the trapezium rule where you input the number of strips and consider how many strips are necessary in order to give the correct value to a certain number of decimal places.

8.3 Simpson's rule

Activity 8

Let $f(x)$ be approximated by the quadratic function $ax^2 + bx + c$ over the interval $-h \le x \le h$.

Show that

$$\int_{-h}^h f(x)\,dx \approx \frac{h}{3}\left(2ah^2 + 6c\right)$$

Activity 9

Given that the quadratic function with equation $y = ax^2 + bx + c$ passes through the points $(-h, f_0)$, $(0, f_1)$ and (h, f_2), show that

$$f_0 + 4f_1 + f_2 = 2ah^2 + 6c$$

Suppose that the region bounded by the curve $y = f(x)$, the lines $x = -h$ and $x = h$ and the x-axis is divided into two strips as shown in the diagram. You can use the the results from Activities 8 and 9 to show that, provided $f(x)$ is approximately a quadratic,

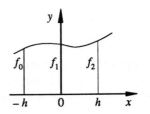

$$\int_{-h}^{h} f(x)\,dx \approx \frac{h}{3}\left(f_0 + 4f_1 + f_2\right)$$

Since the curve $y = f(x)$ has been approximated by a quadratic curve the result above is usually a better approximation than that given by the trapezium rule which approximates the curve $y = f(x)$ by a straight line.

Activity 10

Suppose that f_0, f_1 and f_2 are the ordinates at $x = a$, $x = a + h$ and $x = a + 2h$ respectively. Explain, using the previous result and a translation of the axes, why

$$\int_{a}^{a+2h} f(x)\,dx \approx \frac{h}{3}\left(f_0 + 4f_1 + f_2\right).$$

By taking several **pairs** of strips, the result from Activity 10 can now be extended. If you divide the interval $a \le x \le b$ into n equal strips of width h as before, and again let $f_0, f_1, \ldots, f_n$, be the corresponding ordinates, the above rule applied to each pair of strips in turn gives

$$\int_{a}^{b} f(x)\,dx \approx \frac{h}{3}\left\{\left(f_0 + 4f_1 + f_2\right) + \left(f_2 + 4f_3 + f_4\right) + \right.$$

$$\left. \left(f_4 + 4f_5 + f_6\right) + \ldots + \left(f_{n-2} + 4f_{n-1} + f_n\right)\right\}$$

or, as the formula is more usually written,

$$\int_{x_0}^{x_n} f(x)\,dx \approx \frac{1}{3} h\left[f_0 + f_n + 4\left(f_1 + f_3 + \ldots + f_{n-1}\right) + 2\left(f_2 + f_4 + \ldots + f_{n-2}\right)\right]$$

or, as some find it easier to remember

$$\frac{1}{3}h\left['ends' + 4\times'odds' + 2\times'evens'\right].$$

This result is know as **Simpson's rule**.

Note: n must be even, giving an odd number of ordinates.

It is sometimes interesting to compare the accuracy using Simpson's rule with that from the corresponding application of the trapezium rule. Earlier, the trapezium rule with 5 ordinates was used to find the approximate value of

$$\int_1^3 \frac{1}{\sqrt{(1+x^3)}}\, dx,$$

and the value 0.752 was obtained.

Example

Use Simpson's rule with 5 ordinates to find the approximate value of

$$\int_1^3 \frac{1}{\sqrt{(1+x^3)}}\, dx,$$

giving your answer to three decimal places.

Solution

As in the previous example, $x_0 = 1$, $x_1 = 1.5$, $x_2 = 2.0$, $x_3 = 2.5$, $x_4 = 3.0$ and $h = 0.5$.

Also, $f_0 = 0.7071$, $f_1 = 0.4781$, $f_2 = 0.3333$, $f_3 = 0.2453$, $f_4 = 0.1890$, working to four decimal places.

Using Simpson's rule, the approximate value of the integral is

$$\frac{1}{3} \times 0.5 \left[f_0 + f_4 + 4(f_1 + f_3) + 2f_2 \right]$$

$$= \frac{1}{6} [0.8961 + 1.9124 + 0.9812 + 0.6666]$$

$$\approx 0.743.$$

This answer is in fact correct to three decimal places.

Exercise 8B

1. Use the trapezium rule with 3 ordinates to estimate $\int_1^5 (2x+7)\, dx$.

    Evaluate by integration $\int_1^5 (2x+7)\, dx$.

    Explain your findings.

2. Estimate the value of each of the following definite integrals (1) to (4) using

    (a) the trapezium rule;

    (b) Simpson's rule
       each with
       (i) 3 ordinates,   (ii) 5 ordinates.

    (1) $\int_2^6 \frac{120}{x^3}\, dx$

    (2) $\int_1^2 (x^3 - 3x^2)\, dx$

    (3) $\int_2^4 \ln 2x\, dx$

    (4) $\int_0^1 \frac{1}{\sqrt{(4-x^2)}}\, dx$

3. Evaluate each of the integrals in Question 2 exactly and comment on the accuracy of the approximations.

8.4 Volumes of revolution

Integration is a very powerful tool for finding quantities like areas, volumes and arc lengths. This section will illustrate how integration is used for one particular application, namely the determination of volumes. First, though, some approximate methods will be used.

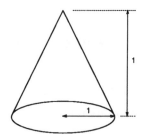

The diagram opposite shows a cone with radius 1 unit, height 1 unit (not to scale). What is its volume?

To find its volume you would probably use the formula

$$V = \tfrac{1}{3}\pi r^2 h$$

but how do you know this formula is correct and why the one third factor? One way to approximate the volume of the cone is to consider it to be made of a series of cylinders.

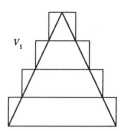

Two methods are shown opposite. V_1 clearly over-estimates the volume, whereas V_2 clearly under-estimates the volume.

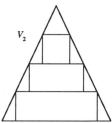

However we do know that the true volume is 'trapped' between the volume V_1 and the volume V_2.

Activity 11

(a) Calculate an approximation of the volume of a cube by 'averaging' the volumes of V_1 and V_2 where $V_1 = A + B + C + D$ and where $V_2 = A' + B' + C'$.

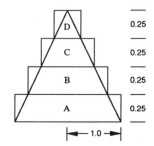

(b) What is the ratio

$$\frac{\pi}{\text{average } V} = \frac{\pi}{\tfrac{1}{2}(V_1 + V_2)} = ?$$

Now repeat with cylinders of height:

(i) 0.2   (ii) 0.1   (iii) 0.05

In each case, calculate the ratio

$$\frac{\pi}{\tfrac{1}{2}(V_1 + V_2)}$$

As the cylinder height approaches zero what does the ratio

$$\frac{\pi}{\tfrac{1}{2}(V_1 + V_2)}$$

approach?

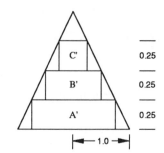

Activity 12

Find an approximation of the volume of a sphere by considering it to be made of a series of cylinders as shown opposite.

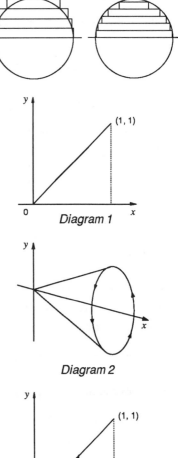

Consider the cone again. *Diagram 1* shows the line $y = x$ from $x = 0$ to $x = 1$.

If you rotate this area about the x-axis through 2π or $360°$ you will generate a cone with radius 1 and length (or height) 1 (*diagram 2*).

Now consider a thin slice of the cone of radius y and length δx. This will be the slice obtained by rotating the shaded strip shown in *diagram 3* .

The volume of this slice is approximately that of a cylinder with volume $\pi y^2 \delta x$ and the smaller we make δx the better the approximation becomes.

The volume of the cone therefore is

$$\approx \Sigma \pi y^2 \delta x$$

where the Σ sign means summing up over all such slices.

Another way of expressing this is to write

$$\delta V \approx \pi y^2 \delta x$$

where δV is the volume corresponding to the small cylindrical disc of height δx. Hence

$$\frac{\delta V}{\delta x} \approx \pi y^2$$

and letting $\delta x \to 0$

gives $\qquad \dfrac{dV}{dx} = \pi y^2.$

Integrating gives an expression for the volume

$$V = \int_0^1 \pi y^2 dx$$

Activity 13

Evaluate the expression for V given above, noting that $y = x$ in this case.

The formula for the volume of revolution of any curve with equation $y = f(x)$ about the x-axis between $x = a$ and $x = b$ is given by

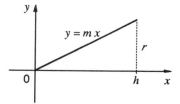

$$V = \int_a^b \pi y^2 dx$$

Activity 14

The diagram opposite shows part of the line $y = mx$ between $x = 0$ and $x = h$. The region bounded by the lines $y = mx$, $y = 0$ and $x = h$ is to be rotated about the x-axis to generate a cone.

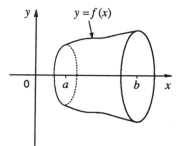

(a) Express m in terms of h and r (radius of the cone).

(b) By evaluating $V = \int_0^h \pi y^2 dx$, show that the volume of a cone is given by

$$V = \tfrac{1}{3} \pi r^2 h$$

What would happen if the line $y = mx$ in the above diagram was rotated about the y-axis?

Activity 15

The diagram opposite is a model of a power station cooling tower. It is necessary to find its volume. The diagram below it shows part of the curve $y = e^x$.

If the region bounded by the curve $y = e^x$ and the lines $x = a$ and $x = b$ is rotated about the x-axis, a shape which is an approximation to the model of the cooling tower will be generated.

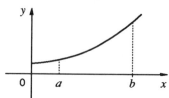

Show that the volume generated is given by

$$\frac{\pi}{2}\left[e^{2b} - e^{2a}\right]$$

Hence calculate the volume when $a = 2$ and $b = 5$.

Activity 16

(a) In order to estimate the amount of liquid that a saucer will

hold, a student decides to use the function $y = \dfrac{x^2}{32}$.

She rotates the area bounded by the line $y = \dfrac{x^2}{32}$ and the line

$y = 2$ about the y-axis. Calculate the volume generated.

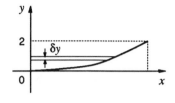

(b) Obtain a 'saucer' of your own and suggest possible improvements to the mathematical model used by this student.

(c) Obtain a 'cup' of your own and, by producing a mathematical model, estimate its volume. Compare your estimated volume with the actual volume. Modify your model to give a better approximation.

Example

The area given by $y^2 \leq x$ and $y \geq x$ is to be rotated about the x-axis to form a 'bowl'. Find the volume of the material in the bowl.

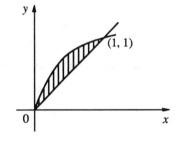

Solution

The points of intersection are $(0, 0)$ and $(1, 1)$. You can think of the bowl as the solid formed by the outer curve y_1 with the inner curve y_2 taken away.

Therefore

$$V = \pi \int y_1^2 \, dx - \pi \int y_2^2 \, dx$$

$$= \pi \int_0^1 x \, dx - \pi \int_0^1 x^2 \, dx$$

$$= \pi \int_0^1 \left(x - x^2 \right) dx$$

$$= \pi \left[\frac{x^2}{2} - \frac{x^3}{3} \right]_0^1$$

$$= \frac{\pi}{6} \text{ cubic units.}$$

Exercise 8C

1. Find the volume of the solid generated when the region bounded by the x-axis, the lines $x = 1$ and $x = 2$ and the curve with equation $y = x^2$, is rotated once about the x-axis.

2. Sketch the curve with equation $y = 1 - \dfrac{4}{x^2}$.

   The region R is bounded by the curve $y = 1 - \dfrac{4}{x^2}$, the x-axis and the lines $x = \frac{1}{2}$ and $x = 1$. Find the volume generated when R is rotated completely about the x-axis.

3. The area bounded by the curve with equation $y = \tan x$, the x-axis and the line $x = \dfrac{\pi}{3}$ is rotated about the x-axis. Calculate the volume of the solid of revolution so formed.

4. Draw a rough sketch of the circle with equation $x^2 + y^2 = 100$ and the curve with equation $9y = 2x^2$. Find the coordinates of the points A and B where they meet. Calculate the area of the region R bounded by the minor arc AB of the circle and the other curve. Find also the volume obtained by rotating R about the y-axis.

5. The region bounded by the curve with equation $y = \sqrt{x} + \dfrac{1}{\sqrt{x}}$, the x-axis and the lines $x = 1$ and $x = 4$, is R. Determine

   (a) the area of R,

   (b) the volume of the solid formed when R is rotated through 2π radians about the x-axis.
   (AEB)

6. A curve has equation $y = \cosh x$ and the points P and Q on the curve have x-coordinates 0 and $\ln 2$ respectively. The region bounded by the arc PQ of the curve, the coordinate axes and the line $x = \ln 2$, is rotated through 2π radians about the x-axis to form a solid of revolution. Show that the volume of the solid is $\pi\left(\frac{1}{2}\ln 2 + \frac{15}{32}\right)$. (AEB)

7. By using suitable approximations for the function to represent the shape for a milk bottle, use integration to find the volume of revolution. Check this result with the expected value.

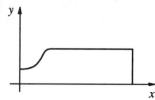

8. The finite region bounded by the curves with equations $y = x^3$ and $y = \sqrt{x}$ is R.

   (a) Determine the area of R.

   (b) Calculate the volume generated when R is rotated through 2π radians about

      (i) the x-axis,

      (ii) the y-axis.

8.5 Lengths of arcs of curves

Suppose P and Q are two points fairly close together which lie on the curve with equation $y = f(x)$, so that P has coordinates (x, y) and Q has coordinates $(x + \delta x, y + \delta y)$. Let the length of the curve between P and Q be δs. This length must be approximately equal to the length of the line segment PQ. Thus

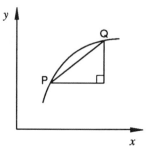

$$\delta s \approx \sqrt{\left((\delta x)^2 + (\delta y)^2\right)}$$

So $\quad \dfrac{\delta s}{\delta x} \approx \sqrt{\left(1 + \left(\dfrac{\delta y}{\delta x}\right)^2\right)}$

Taking the limit as $\delta x \to 0$,

$$\frac{ds}{dx} \approx \sqrt{\left(1 + \left(\frac{dy}{dx}\right)^2\right)}$$

Hence the length of arc of curve from the point where $x = x_1$ to the point where $x = x_2$ is

$$s = \int_{x_1}^{x_2} \sqrt{\left[1 + \left(\frac{dy}{dx}\right)^2\right]}\, dx$$

Example

Find the length of the arc of the curve with equation $y = \frac{4}{3}x^{\frac{3}{2}}$ from the point where $x = \frac{3}{4}$ to the point where $x = 2$.

Solution

Here $\dfrac{dy}{dx} = 2x^{\frac{1}{2}}$,

so $\quad 1 + \left(\dfrac{dy}{dx}\right)^2 = 1 + 4x$

Arc length $\quad s = \displaystyle\int_{\frac{3}{4}}^{2} (1 + 4x)^{\frac{1}{2}}\, dx$

$$= \left[\frac{1}{4} \times \frac{2}{3}(1 + 4x)^{\frac{3}{2}}\right]_{\frac{3}{4}}^{2}$$

$$= \frac{1}{6}(27 - 8) = 3\frac{1}{6}$$

Activity 17

Show that if x and y are expressed in terms of a parameter t, then the arc length between the points on the curve where $t = t_1$ and $t = t_2$ is given by

$$s = \int_{t_1}^{t_2} \sqrt{\left(\dot{x}^2 + \dot{y}^2\right)}\, dt$$

where $\quad \dot{x} = \dfrac{dx}{dt}$ and $\dot{y} = \dfrac{dy}{dt}$

Example

A curve is defined by

$$x = t - \sin t; \quad y = 1 - \cos t$$

where t is a parameter. Calculate the length of the arc of the curve from the point where $t = 0$ to the point where $t = 2\pi$.

Solution

$$\dot{x} = \frac{dx}{dt} = 1 - \cos t; \quad \dot{y} = \frac{dy}{dt} = \sin t$$

$$\dot{x}^2 + \dot{y}^2 = 1 - 2\cos t + \cos^2 t + \sin^2 t$$

But $\quad \cos^2 t + \sin^2 t = 1$

giving $\quad \dot{x}^2 + \dot{y}^2 = 2 - 2\cos t$

$$= 4\sin^2 \tfrac{1}{2} t$$

As $2\sin \tfrac{1}{2} t \geq 0$ for $0 \leq t \leq 2\pi$,

$$\sqrt{\left(\dot{x}^2 + \dot{y}^2\right)} = 2\sin \tfrac{1}{2} t$$

and $\quad s = \int_0^{2\pi} \sqrt{\left(\dot{x}^2 + \dot{y}^2\right)} \, dt$

$$= \int_0^{2\pi} 2\sin \tfrac{1}{2} t \; dt$$

$$= \left[-4\cos \tfrac{1}{2} t\right]_0^{2\pi}$$

$$= -4\cos \pi + 4\cos 0$$

$$= 4 + 4 = 8$$

Exercise 8D

1. Use integration to find the length of the arc of the curve with equation $y = \sqrt{\left(1 - x^2\right)}$ from the point where $x = 0$ to the point where $x = \tfrac{1}{2}$. By identifying the curve, verify your answer.

2. A curve is defined parametrically by
    $x = 2\cos t - \cos 2t$, $y = 2\sin t - \sin 2t$, where t is a parameter. Find the length of the arc of the curve from the point where $t = 0$ to the point where $t = \dfrac{\pi}{4}$.

3. Sketch the curve defined by the parametric equations $x = \cos^3 t$; $y = -\sin^3 t$ $(0 \leq t \leq 2\pi)$ using a graphics calculator or software package.

    Show that the total length of the curve is 6 units, by making use of symmetry properties of the curve.

    Why can you not find the arc length by integrating directly from $t = 0$ to $t = 2\pi$?

4. Given that $y = \ln\sec x$, where $\frac{-\pi}{2} < x < \frac{\pi}{2}$, show that $\frac{dy}{dx} = \tan x$. Hence find the length of the curve with equation $y = \ln\sec x$ from the point where $x = -\frac{\pi}{4}$ to the point where $x = \frac{\pi}{6}$.

5. Show that the length of arc of the parabola with parametric equations $x = at^2$, $y = 2at$ (where $a > 0$), from the point where $t = t_1$ to the point where $t = t_2$, is given by

$$2a\int_{t_1}^{t_2} \sqrt{\left(1 + t^2\right)}\, dt\,.$$

By means of the substitution $t = \sinh\theta$, or otherwise, show that the arc length from the point where $t = 0$ to the point where $t = 3$ is

$$a\left(\sinh^{-1} 3 + 3\sqrt{10}\right).$$

6. Calculate the length of the curve defined by the equations $x = \tanh t$, $y = \operatorname{sech} t$, from the point where $t = -1$ to the point where $t = 2$.

7. Given that a is a positive constant, find the length of the curve defined parametrically by

$$x = at\cos t; \quad y = at\sin t \ \ (0 \le t \le 3\pi).$$

8. The curve defined parametrically by

$$x = (1 - \sin t)\cos t, \quad y = (1 - \sin t)\sin t$$

is sketched for $0 \le t \le 2\pi$.

It is called a cardioid.

What happens when you try to find the total perimeter by integrating from 0 to 2π?

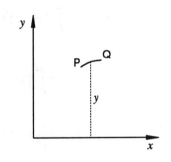

Use symmetry properties to find the perimeter of the cardioid.

8.6 Curved surface areas of revolution

Consider the small arc PQ of length δs of a curve distance y from the x-axis. When the arc is rotated through 2π radians about the x-axis it generates a band with surface area δA approximately equal to $2\pi y \times \delta s$.

Therefore

$$\frac{\delta A}{\delta x} \approx 2\pi y \frac{\delta s}{\delta x}$$

Taking the limit as $\delta x \to 0$ and using the formula for $\frac{ds}{dx}$ obtained in the previous section gives

$$\frac{dA}{dx} = 2\pi y \frac{ds}{dx} = 2\pi y \sqrt{1 + \left(\frac{dx}{dy}\right)^2}.$$

Hence the curved suface area of revolution when the arc of a curve from $x = x_1$ to $x = x_2$ is rotated through 2π radians about the x-axis is

$$\boxed{\int_{x_1}^{x_2} 2\pi y \sqrt{\left[1 + \left(\frac{dy}{dx}\right)^2\right]}\, dx}$$

Example

The arc of the parabola with equation $y^2 = 2x$ from the origin to the point $(4, 2\sqrt{2})$ is rotated through 2π radians about the x-axis.

Calculate the area of the curved surface generated.

Solution

$$y^2 = 2x \Rightarrow 2y\frac{dy}{dx} = 2$$

$$1 + \left(\frac{dy}{dx}\right)^2 = 1 + \frac{1}{y^2} = 1 + \frac{1}{2x} = \frac{2x+1}{2x}$$

Since the arc is on the branch where y is positive, $y = (2x)^{\frac{1}{2}}$ and so curved surface area

$$= \int_0^4 2\pi y \sqrt{\left[1 + \left(\frac{dy}{dx}\right)^2\right]}\, dx$$

$$= \int_0^4 2\pi (2x)^{\frac{1}{2}} \left(\frac{2x+1}{2x}\right)^{\frac{1}{2}} dx$$

$$= 2\pi \int_0^4 (2x+1)^{\frac{1}{2}}\, dx$$

$$= 2\pi \left[\tfrac{1}{2} \times \tfrac{2}{3}(2x+1)^{\frac{3}{2}}\right]_0^4$$

$$= 2\pi \times \frac{1}{3} \times (27 - 1) = \frac{52}{3}\pi$$

The results from Activity 17 give a corresponding result when a curve is expressed in parametric form with parameter t, as below.

Curved surface area is

$$\boxed{\int_{t_1}^{t_2} 2\pi y \sqrt{\left[\dot{x}^2 + \dot{y}^2\right]}\, dt}$$

Activity 18

A curve is defined parametrically by $x = t - \sin t$, $y = 1 - \cos t$.

Show that

$$\dot{x}^2 + \dot{y}^2 = 4 \sin^2 \tfrac{1}{2} t .$$

The part of the curve from $t = 0$ to $t = \pi$ is rotated through 2π radians about the x-axis to form a curved surface.

Show that the surface area can be expressed in the form

$$8\pi \int_0^\pi \sin^3\left(\frac{t}{2}\right) dt$$

Use the substitution $u = \cos \tfrac{1}{2} t$, or otherwise, to show that this surface area has value $\dfrac{32}{3}\pi$.

Exercise 8E

1. The arc of the curve described by $x = \cos^3 t$, $y = \sin^3 t$, from the point where $t = 0$ to the point where $t = \dfrac{\pi}{2}$, is rotated through 2π radians about the x-axis.

    Calculate the area of the surface generated.

2. Calculate the area of the surface generated when each of the following arcs of curves are rotated through 2π radians about the x-axis.

    (a) the part of the line $y = \tfrac{1}{4} x$ from $x = 1$ to $x = 5$;

    (b) the arc of the curve $y = \cosh x$ from $x = 0$ to $x = 2$;

    (c) the portion of the curve $y = e^x$ from $x = 0$ to $x = \ln 3$.

3. The parametric equations of a curve are

    $$x = t - \tanh t, \quad y = \operatorname{sech} t$$

    The arc of the curve between the points with parameters 0 and $\ln 2$ is rotated about the x-axis. Calculate in terms of π the area of the curved surface formed.   (AEB)

4. A curve is defined by

    $$x = t^3, \quad y = 3t^2$$

    where t is a parameter.

    Calculate the area of the surface generated when the portion of the curve from $t = 0$ to $t = 2$ is rotated through 2π radians about the x-axis.

8.7 Reduction formulae in integration

Activity 19

Use integration by parts to show how $I = \int_0^1 x^2 e^{-x} dx$ can be

expressed in terms of $\int_0^1 x e^{-x} dx$.

Evaluate $\int_0^1 x e^{-x} dx$ and hence find the value of I.

If you consider the more general form of this integral

$$I_n = \int_0^1 x^n e^{-x} dx$$

you can use integration by parts to express I_n in terms of I_{n-1}.

Now putting $u = x^n$ and $\dfrac{dv}{dx} = e^{-x}$ gives

$$I_n = \left[-x^n e^{-x}\right]_0^1 + n \int_0^1 x^{n-1} e^{-x} dx$$

Assuming $n > 0$,

$$I_n = -e^{-1} + n I_{n-1}$$

This is an example of a **reduction formula**. Suppose you wish to
find the value of the integral in Activity 19. You need I_2. But

$$I_2 = -e^{-1} + 2 I_1$$

and $\qquad I_1 = -e^{-1} + I_0$

But

$$I_0 = \int_0^1 e^{-x} dx = \left[-e^{-x}\right]_0^1 = 1 - e^{-1}$$

Hence

$$I_1 = -e^{-1} + I_0 = 1 - 2e^{-1}$$

and

$$I_2 = -e^{-1} + 2\left(1 - 2e^{-1}\right) = 2 - 5e^{-1}$$

Activity 20

Use the reduction formula and value of I_2 to obtain the values of

$$\int_0^1 x^3 e^{-x} dx \text{ and } \int_0^1 x^4 e^{-x} dx$$

Example

Given that $I_n = \int_0^{\frac{\pi}{2}} \sin^n x \, dx$, express I_n in terms of I_{n-2} for $n \geq 2$.

Hence evaluate $\int_0^{\frac{\pi}{2}} \sin^5 x \, dx$ and $\int_0^{\frac{\pi}{2}} \sin^6 x \, dx$.

Solution

Using the formula for integration by parts

$$\int u \frac{dv}{dx} dx = uv - \int \frac{du}{dx} v \, dx$$

let $u = \sin^{n-1} x$, $\dfrac{dv}{dx} = \sin x$,

giving $\dfrac{du}{dx} = (n-1)\sin^{n-2} x \cos x$, $v = -\cos x$.

So for $n \geq 2$

$$I_n = \left[-\sin^{n-1} x \cos x \right]_0^{\frac{\pi}{2}} + (n-1)\int_0^{\frac{\pi}{2}} \sin^{n-2} x \cos^2 x \, dx$$

$$= 0 + (n-1)\int_0^{\frac{\pi}{2}} \sin^{n-2} x \left(1 - \sin^2 x\right) dx$$

$$= (n-1)\int_0^{\frac{\pi}{2}} \sin^{n-2} x \, dx - (n-1)\int_0^{\frac{\pi}{2}} \sin^n x \, dx$$

$$= (n-1)I_{n-2} - (n-1)I_n$$

Therefore for $n \geq 2$

$$n I_n = (n-1)I_{n-2}$$

or $$I_n = \frac{(n-1)}{n} I_{n-2}.$$

You need $\quad I_5 = \dfrac{4}{5}I_3 \quad \text{and} \quad I_3 = \dfrac{2}{3}I_1$

Also $\quad I_1 = \displaystyle\int_0^{\frac{\pi}{2}} \sin x \, dx = [-\cos x]_0^{\frac{\pi}{2}} = 1$

and $\quad I_5 = \dfrac{4}{5} \times \dfrac{2}{3} \times 1 = \dfrac{8}{15}.$

Similarly,

$$I_6 = \dfrac{5}{6} \times \dfrac{3}{4} \times \dfrac{1}{2} \times I_0 = \dfrac{15\pi}{96}.$$

Activity 21

(a) Differentiate $\sec^{n-2} \tan x$ with respect to x and express your answer in terms of powers of $\sec x$. By integrating the result with respect to x, establish the reduction formula

$$(n-1)I_n - (n-2)I_{n-2} = \sec^{n-2} x \tan x + \text{constant}$$

where $\quad I_n = \displaystyle\int \sec^n x \, dx.$

(b) Use the reduction formula in (a) to evaluate

$$\int_0^{\frac{\pi}{4}} \sec^4 x \, dx \quad \text{and} \quad \int_{\frac{\pi}{6}}^{\frac{\pi}{4}} \sec^5 x \, dx.$$

Exercise 8F

1. Given that $I_n = \displaystyle\int_0^{\frac{\pi}{2}} \cos^n x \, dx$, prove that

   $I_n = \dfrac{n-1}{n} I_{n-2}$. Hence find I_4 and I_7.

2. Given that $I_n = \displaystyle\int_0^{\frac{\pi}{2}} x^n \cos x \, dx$, establish the reduction formula

   $$\left(n^2 + 4\right) I_n = n(n-1)\, I_{n-2} + 2e^\pi.$$

   Evaluate I_4 and I_5.

3. If $I_n = \displaystyle\int_0^{\frac{\pi}{2}} e^{2x} \sin^n x \, dx$, $n > 1$, show that

   $$\left(n^2 + 4\right) I_n = n(n-1)\, I_{n-2} + 2e^\pi$$

   Hence, or otherwise, find $\displaystyle\int_0^{\frac{\pi}{2}} e^{2x} \sin^3 x \, dx$. (AEB)

4. If $I_n = \displaystyle\int \tan^n x \, dx$, obtain a reduction formula for I_n. Hence, or otherwise, show that

   $$\int_0^{\frac{\pi}{4}} \tan^4 x \, dx = \dfrac{3\pi - 8}{12}. \tag{AEB}$$

5. Simplify $\dfrac{\sin 2n\theta - \sin 2(n-1)\theta}{\sin \theta}.$

   If $I_n = \displaystyle\int \dfrac{\sin 2n\theta}{\sin \theta}\, d\theta$, prove that

   $I_n = I_{n-1} + \dfrac{2}{(2n-1)} \sin(2n-1)\theta$. Hence, or

   otherwise, evaluate $\displaystyle\int_0^{\frac{\pi}{2}} \dfrac{\sin 5\theta}{\sin \theta}\, d\theta.$ (AEB)

6. Given that $p = \ln 2$, write down the values of $\cosh p$ and $\sinh p$. Find a reduction formula relating I_n and I_{n-2} where $I_n = \displaystyle\int_0^p \cosh^n \theta \, d\theta.$ Hence find I_3 and I_4.

8.8 Miscellaneous Exercises

1. Sketch the curve given by the parametric equations $x=t^3; y=3t^2$. Find the length of the arc of the curve from $t=0$ to $t=2$. (AEB)

2. Given that a is a positive constant, find the length of the arc of the curve with equation

$$y=a\cosh\left(\frac{x}{a}\right)$$ between $x=0$ and $x=k$, where k is

a constant. Hence show that, as k varies, the arc length is proportional to the area of the region bounded by the arc, the coordinate axes and the line $x=k$.

3. Given that $xy=3x^2+y^2$, find $\frac{dy}{dx}$, giving your answer in terms of x and y. (AEB)

4. Find the length of the arc l of the curve with equation $y=\ln(\cos x)$ from the point at which $x=0$ to the point at which $x=\frac{1}{6}\pi$. The arc l is rotated completely about the x-axis to form a surface, S. Show that the area of S is

$$\left| 2\pi\int_0^{\frac{\pi}{6}} \frac{\ln(\cos x)}{\cos x} dx \right|$$

Use Simpson's rule with three ordinates to estimate this area, giving your answer to 2 decimal places. (AEB)

5. Given that $I=\int_0^1 \frac{x^2}{\sqrt{(4-x^2)}}dx$,

(a) using Simpson's rule with four equal intervals, working with 4 decimal places, obtain an approximation to I, giving your answer to three significant figures;

(b) by putting $x=2\sin\theta$, show that

$$I=4\int_0^{\frac{\pi}{6}} \sin^2\theta \, d\theta.$$

Hence show that the exact value of I is

$$\frac{\pi}{3}-\frac{\sqrt{3}}{2}.$$ (AEB)

6. Find the gradient at the point $(2, 3)$ on the curve with equation
$3x^2+6xy-2y^3+6=0$. (AEB)

7. A curve has equation $y=x-1+\frac{1}{x+1}$.

Calculate the coordinates of the turning points of the curve and determine their nature.

The finite region bounded by the curve, the x-axis from $x=0$ to $x=4$ and the line $x=4$ is R. Express the area of R as an integral and show that its exact value is $4+\ln 5$. Use Simpson's rule with four equal intervals to find an estimate of the same integral, giving your answer to three decimal places. Hence find an approximation for $\ln 5$, giving your answer to two decimal places. (AEB)

8. Shade on a sketch the finite region R in the first quadrant bounded by the x-axis, the curve with equation $y=\ln x$ and the line $x=5$. By means of integration, calculate the area of R. The region R is rotated completely about the x-axis to form a solid of revolution S.

x	1	2	3	4	5
$(\ln x)^2$	0	0.480	1.207	1.922	2.590

Use the given table of values and apply the trapezium rule to find an estimate of the volume of S, giving your answer to one decimal place. (AEB)

9. Showing your working in the form of a table, use Simpson's rule with 4 equal intervals to estimate

$\int_0^2 \ln(1+x^2)dx$, giving your answer to 3 decimal places. Deduce an approximate value for

$\int_0^2 \ln\sqrt{(1+x^2)}dx$. (AEB)

10. Given that $x>0$ and that $y=\frac{\ln x}{x}$, find $\frac{dy}{dx}$. State the set of values of x for which $\frac{dy}{dx}>0$ and the set of values of x for which $\frac{dy}{dx}<0$. Hence show that y has a maximum value of $\frac{1}{e}$.

Find the area of the finite region R bounded by the curve $y=\frac{\ln x}{x}$, the x-axis and the line $x=5$. The region R is rotated completely about the x-axis to form a solid of revolution S. Use Simpson's rule, taking ordinates at $x=1, 2, 3, 4$ and 5 to estimate, to 2 significant figures, the volume of S. (AEB)

11. The following approximate measurements were made of two related variables x and y.

x	2.0	2.5	3.0	3.5	4.0
y	10.9	17.5	27.0	40.3	59.1

Use the trapezium rule with five ordinates to estimate the value of $\int_2^4 y\,dx$ giving your answer to 1 decimal place. (AEB)

12. Evaluate $\int_1^5 \frac{x}{x^2+1}\,dx$ giving your answer in terms of a natural logarithm. Use Simpson's rule with four intervals to find an estimate of the integral. Hence find an approximation for $\ln 13$, giving your answer to two decimal places. (AEB)

13. Given that $I_n = \int_0^{\frac{1}{4}\pi} \tan^n x\,dx$, show that for $n \geq 0$,

$I_{n+2} + I_n = \frac{1}{n+1}$. Calculate the values of I_4 and I_5.

(AEB)

14. A curve has equation $9ay^2 = 8x^3$, where a is a positive constant. The tangent at $P\left(a, \frac{2\sqrt{2}}{3}a\right)$

meets the curve again at Q. Prove that the x-coordinate of Q is $\frac{1}{4}a$ and show further that QP is the normal to the curve at Q. Show that

$1 + \left(\frac{dy}{dx}\right)^2 = 1 + \frac{2x}{a}$. Find, in terms of a, the length of the arc QP of the curve. (AEB)

15. Sketch the curve with equation $y = \sec 2x$ for $-\frac{1}{2}\pi \leq x \leq \frac{1}{2}\pi$. The region bounded by the curve, the x-axis and the lines $x = -\frac{\pi}{6}$ and $x = \frac{\pi}{6}$ is R.

Show that $\left(\frac{dy}{dx}\right)^2 + 1 = \left(2\sec^2 2x - 1\right)^2$ and hence prove that the perimeter of R is $4 + 2\sqrt{3}$. (AEB)

16. A curve has equation $y = \cosh x$ and the points P and Q on the curve have x-coordinates 0 and $\ln 2$ respectively. Find the length of the arc PQ of the curve. (AEB)

17. Given that $I_n = \int_0^1 x^n \sqrt{(1-x)}\,dx$, prove that, if $n > 0$, then $(2n+3)I_n = 2n I_{n-1}$.

A curve has equation $y^2 = x^4(1-x)$.

(a) Find the coordinates of the turning point of the curve and sketch its graph.

(b) Find the area of the loop of the curve. (AEB)

18. Derive a reduction formula for I_n in terms of I_{n-1} when $I_n = \int x^3 (\ln x)^n dx$.

Hence find $\int x^3 (\ln x)^3 dx$. (AEB)

19. The tangent at a point P on the curve whose parametric equations are $x = a\left(t - \frac{1}{3}t^3\right)$, $y = at^2$, cuts the x-axis at T. Prove that the distance of the point T from the origin O is one half of the length of the arc OP. (AEB)

20. A curve is given by the parametric equations

$x = 4\cos t + \cos 2t$, $y = \sin 2t + 4\sin t + 2t$.

Find the length of the curve between the points $t = 0$ and $t = \frac{\pi}{4}$. (AEB)

21. A curve has parametric equations

$x = 4t^2$; $y = t^4 - 4\ln t$.

Find the length of the arc of the curve from $t = 1$ to $t = 2$. Find also the area of the surface formed when this arc is rotated completely about the y-axis. (AEB)

22. Given that $I_n = \int \frac{x^n}{\left(a^2 + x^2\right)^{\frac{1}{2}}}\,dx$, where a is a constant, show that for $n \geq 2$

$n I_n = x^{n-1}\left(a^2 + x^2\right)^{\frac{1}{2}} - (n-1)a^2 I_{n-2}$ + constant.

Evaluate $\int_0^{\sqrt{3}} \frac{x^5}{\left(1+x^2\right)^{\frac{1}{2}}}\,dx$ and $\int_0^1 \frac{x^4}{\left(4+x^2\right)^{\frac{1}{2}}}\,dx$.

9 MATRICES AND TRANSFORMATIONS

Objectives

After studying this chapter you should

- be able to handle matrix (and vector) algebra with confidence, and understand the differences between this and scalar algebra;

- be able to determine inverses of 2×2 matrices, recognising the conditions under which they do, or do not, exist;

- be able to express plane transformations in algebraic and matrix form;

- be able to recognise and use the standard matrix form for less straightforward transformations;

- be able to use the properties of invariancy to help describe transformations;

- appreciate the composition of simple transformations;

- be able to derive the eigenvalues and eigenvectors of a given 2×2 matrix, and interpret their significance in relation to an associated plane transformation.

9.0 Introduction

A **matrix** is a rectangular array of numbers. Each entry in the matrix is called an **element**. Matrices are classified by the number of rows and the number of columns that they have; a matrix **A** with m rows and n columns is an $m \times n$ (said 'm by n') matrix, and this is called the **order** of **A**.

Example

Given

$$\mathbf{A} = \begin{bmatrix} 1 & 4 & 2 \\ 3 & -1 & 0 \end{bmatrix},$$

then **A** has order 2×3 (rows first, columns second.) The elements of **A** can be denoted by a_{ij}, being the element in the ith row and jth column of **A**. In the above case, $a_{11} = 1, a_{23} = 0$, etc.

Addition and subtraction of matrices is defined only for matrices of equal order; the sum (difference) of matrices **A** and **B** is the matrix obtained by adding (subtracting) the elements in corresponding positions of **A** and **B**.

Thus

$$A = \begin{bmatrix} 1 & 4 & 2 \\ 3 & -1 & 0 \end{bmatrix} \text{ and } B = \begin{bmatrix} -1 & 2 & 3 \\ 4 & 3 & -3 \end{bmatrix}$$

$$\Rightarrow \quad A + B = \begin{bmatrix} 0 & 6 & 5 \\ 7 & 2 & -3 \end{bmatrix} \text{ and } A - B = \begin{bmatrix} 2 & 2 & -1 \\ -1 & -4 & 3 \end{bmatrix}.$$

However, if

$$C = \begin{bmatrix} 2 & 3 \\ 1 & 4 \end{bmatrix},$$

then **C** can neither be added to nor subtracted from either of **A** or **B**.

If you think of matrices as stores of information, then the addition (or subtraction) of corresponding elements makes sense.

Example

A milkman delivers three varieties of milk Pasteurised (PA), Semi-skimmed (SS) and Skimmed (SK)) to four houses (E, F, G and H) over a two-week period. The number of pints of each type of milk delivered to each house in week 1 is given in matrix **M**, while **N** records similar information for week 2.

$$\begin{array}{c} \quad\;\; \text{PA SS SK} \\ \begin{array}{c} E \\ F \\ G \\ H \end{array} \begin{bmatrix} 8 & 4 & 3 \\ 12 & 0 & 3 \\ 2 & 7 & 6 \\ 6 & 9 & 0 \end{bmatrix} = M \end{array} \qquad \begin{array}{c} \quad\;\; \text{PA SS SK} \\ \begin{array}{c} E \\ F \\ G \\ H \end{array} \begin{bmatrix} 4 & 7 & 8 \\ 10 & 0 & 5 \\ 0 & 8 & 7 \\ 8 & 10 & 0 \end{bmatrix} = N \end{array}$$

Then

$$M + N = \begin{bmatrix} 12 & 11 & 11 \\ 22 & 0 & 8 \\ 2 & 15 & 13 \\ 14 & 19 & 0 \end{bmatrix}$$

records the total numbers of pints of each type of milk delivered to each of the houses over the fortnight, and

$$N - M = \begin{bmatrix} -4 & 3 & 5 \\ -2 & 0 & 2 \\ -2 & 1 & 1 \\ 2 & 1 & 0 \end{bmatrix}$$

records the increase in delivery for each type of milk for each of the houses in the second week.

Suppose now that we consider the 3×2 matrix, P, giving the prices of each type of milk, in pence, as charged by two dairy companies:

$$\begin{array}{cc} & 1 \quad 2 \\ \begin{array}{c} PA \\ SS \\ SK \end{array} & \begin{bmatrix} 35 & 36 \\ 32 & 30 \\ 27 & 27 \end{bmatrix} = P \end{array}$$

What are the possible weekly milk costs to each of the four households?

Define the cost matrix as

$$\begin{array}{cc} & 1 \qquad 2 \\ \begin{array}{c} E \\ F \\ G \\ H \end{array} & \begin{bmatrix} c_{11} & c_{12} \\ c_{21} & c_{22} \\ c_{31} & c_{32} \\ c_{41} & c_{42} \end{bmatrix} = C \end{array}$$

Now c_{11} is the cost to household E if company 1 delivers the milk (in the week for which the matrix M records the deliveries) and so

$$c_{11} = 8 \times 35 + 4 \times 32 + 3 \times 27$$
$$= 489p$$

Essentially this is the first row $\begin{bmatrix} 8 & 4 & 3 \end{bmatrix}$ of M 'times' the first

column $\begin{bmatrix} 35 \\ 32 \\ 27 \end{bmatrix}$ of P.

Similarly, for example, c_{32} can be thought of as the 'product' of the

third row of M, $\begin{bmatrix} 2 & 7 & 6 \end{bmatrix}$, with the second column of P, $\begin{bmatrix} 36 \\ 30 \\ 27 \end{bmatrix}$, so

that
$$c_{32} = 2 \times 36 + 7 \times 30 + 6 \times 27$$
$$= 444p$$

This is the cost to household G if they get company 2 to deliver their milk.

Matrix multiplication is defined in this way. You will see that multiplication of matrices $\mathbf{X}$ and $\mathbf{Y}$ is only possible if

> the number of columns $\mathbf{X}$ = the number of rows of $\mathbf{Y}$

Then, if $\mathbf{X}$ is an $(a \times b)$ matrix and $\mathbf{B}$ a $(c \times d)$ matrix, the product matrix $\mathbf{XY}$ exists if and only if $b = c$ and $\mathbf{XY}$ is then an $(a \times d)$ matrix. Thus, for $\mathbf{P} = \mathbf{XY}$,

$$\mathbf{P} = \left(p_{ij} \right),$$

where the entry p_{ij} is the scalar product of the ith row of $\mathbf{X}$ (taken as a row vector) with the jth column of $\mathbf{Y}$ (taken as a column vector).

Example

Find $\mathbf{AB}$ when

$$\mathbf{A} = \begin{bmatrix} 1 & 4 & 2 \\ 3 & -1 & 0 \end{bmatrix}, \quad \mathbf{B} = \begin{bmatrix} 2 & 5 \\ 2 & 0 \\ -1 & 3 \end{bmatrix}$$

Solution

$\mathbf{A}$ is a 2×3 matrix, $\mathbf{B}$ is a 3×2 matrix. Since the number of columns of $\mathbf{A}$ = the number of rows of $\mathbf{B}$, the product matrix $\mathbf{AB}$ exists, and has order 2×2.

$$\mathbf{P} = \mathbf{AB} = \begin{bmatrix} p_{11} & p_{12} \\ p_{21} & p_{22} \end{bmatrix}$$

$$p_{11} = \begin{bmatrix} 1 & 4 & 2 \end{bmatrix} \cdot \begin{bmatrix} 2 \\ 2 \\ -1 \end{bmatrix} = 2 + 8 - 2 = 8, \text{ etc}$$

giving

$$\mathbf{P} = \begin{bmatrix} 8 & 11 \\ 4 & 15 \end{bmatrix}$$

The answers to the questions in the activity below should help you discover a number of important points relating the matrix arithmetic and algebra. Some of them are exactly as they are with ordinary real numbers, that is, scalars. More significantly, there are a few important differences.

Activity 1

(1) In the example above, suppose that $Q = BA$. What is the order of Q? Comment.

(2) (a) Take $C = \begin{bmatrix} 4 & 1 \\ 3 & 2 \end{bmatrix}$ and $D = \begin{bmatrix} -1 & 0 & 3 \\ 2 & 5 & 7 \end{bmatrix}$. What is the order of CD? What is the order of DC? Comment.

(b) Take $E = \begin{bmatrix} 0 & 3 \\ -7 & 2 \end{bmatrix}$ and $F = \begin{bmatrix} 2 & 2 \\ 8 & -1 \end{bmatrix}$. What is the order of FE? Work out EF and FE. Comment.

(c) (i) Work out CE and FC

(ii) Work out $CE \times F$ and $C \times EF$. Comment.

(iii) Work out $F \times CE$ and $FC \times E$. Comment.

(3) Using the matrices given above, work out

$$CF, \quad C+F, \quad E+F.$$

Answer the following questions and comment on your answers.

(a) Is $CE + CF = C(E + F)$?

(b) Is $CE + FE = (C + F)E$?

(c) Is $CE + EF = E(C + F)$?

(d) Is $CE + EF = (C + F)E$?

Summary of observations

You should have noted that, for matrices M and N, say:

- the product matrix MN may exist, even if NM does not.
- even if MN and NM both exist, they may have different orders.
- even if MN and NM both exist and have the same order, it is generally not the case that $MN = NM$. (Matrix multiplication does not obey the **commutative law**. Matrix addition does: $A + B = B + A$ provided that A and B are of the same order.)
- when multiplying more than two matrices together, the order in which they appear is important, but the same result is obtained however they are multiplied within that order. (Matrix multiplication is said to obey the **associative law**.)

- A matrix can be pre-multiplied or post-multiplied by another. Multiplication of brackets and, conversely, factorisation is possible provided the left-to-right order of the matrices involved is maintained.

For a sensible matrix algebra to be developed, it is necessary to ensure that **MN** and **NM** both exist, and have the same order as **M** and **N**. That is, **M** and **N** must be square matrices. In the work that follows you will be working with 2×2 matrices, as well as with row vectors (1×2 matrices) and column vectors (2×1 matrices).

Exercise 9A

1. Work out the values of x and y in the following cases:

   (a) $\begin{bmatrix} 4 & 1 \\ -19 & -5 \end{bmatrix} \begin{bmatrix} 5 \\ -22 \end{bmatrix} = \begin{bmatrix} x \\ y \end{bmatrix}$

   (b) $\begin{bmatrix} 4 & 1 \\ -19 & -5 \end{bmatrix} \begin{bmatrix} x \\ y \end{bmatrix} = \begin{bmatrix} 5 \\ -22 \end{bmatrix}$

   (c) $\begin{bmatrix} 3 & 2 \\ 4 & -1 \end{bmatrix} \begin{bmatrix} x \\ y \end{bmatrix} = \begin{bmatrix} 8 \\ 18 \end{bmatrix}$

   (d) $\begin{bmatrix} 15 & -5 \\ -6 & 2 \end{bmatrix} \begin{bmatrix} x \\ y \end{bmatrix} = \begin{bmatrix} 20 \\ -8 \end{bmatrix}$

   (e) $\begin{bmatrix} 1 & -7 \\ -3 & 21 \end{bmatrix} \begin{bmatrix} x \\ y \end{bmatrix} = \begin{bmatrix} 4 \\ 14 \end{bmatrix}$

   Comment on your responses to parts (d) and (e).

2. $A = \begin{bmatrix} 1 & -1 \\ 2 & 1 \end{bmatrix}$. Find A^2 and A^3. If we say $A^1 = A$, is there any meaning to A^0?

3. The transpose of $A = \begin{bmatrix} a & b \\ c & d \end{bmatrix}$ is the matrix A^T obtained by swapping the rows and columns of A; i.e. $A^T = \begin{bmatrix} a & c \\ b & d \end{bmatrix}$. Find the conditions necessary for it to be true that $AA^T = A^TA$.

4. (a) Find the value of h for which
   $$\begin{bmatrix} 4 & 1 \\ 6 & -1 \end{bmatrix} \begin{bmatrix} 1 \\ 1 \end{bmatrix} = h \begin{bmatrix} 1 \\ 1 \end{bmatrix}$$

   (b) Find the values of a and b for which
   $$\begin{bmatrix} 4 & 1 \\ 6 & -1 \end{bmatrix} \begin{bmatrix} a \\ b \end{bmatrix} = -2 \begin{bmatrix} a \\ b \end{bmatrix}$$

5. (a) Find a matrix **B** such that
   $$B \begin{bmatrix} 2 & 5 \\ -4 & 9 \end{bmatrix} = \begin{bmatrix} 12 & 30 \\ -24 & 54 \end{bmatrix}$$

   (b) Find two 2×2 matrices **M** and **N** such that
   $$MN = \begin{bmatrix} 0 & 0 \\ 0 & 0 \end{bmatrix}$$
   without any of the elements in **M** or **N** being zero.

9.1 Special matrices

The 2×2 matrix $I = \begin{bmatrix} 1 & 0 \\ 0 & 1 \end{bmatrix}$ has the property that, for any 2×2 matrix **A**,

$$\boxed{IA = AI = A}$$

In other words, multiplication by **I** (either pre-multiplication or post-multiplication) leaves the elements of **A** unchanged.

I is called the **identity matrix** and it is analogous to the real number 1 in ordinary multiplication.

The 2×2 matrix $\mathbf{Z} = \begin{bmatrix} 0 & 0 \\ 0 & 0 \end{bmatrix}$ is such that

$$\mathbf{Z} + \mathbf{A} = \mathbf{A} + \mathbf{Z} = \mathbf{A}$$

and $\qquad \mathbf{ZA} = \mathbf{AZ} = \mathbf{Z};$

that is, **Z** leaves **A** unchanged under matrix addition, and itself remains unchanged under matrix multiplication. For obvious reasons, **Z** is called the **zero matrix**.

Next, although it is possible to define matrix multiplication meaningfully, there is no practical way of approaching division. However, in ordinary arithmetic, division can be approached as multiplication by reciprocals. For instance, the reciprocal of 2 is $\frac{1}{2}$, and 'multiplication by $\frac{1}{2}$' is the same as 'division by 2'. The equation $2x = 7$ can then be solved by multiplying both sides by $\frac{1}{2}$:

$$\tfrac{1}{2} \times 2x = \tfrac{1}{2} \times 7 \Rightarrow x = 3 \times 5$$

It is not necessary to have division defined as a process: instead, the use of the relations $\left(\frac{1}{2} \right) \times 2 = 1$ and $1 \times x = x$ suffices.

In matrix arithmetic we thus require, for a given matrix **A**, the matrix **B** for which,

$$\mathbf{AB} = \mathbf{BA} = \mathbf{I}.$$

B is denoted by $\mathbf{A}^{-1}$ (just as $2^{-1} = \frac{1}{2}$) and is called the **inverse matrix** of **A**, giving

$$\boxed{\mathbf{AA}^{-1} = \mathbf{A}^{-1}\mathbf{A} = \mathbf{I}}$$

Activity 2   To find an inverse matrix

Let $\quad \mathbf{A} = \begin{bmatrix} a & b \\ c & d \end{bmatrix}$. You need to find matrix **B**, of the form $\begin{bmatrix} e & f \\ g & h \end{bmatrix}$ say, such that $\mathbf{AB} = \mathbf{I}$.

Calculate the product matrix **AB** and equate it, element by element, with the corresponding elements of **I**. This will give two pairs of simultaneous equations: two equations in e and g, and two more equations in f and h. Solve for e, f, g, h in terms of a, b, c, d and you will have found $\mathbf{A}^{-1}$ (i.e. **B**). Check that $\mathbf{BA} = \mathbf{I}$ also.

Summary

For $\quad \mathbf{A} = \begin{bmatrix} a & b \\ c & d \end{bmatrix}$,

$$\mathbf{A}^{-1} = \frac{1}{(ad-bc)} \begin{bmatrix} d & -b \\ -c & a \end{bmatrix}$$

and $\quad \mathbf{A}^{-1}\mathbf{A} = \mathbf{A}\mathbf{A}^{-1} = \mathbf{I}$.

The factor $(ad-bc)$ present in each term, is called the **determinant** of matrix $\mathbf{A}$, and is a scalar (a real number), denoted det $\mathbf{A}$.

If $ad = bc$, then $\dfrac{1}{ad-bc} = \dfrac{1}{0}$, which is not defined. In this case, $\mathbf{A}^{-1}$ does not exist and the matrix $\mathbf{A}$ is described as **singular** (non-invertible). If $\mathbf{A}^{-1}$ does exist the matrix $\mathbf{A}$ is described as being **non-singular** (invertible).

For $\quad \mathbf{A} = \begin{bmatrix} a & b \\ c & d \end{bmatrix}$, we write

$$\det \mathbf{A} = \begin{vmatrix} a & b \\ c & d \end{vmatrix} = ad-bc.$$

So a matrix $\mathbf{A}$ has an inverse if and only if det $\mathbf{A} \neq 0$.

Example

Find the inverse of $\quad \mathbf{X} = \begin{bmatrix} 2 & 4 \\ 5 & -1 \end{bmatrix}$.

Hence solve the simultaneous equations

$$2x + 4y = 1$$
$$5x - y = 8$$

Solution

det $\mathbf{X} = 2 \times (-1) - 4 \times 5 = -22$.

So $\quad \mathbf{X}^{-1} = -\dfrac{1}{22} \begin{bmatrix} -1 & -4 \\ -5 & 2 \end{bmatrix}$

$$= \begin{bmatrix} \frac{1}{22} & \frac{2}{11} \\ \frac{5}{22} & -\frac{1}{11} \end{bmatrix}$$

The equations can be written in matrix form as

$$\begin{bmatrix} 2 & 4 \\ 5 & -1 \end{bmatrix} \begin{bmatrix} x \\ y \end{bmatrix} = \begin{bmatrix} 1 \\ 8 \end{bmatrix} \text{ or } \mathbf{Xu} = \mathbf{v}$$

where **u** and **v** are the column vectors $\begin{bmatrix} x \\ y \end{bmatrix}$ and $\begin{bmatrix} 1 \\ 8 \end{bmatrix}$ respectively.

(Pre-) Multiplying both sides by $\mathbf{X}^{-1}$ gives

$$\mathbf{X}^{-1}\mathbf{Xu} = \mathbf{X}^{-1}\mathbf{v}$$

$$\Rightarrow \quad \mathbf{Iu} = \mathbf{X}^{-1}\mathbf{v}$$

$$\Rightarrow \quad \mathbf{u} = \mathbf{X}^{-1}\mathbf{v}$$

Thus
$$\begin{bmatrix} x \\ y \end{bmatrix} = \frac{1}{22}\begin{bmatrix} 1 & 4 \\ 5 & -2 \end{bmatrix} \begin{bmatrix} 1 \\ 8 \end{bmatrix}$$
$$= \frac{1}{22}\begin{bmatrix} 1+32 \\ 5-16 \end{bmatrix}$$
$$= \begin{bmatrix} 1\frac{1}{2} \\ \frac{1}{2} \end{bmatrix}$$

so that $x = \frac{3}{2}, \quad y = \frac{1}{2}.$

Exercise 9B

1. Evaluate the following determinants

   (a) $\begin{vmatrix} 12 & 5 \\ 27 & 11 \end{vmatrix}$ (b) $\begin{vmatrix} 36 & -9 \\ -4 & 1 \end{vmatrix}$

   (c) $\begin{vmatrix} x+2 & 4-x \\ x & 7 \end{vmatrix}$

2. Find the inverses of **A**, **B** and **C**, where

   $\mathbf{A} = \begin{bmatrix} 7 & 19 \\ 2 & 6 \end{bmatrix}$ $\mathbf{B} = \begin{bmatrix} 5 & \frac{1}{2} \\ 20 & 2 \end{bmatrix}$ $\mathbf{C} = \begin{bmatrix} a & -4 \\ 1 & 3 \end{bmatrix}$

3. Find all values of k for which the matrix

   $\mathbf{M} = \begin{bmatrix} 3 & k+2 \\ -k & k-2 \end{bmatrix}$ is singular.

4. By finding $\begin{bmatrix} 3 & 7 \\ 1 & 6 \end{bmatrix}^{-1}$ solve the equations

   $3x + 7y = 9$
   $x + 6y = 5$

5. Given $\mathbf{X} = \begin{bmatrix} 2 & 3 \\ -2 & 1 \end{bmatrix}$, show that $\mathbf{X}^2 - 3\mathbf{X} + 8\mathbf{I} = \mathbf{Z}$.

   Deduce that $\mathbf{X}^{-1} = \frac{1}{8}(3\mathbf{I} - \mathbf{X})$.

   [Note: $3\mathbf{X} \equiv (3\mathbf{I})\mathbf{X}$, for instance.]

6. Take $\mathbf{A} = \begin{bmatrix} a & b \\ c & d \end{bmatrix}$ and $\mathbf{B} = \begin{bmatrix} p & q \\ r & s \end{bmatrix}$. Prove that

   $\det(\mathbf{AB}) = \det\mathbf{A}\det\mathbf{B}$.

7. Show that all matrices of the form

   $\begin{bmatrix} 6a+b & a \\ 3a & b \end{bmatrix}$

   commute with

   $\mathbf{A} = \begin{bmatrix} 2 & 1 \\ 3 & -4 \end{bmatrix}$

   [A and B commute if $\mathbf{AB} = \mathbf{BA}$]

8. Given $\mathbf{A} = \begin{bmatrix} 3 & 7 \\ 1 & 2 \end{bmatrix}$ and $\mathbf{B} = \begin{bmatrix} 4 & -1 \\ -3 & 1 \end{bmatrix}$, find $\mathbf{AB}$ and $(\mathbf{AB})^{-1}$.

   (a) Show that $(\mathbf{AB})^{-1} \neq \mathbf{A}^{-1}\mathbf{B}^{-1}$.

   (b) Prove that $(\mathbf{AB})^{-1} = \mathbf{B}^{-1}\mathbf{A}^{-1}$ for all 2×2 non-singular matrices $\mathbf{A}$ and $\mathbf{B}$.

9. $\mathbf{A} = \begin{bmatrix} a & b \\ c & d \end{bmatrix}$, $\mathbf{B} = \begin{bmatrix} 0 & 1 \\ 1 & 0 \end{bmatrix}$, $\mathbf{C} = \begin{bmatrix} 1 & 1 \\ 0 & 1 \end{bmatrix}$, $\mathbf{D} = \begin{bmatrix} 1 & 0 \\ -1 & 1 \end{bmatrix}$,

   $\mathbf{E} = \begin{bmatrix} k & 0 \\ 0 & 1 \end{bmatrix}$, $\mathbf{F} = \begin{bmatrix} 1 & m \\ 0 & 1 \end{bmatrix}$.

   Describe the effect on the rows of $\mathbf{A}$ of pre-multiplying $\mathbf{A}$ by (i) $\mathbf{B}$, (ii) $\mathbf{C}$, (iii) $\mathbf{D}$, (iv) $\mathbf{E}$, (v) $\mathbf{F}$. (That is, $\mathbf{BA}$, $\mathbf{CA}$, etc).

10. (a) Show that the 2×2 matrix $\mathbf{M} = \begin{bmatrix} a & b \\ c & d \end{bmatrix}$ is singular if and only if one row (or column) is a multiple of the other row (or column).

    (b) Prove that, if the matrix $(\mathbf{M} - \lambda \mathbf{I})$ is singular, where λ is some real (or complex) constant, then λ satisfies a certain quadratic equation, which you should find

9.2 Transformation matrices

Pre-multiplication of a 2×1 column vector by a 2×2 matrix results in a 2×1 column vector; for example,

$$\begin{bmatrix} 3 & 4 \\ -1 & 2 \end{bmatrix} \begin{bmatrix} 7 \\ -1 \end{bmatrix} = \begin{bmatrix} 17 \\ -9 \end{bmatrix}$$

If the vector $\begin{bmatrix} 7 \\ -1 \end{bmatrix}$ is thought of as a position vector (that is, representing the point with coordinates $(7, -1)$, then the matrix has changed the point $(7, -1)$ to the point $(17, -9)$. Similarly, the matrix has an effect on each point of the plane. Calling the transformation $\mathbf{T}$, this can be written

$$\mathbf{T}: \begin{bmatrix} x \\ y \end{bmatrix} \to \begin{bmatrix} x' \\ y' \end{bmatrix}.$$

$\mathbf{T}$ maps points (x, y) onto image points (x', y').

Using the above matrix,

$$\begin{bmatrix} x' \\ y' \end{bmatrix} = \begin{bmatrix} 3 & 4 \\ -1 & 2 \end{bmatrix} \begin{bmatrix} x \\ y \end{bmatrix}$$

$$= \begin{bmatrix} 3x + 4y \\ -x + 2y \end{bmatrix}$$

and the transformation can also be written in the form

$$\mathbf{T}:x'=3x+4y,\ y'=-x+2y.$$

[The handling of either form may be required.]

Activity 3

You may need squared paper for this activity.

Express each of the following transformations in the form

$$x'=ax+by,\ y'=cx+dy$$

for some suitable values of the constants a, b, c and d (positive, zero or negative). Then re-write in matrix form as

$$\begin{bmatrix} x' \\ y' \end{bmatrix} = \begin{bmatrix} a & b \\ c & d \end{bmatrix} \begin{bmatrix} x \\ y \end{bmatrix}$$

You may find it helpful at first to choose specific points (i.e. to choose some values for x and y).

(a) Reflection in the x-axis.

(b) Reflection in the y-axis.

(c) Reflection in the line $y=x$.

(d) Reflection in the line $y=-x$.

(e) Rotation through $90°$ (anticlockwise) about the origin.

(f) Rotation through $180°$ about the origin.

(g) Rotation through $-90°$ (i.e. $90°$ clockwise) about the origin.

(h) Enlargement with scale factor 5, centre the origin.

9.3 Invariancy and the basic transformations

An **invariant** (or fixed) **point** is one which is mapped onto itself; that is, it is its own image. An **invariant** (or fixed) **line** is a line all of whose points have image points also on this line. In the special case when all the points on a given line are invariant – in other words, they not only map onto other points on the line, but each maps onto itself – the line is called a **line of invariant points** (or a pointwise invariant line).

The invariant points and lines of a transformation are often its key features and, in most cases, help determine the nature of the transformation in question.

Example

Find the invariant points of the transformations defined by

(a) $x'=1-2y, \quad y'=2x-3$

(b) $\begin{bmatrix} x' \\ y' \end{bmatrix} = \begin{bmatrix} \frac{21}{5} & \frac{8}{5} \\ \frac{8}{5} & \frac{9}{5} \end{bmatrix} \begin{bmatrix} x \\ y \end{bmatrix}$

Solution

(a)   For invariant points, $x'=x$ and $y'=y$.

Thus

$x = 1 - 2y$ and $y = 2x - 3$

giving $x = 1 - 2\{2x - 3\}$

$\Rightarrow \qquad x = 1 - 4x + 6$

$\Rightarrow \qquad 5x = 7$ and $x = \frac{7}{5}, y = -\frac{1}{5}$

The invariant point is $\left(\frac{7}{5}, -\frac{1}{5}\right)$.

(b) $x' = x, y' = y$ for invariant points

$\Rightarrow \qquad x = \frac{21}{5}x + \frac{8}{5}y \quad$ and $\quad y = \frac{8}{5}x + \frac{9}{5}y$

$\Rightarrow \qquad 5x = 21x + 8y \qquad 5y = 8x + 9y$

$\Rightarrow \qquad y = -2x \qquad\qquad y = -2x$

and all points on the line $y = -2x$ are invariant.

Example

Find, in the form $y = mx + c$, the equations of all invariant lines of the transformation given by

$$\begin{bmatrix} x' \\ y' \end{bmatrix} = \begin{bmatrix} 7 & 24 \\ 24 & -7 \end{bmatrix} \begin{bmatrix} x \\ y \end{bmatrix}$$

Solution

Firstly, note that if $y = mx + c$ is an invariant line, then all such points (x, y) on this line have image points (x', y') with $y' = mx' + c$ also.

Now $x' = 7x + 24y = 7x + 24(mx + c) = (7 + 24m)x + 24c$

and $y' = 24x - 7y = 24x - 7(mx + c) = (24 - 7m)x - 7c$

Therefore, as $y' = mx' + c$, we can deduce that

$$(24 - 7m)x - 7c = m[(7 + 24m)x + 24c] + c$$

$$\Rightarrow \quad 0 = (24m^2 + 14m - 24)x + (24m + 8)c$$

Since x is a variable taking any real value while m and c are constants taking specific values, this statement can **only** be true if the RHS is identically zero; whence

$$24m^2 + 14m - 24 = 0 \text{ and } (24m + 8)c = 0.$$

The first of these equations

$$\Rightarrow \quad 2(4m - 3)(3m + 4) = 0$$

$$\Rightarrow \quad m = \tfrac{3}{4} \text{ or } -\tfrac{4}{3}.$$

The second equation

$$\Rightarrow \quad m = -\tfrac{1}{3} \text{ or } c = 0.$$

Clearly, then, $m \neq -\tfrac{1}{3}$ since in this case the coefficient of x, $24m^2 + 14m - 24$, would not then be zero.

There are, then, two cases:

(i) $m = \tfrac{3}{4}, c = 0$ giving the invariant line $y = \tfrac{3}{4}x$;

(ii) $m = -\tfrac{4}{3}, c = 0$ giving a second invariant line $y = -\tfrac{4}{3}x$.

Note that a transformation of the plane that can be represented by a 2×2 matrix must always include the origin as an invariant point, since

$$\mathbf{A}\begin{bmatrix} 0 \\ 0 \end{bmatrix} = \begin{bmatrix} 0 \\ 0 \end{bmatrix} \text{ for any matrix } \mathbf{A}.$$

Therefore clearly not all transformations are matrix representable.

The six basic transformations, together with their respective characteristics and defining features, are given below. You will return to them again, and their possible matrix representations, in later sections.

Translation

Under a **translation** each point is moved a fixed distance in a given direction:

$$\begin{bmatrix} x' \\ y' \end{bmatrix} = \begin{bmatrix} x \\ y \end{bmatrix} + \begin{bmatrix} a \\ b \end{bmatrix}$$

The vector $\begin{bmatrix} a \\ b \end{bmatrix}$ is called the **translation vector**, which completely defines the transformation. Distances and areas are preserved, and (provided that $\begin{bmatrix} a \\ b \end{bmatrix} \neq \begin{bmatrix} 0 \\ 0 \end{bmatrix}$) there are no invariant points. Thus a non-zero translation is not 2×2 matrix representable. Any line parallel to the translation vector is invariant.

Stretch

A **stretch** is defined parallel to a specified line or direction. Any line parallel to this direction is invariant, and there will be one line of invariant points perpendicular to this direction. Points of the plane are moved so that their distances from the line of invariant points are increased by a factor of k. Distances are, in general, not preserved and areas are increased by a factor of k.

Example

The transformation

$$\mathbf{T}: x' = x, \ y' = 2y$$

is a stretch of factor 2 in the direction of the y-axis. The line of invariant points is the x-axis.

Enlargement

Under an **enlargement** of factor k and centre C, each point P is moved k times further from point C, the single invariant point of the transformation, such that $\overrightarrow{CP'} = k\overrightarrow{CP}$. Any line through C is invariant. Distances are not preserved (unless $k = 1$); areas are increased by a factor of k^2.

Example

The transformation

$$\mathbf{T}: x' = 2x - 1, \ y' = 2y$$

is an enlargement of factor 2 with centre $(1, 0)$. For each (x, y),

$$(x', y') - (1, 0) = 2((x, y) - (1, 0)).$$

Projection

A trivial transformation whereby the whole plane is collapsed (projected) onto a single line or, in extreme cases, a single point.

Example

The transformation

$$\mathbf{T}:x'=0,\ y'=y$$

projects the whole plane onto the y-axis.

Reflection

A **reflection** is defined by its axis or line of symmetry, i.e. the 'mirror' line. Each point P is mapped onto the point P' which is the mirror-image of P in the mirror line; i.e. such that PP' is perpendicular to the mirror and such that their distances from it are equal, with P and P' on opposite sides of the line. Thus all points on the axis are invariant, and any lines perpendicular to it are also invariant. A reflection preserves distances and is area-preserving.

Example

The transformation

$$\mathbf{T}:x'=2-x,\ y'=y$$

is a reflection in the line $x=1$.

Rotation

A **rotation** is defined by its centre, C, the single invariant point and an angle of rotation (note that anticlockwise is taken to be the positive direction: thus a clockwise rotation of 90° can simply be described as a rotation of 270°). Points P are mapped to points P' such that CP'=CP and $\hat{PCP'}=\theta$, the angle of rotation. There are no invariant lines, with the exception of the case of a 180° (or multiples of 180°) rotation, when all lines through C will be invariant: note that a 180° rotation is identical to an enlargement, scale factor –1, and centre C. Distances and areas are preserved.

Example

The transformation

$$\mathbf{T}:x'=-y,\ y'=x$$

is a rotation of 90° with centre the origin.

Exercise 9C

1. Find the invariant points of the following transformations:

(a) $x'=2x+1,\ y'=3-2y$;

(b) $\begin{bmatrix} x' \\ y' \end{bmatrix} = \begin{bmatrix} x+y-1 \\ 1-2x \end{bmatrix}$;

(c) $\begin{bmatrix} x' \\ y' \end{bmatrix} = \begin{bmatrix} 8 & -15 \\ -7 & 16 \end{bmatrix} \begin{bmatrix} x \\ y \end{bmatrix}$;

(d) $x'=x,\ y'=2-y$

(e) $5x'=9x+8y-12$
   $5y'=8x+21y-24$

(f) $\begin{bmatrix} x' \\ y' \end{bmatrix} = \begin{bmatrix} \frac{3}{5} & -\frac{4}{5} \\ \frac{4}{5} & \frac{3}{5} \end{bmatrix} \begin{bmatrix} x \\ y \end{bmatrix} + \begin{bmatrix} 2 \\ 0 \end{bmatrix}$

(g) $x'=5x+6y-1,$
   $y'=2x+4y-4$

2. A transformation of the plane is given by the matrix

$$A = \begin{bmatrix} 1 & 4 \\ 4 & 1 \end{bmatrix}$$

Find the invariant lines of the transformation.

3. A transformation of the plane, T, is given by

$$x'=5-2y,\ y'=4-2x.$$

Find the invariant point and the invariant lines of T.

4. A transformation of the plane is given by the matrix

$$\begin{bmatrix} 2 & 2 \\ 1 & 3 \end{bmatrix}$$

Find all the invariant lines of the transformation.

5. Determine any fixed lines of the transformation given by

$$x'=\tfrac{1}{2}x+\tfrac{1}{4}y,\ y'=x+\tfrac{1}{2}y$$

Describe the transformation geometrically.

9.4   The determinant

If a plane transformation **T** is represented by a 2×2 matrix **A**, then det **A**, the determinant of **A**, represents the scale factor of the area increase produced by **T**.

To illustrate this, consider the effect of the transformation given by the matrix

$$A = \begin{bmatrix} a & b \\ c & d \end{bmatrix}$$

on the unit square, with vertices at $(0, 0)$, $(1, 0)$, $(0, 1)$ and $(1, 1)$, and of area 1.

The images of the square's vertices are on the diagram at $(0, 0)$, (a, c), (b, d) and $(a+b, c+d)$ respectively. You will see that the square is transformed into a parallelogram.

By drawing in rectangles and triangles it is easily shown that the area of this parallelogram is

$$(a+b)(c+d)-2\left[bc+\tfrac{1}{2}bd+\tfrac{1}{2}ac\right]$$

$$= ad-bc$$

$$= \det A$$

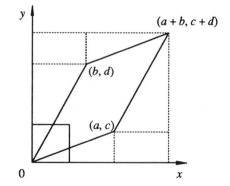

Note that if the cyclic order of the vertices of a plane figure is reversed (from clockwise to anticlockwise, or vice versa) then the area factor is actually $-\det \mathbf{A}$. Strictly speaking then, you should take $|-\det \mathbf{A}|$, the absolute value of the determinant.

Activity 4

Write down the numerical value of some determinants of matrices which represent

(a) a stretch;   (b) an enlargement;   (c) a projection;

(d) a reflection;   (e) a rotation.

9.5 The rotation and reflection matrices

Rotation about the origin

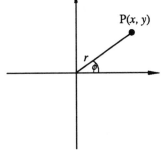

Let O be the origin $(0, 0)$ and consider a point $P(x, y)$ in the plane, with $OP = r$ and angle between OP and the x-axis equal to ϕ.

[Note that $r = \sqrt{x^2 + y^2}$ and $x = r \cos \phi$, $y = r \sin \phi$.]

Let the image of P after an anticlockwise rotation about O through an angle θ be $P'(x', y')$.

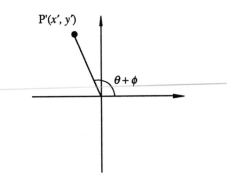

Then, $x' = r \cos(\theta + \phi)$

$\qquad = r(\cos \theta \cos \phi - \sin \theta \sin \phi)$

$\qquad = r \cos \phi \cos \theta - r \sin \phi \sin \theta$

$\qquad = x \cos \theta - y \sin \theta$

Also, $y' = r \sin(\theta + \phi)$

$\qquad = r(\sin \theta \cos \phi + \cos \theta \sin \phi)$

$\qquad = r \cos \phi \sin \theta + r \sin \phi \cos \theta$

$\qquad = x \sin \theta + y \cos \theta$

Thus

$$\begin{bmatrix} x' \\ y' \end{bmatrix} = \begin{bmatrix} \cos \theta & -\sin \theta \\ \sin \theta & \cos \theta \end{bmatrix} \begin{bmatrix} x \\ y \end{bmatrix}$$

For a clockwise rotation through θ about O either

(i) replace θ by $-\theta$ and use $\cos(-\theta) = \cos\theta$,
     $\sin(-\theta) = -\sin\theta$ to get the matrix

$$\begin{bmatrix} \cos\theta & \sin\theta \\ -\sin\theta & \cos\theta \end{bmatrix};$$

or

(ii) find $\begin{bmatrix} \cos\theta & -\sin\theta \\ \sin\theta & \cos\theta \end{bmatrix}^{-1}$

$$\begin{vmatrix} \cos\theta & -\sin\theta \\ \sin\theta & \cos\theta \end{vmatrix} = \cos^2\theta + \sin^2\theta = 1 \text{ (which it clearly should}$$

be, since rotating plane figures leaves area unchanged), and the above matrix is again obtained.

Check the following results with your answers to parts (e) – (g) in Activity 3.

Putting $\theta = 90°$ gives the matrix $\begin{bmatrix} 0 & -1 \\ 1 & 0 \end{bmatrix}$

$\theta = 180°$ gives the matrix $\begin{bmatrix} -1 & 0 \\ 0 & -1 \end{bmatrix}$

$\theta = -90°$ or $270°$ gives $\begin{bmatrix} 0 & 1 \\ -1 & 0 \end{bmatrix}$

Reflection in a line through the origin

Consider the point P(x, y), a distance d from the line $y = x \tan\theta$ (where θ is the angle between the line and the positive x-axis), and its image P'(x', y') after reflection in this line.

Method 1

Using the formula for the distance of a point P(x, y) from the line $mx - y = 0$, where $m = \tan\theta$, the distance

$$d = \frac{mx - y}{\sqrt{1 + m^2}}$$

$$= \frac{x \tan\theta - y}{\sqrt{1 + \tan^2\theta}}$$

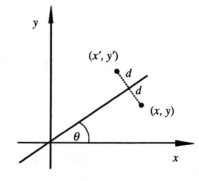

$$= \frac{x\tan\theta - y}{\sec\theta} \qquad \text{since} \quad 1 + \tan^2\theta = \sec^2\theta$$

$$= x\sin\theta - y\cos\theta.$$

Then,

$$x' = x - 2d\sin\theta$$

$$= x - 2\sin\theta(x\sin\theta - y\cos\theta)$$

$$= x(1 - 2\sin^2\theta) + y \times 2\sin\theta\cos\theta$$

$$= x\cos 2\theta + y\sin 2\theta.$$

Also, $\qquad y' = y + 2d\cos\theta$

$$= y + 2\cos\theta(x\sin\theta - y\cos\theta)$$

$$= x \times 2\sin\theta\cos\theta + y(1 - 2\cos^2\theta)$$

$$= x\sin 2\theta - y\cos 2\theta.$$

Thus

$$\begin{bmatrix} x' \\ y' \end{bmatrix} = \begin{bmatrix} \cos 2\theta & \sin 2\theta \\ \sin 2\theta & -\cos 2\theta \end{bmatrix} \begin{bmatrix} x \\ y \end{bmatrix}$$

This method is somewhat clumsy, and certainly not in the spirit of work on transformations. The following approach is both useful and powerful, requiring a few pre-requisites which cannot be quickly deduced. You should make note of it.

Method 2

Write the reflection as the composition of three simple transformations, as follows

   (i)   rotate the plane through θ clockwise about O, so that the line is mapped onto the x-axis. Call this T_1;

   (ii) reflect in this new x-axis. Call this T_2;

   (iii) rotate back through θ anticlockwise about O, so that the line is now in its original position. Call this T_3.

$\qquad T_1$ has matrix $\qquad \begin{bmatrix} \cos\theta & \sin\theta \\ -\sin\theta & \cos\theta \end{bmatrix}$,

$\mathbf{T_2}$ has matrix $\begin{bmatrix} 1 & 0 \\ 0 & -1 \end{bmatrix}$ (see Activity 3 part (a)),and

$\mathbf{T_3}$ is given by $\begin{bmatrix} \cos\theta & -\sin\theta \\ \sin\theta & \cos\theta \end{bmatrix}$.

Now, the application of these three simple transformations correspond to pre-multiplication of the position vector $\begin{bmatrix} x \\ y \end{bmatrix}$ by these three matrices in turn in the order $\mathbf{T_1}$, $\mathbf{T_2}$, $\mathbf{T_3}$.

Applying $\mathbf{T_1}$ first gives $\qquad \mathbf{T_1}\begin{bmatrix} x \\ y \end{bmatrix}$

Applying $\mathbf{T_2}$ to this gives $\qquad \mathbf{T_2}\left\{ \mathbf{T_1}\begin{bmatrix} x \\ y \end{bmatrix}\right\} = (\mathbf{T_2 T_1})\begin{bmatrix} x \\ y \end{bmatrix}$

Applying $\mathbf{T_3}$ then gives $\qquad \mathbf{T_3}\left\{ (\mathbf{T_2 T_1})\begin{bmatrix} x \\ y \end{bmatrix}\right\} = (\mathbf{T_3 T_2 T_1})\begin{bmatrix} x \\ y \end{bmatrix}$.

In this way, you will see that it is the product $\mathbf{T_3 T_2 T_1}$ that is required and not the product $\mathbf{T_1 T_2 T_3}$: it is the order of application and not the usual left-to-right writing which is important.

The transformation is then given by the matrix

$$\begin{bmatrix} \cos\theta & -\sin\theta \\ \sin\theta & \cos\theta \end{bmatrix} \begin{bmatrix} 1 & 0 \\ 0 & -1 \end{bmatrix} \begin{bmatrix} \cos\theta & \sin\theta \\ -\sin\theta & \cos\theta \end{bmatrix}$$

$$= \begin{bmatrix} \cos\theta & \sin\theta \\ \sin\theta & -\cos\theta \end{bmatrix} \begin{bmatrix} \cos\theta & \sin\theta \\ -\sin\theta & \cos\theta \end{bmatrix}$$

$$= \begin{bmatrix} \cos^2\theta - \sin^2\theta & \cos\theta\sin\theta + \sin\theta\cos\theta \\ \sin\theta\cos\theta + \cos\theta\sin\theta & \sin^2\theta - \cos^2\theta \end{bmatrix}$$

$$= \begin{bmatrix} \cos 2\theta & \sin 2\theta \\ \sin 2\theta & -\cos 2\theta \end{bmatrix} \text{ as before.}$$

By substituting in values of θ, you can check the matrices obtained in Activity 3 parts (a) – (d). (Parts (a) and (b) are so straightforward they hardly need checking: in fact, we used (a) in Method 2 in order to establish the more general result.) The line $y = x$ is given by $\theta = 45°$ and $y = -x$ by $\theta = 135°$ or $-45°$.

Example

Find a matrix which represents a reflection in the line $y = 2x$.

Solution

In the diagram shown opposite, $\tan \theta = 2 = \dfrac{2}{1}$. Drawing a right-angled triangle with angle θ and sides 2 and 1, Pythagoras' theorem gives the hypotenuse $\sqrt{5}$ whence $\cos \theta = \dfrac{1}{\sqrt{5}}$ and

$\sin \theta = \dfrac{2}{\sqrt{5}}$.

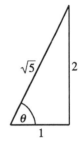

Then

$$\cos 2\theta = 2\cos^2 \theta - 1 = 2 \times \left(\frac{1}{\sqrt{5}}\right)^2 - 1 = -\frac{3}{5}$$

and

$$\sin 2\theta = 2\sin \theta \cos \theta = 2 \times \frac{2}{\sqrt{5}} \times \frac{1}{\sqrt{5}} = \frac{4}{5}.$$

The required matrix is thus

$$\begin{bmatrix} -\frac{3}{5} & \frac{4}{5} \\ \frac{4}{5} & \frac{3}{5} \end{bmatrix}$$

[Alternatively, the well known $t = \tan \theta$ (or $t = \tan \frac{1}{2} A$) substitution, gives $\cos 2\theta = \dfrac{1-t^2}{1+t^2} = -\dfrac{3}{5}$ and $\sin 2\theta = \dfrac{2t}{1+t^2} = \dfrac{4}{5}$ immediately.]

Example

A plane transformation has matrix $\begin{bmatrix} -\frac{\sqrt{3}}{2} & \frac{1}{2} \\ -\frac{1}{2} & -\frac{\sqrt{3}}{2} \end{bmatrix}$. Describe this transformation geometrically.

Solution

The matrix has the form $\begin{bmatrix} \cos \theta & -\sin \theta \\ \sin \theta & \cos \theta \end{bmatrix}$, where $\cos \theta = -\dfrac{\sqrt{3}}{2}$ and $\sin \theta = -\dfrac{1}{2}$, in which case $\theta = 210°$. The matrix then represents a rotation about O through $210°$ anticlockwise.

Exercise 9D

1. Describe geometrically the plane transformations with matrices

   (a) $\begin{bmatrix} \frac{2}{\sqrt{5}} & -\frac{1}{\sqrt{5}} \\ \frac{1}{\sqrt{5}} & \frac{2}{\sqrt{5}} \end{bmatrix}$;   (b) $\begin{bmatrix} \frac{2}{\sqrt{5}} & \frac{1}{\sqrt{5}} \\ \frac{1}{\sqrt{5}} & -\frac{2}{\sqrt{5}} \end{bmatrix}$;

   (c) $\begin{bmatrix} -\frac{1}{9} & \frac{4\sqrt{5}}{9} \\ \frac{4\sqrt{5}}{9} & \frac{1}{9} \end{bmatrix}$;   (d) $\begin{bmatrix} 0.6 & 0.8 \\ -0.8 & 0.6 \end{bmatrix}$;

   (e) $\begin{bmatrix} -0.28 & -0.96 \\ -0.96 & 0.28 \end{bmatrix}$.

2. Write down the matrices representing the following transformations:

   (a) Reflection in the line through the origin which makes an angle of 60° with the positive x-axis;

   (b) Rotation through 135° anticlockwise about O;

   (c) Rotation through $\cos^{-1}\left(\frac{1}{3}\right)$, clockwise about O;

   (d) Reflection in the line $y = -3x$.

9.6 Stretch and enlargement matrices

A stretch parallel to the x-axis, **scale factor** k, has matrix

$$\begin{bmatrix} k & 0 \\ 0 & 1 \end{bmatrix}.$$

Thus $\begin{bmatrix} x' \\ y' \end{bmatrix} = \begin{bmatrix} kx \\ y \end{bmatrix}$ and points (x,y) are transformed into points with the same y-coordinate, but with x-coordinate k times further from the y-axis than they were originally.

Similarly, a stretch parallel to the y-axis, **scale factor** k is represented by the matrix

$$\begin{bmatrix} 1 & 0 \\ 0 & k \end{bmatrix}.$$

An enlargement, centre O and scale factor k, has matrix

$$\begin{bmatrix} k & 0 \\ 0 & k \end{bmatrix} = k\begin{bmatrix} 1 & 0 \\ 0 & 1 \end{bmatrix} = k\mathbf{I},$$

so that $x' = kx$ and $y' = ky$.

9.7 Translations and standard forms

Having obtained matrix forms for some of the elementary plane transformations, it is now possible to extend the range of simple techniques to more complex forms of these transformations. The method employed is essentially the same as that used in the second method for deriving the general matrix for a reflection; namely, treating more complicated transformations as a succession of simpler ones for which results can be quoted without proof.

Rotation not about the origin

A rotation through θ anticlockwise about the point (a, b) can be built up in the following way:

(i) translate the plane by $\begin{bmatrix} -a \\ -b \end{bmatrix}$ so that the centre of rotation is now at the origin;

(ii) rotate about this origin through θ anticlockwise;

(iii) translate the plane back by $\begin{bmatrix} a \\ b \end{bmatrix}$ to its original position.

This leads to

$$\begin{bmatrix} x' \\ y' \end{bmatrix} = \begin{bmatrix} \cos\theta & -\sin\theta \\ \sin\theta & \cos\theta \end{bmatrix} \begin{bmatrix} x-a \\ y-b \end{bmatrix} + \begin{bmatrix} a \\ b \end{bmatrix},$$

or

$$\begin{bmatrix} x'-a \\ y'-b \end{bmatrix} = \begin{bmatrix} \cos\theta & -\sin\theta \\ \sin\theta & \cos\theta \end{bmatrix} \begin{bmatrix} x-a \\ y-b \end{bmatrix}.$$

The second form is more instructive, since it maintains the notion of a straightforward rotation with the point (a, b) as centre. This is the standard form of this (ostensibly) more complicated transformation.

Reflection in a line not through the origin

For a reflection in $y = x\tan\theta + c$,

(i) translate the plane by $\begin{bmatrix} 0 \\ -c \end{bmatrix}$ so that the crossing point of the line on the y-axis is mapped onto the origin;

(ii) reflect in this line through O;

(iii) translate back by $\begin{bmatrix} 0 \\ c \end{bmatrix}$, to get the standard form

$$\begin{bmatrix} x' \\ y'-c \end{bmatrix} = \begin{bmatrix} \cos 2\theta & \sin 2\theta \\ \sin 2\theta & -\cos 2\theta \end{bmatrix} \begin{bmatrix} x \\ y-c \end{bmatrix}.$$

The one case that needs to be examined separately is reflection in a vertical line, $x = a$, say:

(i) translate the plane by $\begin{bmatrix} -a \\ 0 \end{bmatrix}$ so that the line becomes the

y-axis;

(ii) reflect in the y-axis;

(iii) translate by $\begin{bmatrix} a \\ 0 \end{bmatrix}$, to get

$$\begin{bmatrix} x'-a \\ y' \end{bmatrix} = \begin{bmatrix} -1 & 0 \\ 0 & 1 \end{bmatrix} \begin{bmatrix} x-a \\ y \end{bmatrix}.$$

Enlargement, centre not the origin

An enlargement, centre (a, b) and scale factor k, has standard form

$$\begin{bmatrix} x'-a \\ y'-b \end{bmatrix} = \begin{bmatrix} k & 0 \\ 0 & k \end{bmatrix} \begin{bmatrix} x-a \\ y-b \end{bmatrix}$$

in the same way as above.

9.8　Linear transformations of the plane

If a point P(x, y) is mapped onto point P'(x', y') by a transformation T such that

$$x' = ax + by + c, \quad y' = dx + ey + f,$$

for constants a, b, c, d, e and f, then T is said to be a **linear plane transformation**.

Such a transformation can be written algebraically, as above, or in matrix form (possibly in the translated 'standard' form discussed above),

$$\begin{bmatrix} x'-\alpha \\ y'-\beta \end{bmatrix} = \mathbf{M} \begin{bmatrix} x-\alpha \\ y-\beta \end{bmatrix},$$

where $\mathbf{M}$ is a 2×2 matrix.

Example

Express algebraically the transformation which consists of a reflection in the line $x + y = 1$.

Solution

Line is $y = -x + 1$ with gradient $\tan 135°$.

A reflection in this line can then be written as

$$\begin{bmatrix} x' \\ y'-1 \end{bmatrix} = \begin{bmatrix} \cos 270° & \sin 270° \\ \sin 270° & -\cos 270° \end{bmatrix} \begin{bmatrix} x \\ y-1 \end{bmatrix}$$

$$= \begin{bmatrix} 0 & -1 \\ -1 & 0 \end{bmatrix} \begin{bmatrix} x \\ y-1 \end{bmatrix}$$

$$= \begin{bmatrix} -y+1 \\ -x \end{bmatrix}$$

and this is written algebraically as $x' = 1 - y, \quad y' = 1 - x$.

Example

A transformation **T** has algebraic form

$$x' = \frac{3}{5}x - \frac{4}{5}y + 6, \quad y' = \frac{4}{5}x + \frac{3}{5}y - 2.$$

Give a full geometrical description of **T**.

Solution

Firstly, find any invariant (fixed) points of **T**, given by $x' = x, \quad y' = y$: i.e.

$$x = \frac{3}{5}x - \frac{4}{5}y + 6,$$

$$y = \frac{4}{5}x + \frac{3}{5}y - 2.$$

Solving simultaneously gives $(x, y) = (5, 5)$.

T can be then written in standard matrix form

$$\begin{bmatrix} x'-5 \\ y'-5 \end{bmatrix} = \begin{bmatrix} \frac{3}{5} & -\frac{4}{5} \\ \frac{4}{5} & \frac{3}{5} \end{bmatrix} \begin{bmatrix} x-5 \\ y-5 \end{bmatrix},$$

and the matrix is clearly that of a rotation, with

$$\cos\theta = \frac{3}{5}, \quad \sin\theta = \frac{4}{5},$$

giving $\quad \theta = \cos^{-1}\left(\frac{3}{5}\right) \quad (\approx 53.13°).$

Hence **T** is a rotation through an angle of $\cos^{-1}\left(\frac{3}{5}\right)$ anticlockwise about $(5, 5)$.

Example

Show that the transformation $5x' = 21x + 8y, \quad 5y' = 8x + 9y$ is a stretch in a fixed direction leaving every point of a certain line invariant. Find this line and the amount of the stretch.

Solution

Firstly, $x' = x, \ y' = y$ for invariant points, giving

$$5x = 21x + 8y \text{ and } 5y = 8x + 9y.$$

Both equations give $y = -2x$ and so this is the line of invariant points.

Next, consider all possible lines perpendicular to $y = -2x$. These will be of the form $y = \frac{1}{2}x + c$ (for constant c). Now for any point on the line $y = \frac{1}{2}x + c,$

$$x' = \frac{21}{5}x + \frac{8}{5}y = \frac{21}{5}x + \frac{8}{5}\left(\frac{1}{2}x + c\right) = 5x + \frac{8}{5}c,$$

and $\quad y' = \frac{8}{5}x + \frac{9}{5}y = \frac{8}{5}x + \frac{9}{5}\left(\frac{1}{2}x + c\right) = \frac{5x}{2} + \frac{9}{5}c,$

whence $y' = \frac{1}{2}x' + c$ also. Hence all lines perpendicular to $y = -2x$ are invariant and the transformation is a stretch.

Finally, $\begin{bmatrix} x' \\ y' \end{bmatrix} = A \begin{bmatrix} x \\ y \end{bmatrix}$ where $A = \begin{bmatrix} \frac{21}{5} & \frac{8}{5} \\ \frac{8}{5} & \frac{9}{5} \end{bmatrix}$ and

$\det A = \begin{vmatrix} \frac{21}{5} & \frac{8}{5} \\ \frac{8}{5} & \frac{9}{5} \end{vmatrix} = \frac{189}{25} - \frac{64}{25} = 5$, so the stretch has scale factor 5.

Exercise 9E

1. Determine the standard matrix forms of

   (a) an enlargement, centre $(a, 0)$ and scale factor k;

   (b) a rotation of $45°$ anticlockwise about the point $(1,0)$.

2. Give a full geometrical description of the plane transformations having matrices **A** and **B**, where

   $$A = \frac{1}{\sqrt{2}}\begin{bmatrix} 1 & 1 \\ 1 & -1 \end{bmatrix} \text{ and } B = \frac{1}{\sqrt{2}}\begin{bmatrix} 1 & -1 \\ 1 & 1 \end{bmatrix}.$$

   Determine the product matrices **AB** and **BA**. Give also a full geometrical description of the plane transformations having matrices **AB** and **BA**.

3. (a) The transformation **T** of the plane is defined by $x'=x, y'=2-y$. Describe this transformation geometrically.

   (b) Express algebraically the transformation **S** which is a clockwise rotation through $45°$ about the origin.

4. Describe geometrically the single transformations given algebraically by

   (a) $5x'=-3x+4y+12$, $5y'=-4x-3y+16$;

   (b) $5x'=3x-4y+6$, $5y'=-4x-3y+12$;

   (c) $5x'=9x+8y-12$, $5y'=8x+21y-24$.

5. Express each of the following transformations in the form $x'=ax+by+p, y'=cx+dy+q$, giving the values of a, b, c, d, p and q in each case:

   (a) a reflection in the line $x+y=0$;

   (b) a reflection in the line $x-y=2$;

   (c) a rotation through $90°$ anticlockwise about the point $(2,-1)$;

   (d) a rotation through $60°$ clockwise about the point $(3,2)$.

6. Find the matrix which represents a stretch, scale factor k, parallel to the line $y=x\tan\theta$.

9.9 Composition of transformations

If a transformation of the plane T_1 is followed by a second plane transformation T_2 then the result may itself be represented by a single transformation **T** which is the composition of T_1 and T_2 taken in that order. This is written $T = T_2 T_1$.

Note, again, that the order of application is from the right: this is in order to be consistent with the pre-multiplication order of the matrices that represent these transformations.

Example (non-matrix composition)

The transformation **T** is the composition of transformations T_1 and T_2, taken in that order, where

$$T_1: \quad x'=2x+1, \quad y'=3-2y$$

and $\quad T_2: \quad x'=x+y-1, \quad y'=1-2x$

Express **T** algebraically.

Solution

As T_2 is the 'second stage' transformation, write,

$$T_2: \quad x''=x'+y'-1, \quad y''=1-2x' \,,$$

where x' and y' represent the intermediate stage, after T_1 has been applied.

Thus
$$T_2 T_1: \quad x''=(2x+1)+(3-2y)-1=2x-2y+3$$

$$y''=1-2(2x+1)=-4x-1$$

and we can write

$$T: \quad x'=2x-2y+3, \quad y'=-4x-1.$$

The inverse of a transformation **T** can be thought of as that transformation **S** for which $TST = TS = I$, the identity transformation represented by the matrix $\begin{bmatrix} 1 & 0 \\ 0 & 1 \end{bmatrix}$. **S** is then denoted by T^{-1}.

Example (non-matrix inversion)

Find T^{-1}, when **T**: $x'=x+y-1, \quad y'=2x-y+4.$

Interchanging x for x' and y for y' gives

$$x = x'+y'-1, \quad y=2x'-y'+4.$$

These can be treated as simultaneous equations and solved for x', y' in terms of x, y.

Adding $\quad x+y=3x'+3 \Rightarrow x'=\dfrac{1}{3}x+\dfrac{1}{3}y-1;$

substituting back

$$x = \left(\frac{1}{3}x+\frac{1}{3}y-1\right)+y'-1 \Rightarrow y'=\frac{2}{3}x-\frac{1}{3}y+2$$

Therefore, $\quad$ **T^{-1}**: $\quad x'=\dfrac{1}{3}x+\dfrac{1}{3}y-1, \quad y'=\dfrac{2}{3}x-\dfrac{1}{3}y+2.$

Finding a composite transformation when its constituent parts are given in matrix form is easy, simply involving the multiplication of the respective matrices which represent those constituents. Inverses, similarly, require the finding of an inverse matrix, provided that the **T**'s matrix is non-singular: only a projection has a singular matrix.

Example

The transformation $\mathbf{T}$ is defined by $\mathbf{T} = (\mathbf{CBA})$, where $\mathbf{A}$, $\mathbf{B}$ and $\mathbf{C}$ are the transformations:

A: a rotation about O through $30°$ anticlockwise;

B: a reflection in the line through O that makes an angle of $120°$ with the x-axis;

C: a rotation about O through $210°$ anticlockwise.

Give the complete geometrical description of $\mathbf{T}$.

Solution

$\mathbf{A}$ has matrix $\begin{bmatrix} \cos 30° & -\sin 30° \\ \sin 30° & \cos 30° \end{bmatrix} = \dfrac{1}{2}\begin{bmatrix} \sqrt{3} & -1 \\ 1 & \sqrt{3} \end{bmatrix}$,

while $\mathbf{B}$ has matrix

$$\begin{bmatrix} \cos 240° & \sin 240° \\ \sin 240° & -\cos 240° \end{bmatrix} = \dfrac{1}{2}\begin{bmatrix} -1 & -\sqrt{3} \\ -\sqrt{3} & 1 \end{bmatrix}$$

and $\mathbf{C}$ has matrix

$$\begin{bmatrix} \cos 210° & -\sin 210° \\ \sin 210° & \cos 210° \end{bmatrix} = \dfrac{1}{2}\begin{bmatrix} -\sqrt{3} & 1 \\ -1 & -\sqrt{3} \end{bmatrix}.$$

Thus $\mathbf{T} = \mathbf{CBA}$ has matrix

$$\dfrac{1}{8}\begin{bmatrix} -\sqrt{3} & 1 \\ -1 & -\sqrt{3} \end{bmatrix}\begin{bmatrix} -1 & -\sqrt{3} \\ -\sqrt{3} & 1 \end{bmatrix}\begin{bmatrix} \sqrt{3} & -1 \\ 1 & \sqrt{3} \end{bmatrix}$$

$$= \dfrac{1}{8}\begin{bmatrix} 0 & 4 \\ 4 & 0 \end{bmatrix}\begin{bmatrix} \sqrt{3} & -1 \\ 1 & \sqrt{3} \end{bmatrix}$$

$$= \begin{bmatrix} \frac{1}{2} & \frac{\sqrt{3}}{2} \\ \frac{\sqrt{3}}{2} & -\frac{1}{2} \end{bmatrix} = \begin{bmatrix} \cos 60° & \sin 60° \\ \sin 60° & -\cos 60° \end{bmatrix}$$

and $\mathbf{T}$ is a reflection in $y = x \tan 30°$; i.e. $y = \dfrac{x}{\sqrt{3}}$.

Example

Describe fully the transformation **T** given algebraically by

$$x' = 8x - 15y - 37$$
$$y' = 15x + 8y - 1$$

Solution

For invariant points, set $x' = x$ and $y' = y$, giving

$$0 = 7x - 15y - 37$$

and

$$0 = 15x + 7y - 1.$$

Solving simultaneously gives the single invariant point
$(x, y) = (1, -2)$. **T** can then be written as

$$\begin{bmatrix} x'-1 \\ y'+2 \end{bmatrix} = \begin{bmatrix} 8 & -15 \\ 15 & 8 \end{bmatrix} \begin{bmatrix} x-1 \\ y+2 \end{bmatrix}$$

$$= 17 \begin{bmatrix} \frac{8}{17} & -\frac{15}{17} \\ \frac{15}{17} & \frac{8}{17} \end{bmatrix} \begin{bmatrix} x-1 \\ y+2 \end{bmatrix}$$

$$= \begin{bmatrix} 17 & 0 \\ 0 & 17 \end{bmatrix} \begin{bmatrix} \frac{8}{17} & -\frac{15}{17} \\ \frac{15}{17} & \frac{8}{17} \end{bmatrix} \begin{bmatrix} x-1 \\ y+2 \end{bmatrix}$$

and **T** is a rotation through $\cos^{-1}\left(\dfrac{8}{17}\right)$ ($\approx 61.93°$) anticlockwise
about the point $(1, -2)$ together with an enlargement, centre $(1, -2)$
and scale factor 17.

Note that the two matrices involved here commute (remember: if
AB = BA then **A** and **B** are said to commute) so that the two
components of this composite transformation may be taken in
either order. This rotation-and-enlargement having the same centre
is often referred to as a **spiral similarity**.

Exercise 9F

1. Write down the 2×2 matrices corresponding to:

    (a) a reflection in the line through O at 60° to
    the positive x-axis,

    (b) a rotation anticlockwise about O through
    90°, and

    (c) a reflection in the line through O at 120° to
    the positive x-axis.

    Describe geometrically the resultant

    (i) of (a) and (b);

    (ii) of (a), (b) and (c); taken in the given
    order.

2. Give a full geometrical description of the transformation T_1 given by

    $T_1 = x' = 5 - y, \quad y' = x - 1.$

    Express in algebraic form T_2, which is a reflection in the line $y = x + 2$.

    Hence express $T_3 = T_2 T_1 T_2$ algebraically and give a full geometrical description of T_3.

3. Prove that a reflection in the line $y = x \tan \theta$ followed by a reflection in the line $y = x \tan \phi$ is equivalent to a rotation. Describe this rotation completely.

4. Transformations A, B and C are defined algebraically by

    $A: \quad x' = -y, \quad y' = -x,$

    $B: \quad x' = y + 2, \quad y' = x - 2,$

    $C: \quad x' = -y + 1, \quad y' = x - 3.$

    Transformations U and V are defined by

    $U = BCA$ and $V = AC^{-1}BC$. Express U and V algebraically. Show that V has no invariant points, and that U has a single invariant point. Give a simple geometrical description of U.

5. Given $\quad T_1: \quad x' = 1 - 2y, \quad y = 2x - 3$ and
    $\qquad\qquad T_2: \quad x' = 1 - y, \quad y = 1 - x$

    define T_3 algebraically, where T_3 is T_1 followed by T_2. Show that T_3 may be expressed as a reflection in the line $x = \dfrac{4}{3}$ followed by an enlargement, and give the centre and scale factor of this enlargement.

9.10 Eigenvalues and eigenvectors

Consider the equation

$$A\begin{bmatrix} x \\ y \end{bmatrix} = \lambda \begin{bmatrix} x \\ y \end{bmatrix}$$

where A is a 2×2 matrix and λ is a scalar. This is equivalent to

$$A\begin{bmatrix} x \\ y \end{bmatrix} = \lambda I \begin{bmatrix} x \\ y \end{bmatrix} \quad \text{or} \quad (A - \lambda I)\begin{bmatrix} x \\ y \end{bmatrix} = \begin{bmatrix} 0 \\ 0 \end{bmatrix}.$$

Now in the case when the matrix $(A - \lambda I)$ is non-singular (i.e. its inverse exists) we can pre-multiply this equation by $(A - \lambda I)^{-1}$ to deduce that

$$\begin{bmatrix} x \\ y \end{bmatrix} = (A - \lambda I)^{-1}\begin{bmatrix} 0 \\ 0 \end{bmatrix} = \begin{bmatrix} 0 \\ 0 \end{bmatrix}.$$

In other words, if $\det (A - \lambda I) \neq 0$ then the only vector $\begin{bmatrix} x \\ y \end{bmatrix}$ which

satisfies the equation $A\begin{bmatrix} x \\ y \end{bmatrix} = \lambda \begin{bmatrix} x \\ y \end{bmatrix}$ is the zero vector $\begin{bmatrix} 0 \\ 0 \end{bmatrix}$.

The other cases, when $\det(A - \lambda I) = 0$, are more interesting. The equation $A\begin{bmatrix} x \\ y \end{bmatrix} = \lambda \begin{bmatrix} x \\ y \end{bmatrix}$ has a non-trivial solution and it it easy to check that if $\begin{bmatrix} x \\ y \end{bmatrix}$ is a solution so is any scalar multiple of $\begin{bmatrix} x \\ y \end{bmatrix}$. In other words the solutions form a line through the origin, and indeed an invariant line of the transformation represented by A.

(In the special case when $\lambda = 1$, $\begin{bmatrix} x' \\ y' \end{bmatrix} = A\begin{bmatrix} x \\ y \end{bmatrix} = \begin{bmatrix} x \\ y \end{bmatrix}$, and such

vectors $\begin{bmatrix} x \\ y \end{bmatrix}$ give a line of invariant points. For all other values of λ, the line will simply be an invariant line.)

Example

The matrix $A = \begin{bmatrix} \frac{3}{5} & \frac{4}{5} \\ \frac{4}{5} & -\frac{3}{5} \end{bmatrix}$ represents a reflection in the line

$y = x\tan\theta$, with $\cos 2\theta = \dfrac{3}{5}$, $\sin 2\theta = \dfrac{4}{5}$, giving $\tan\theta = \dfrac{1}{2}$. Then

the line $y = \dfrac{1}{2}x$ is a line of invariant points under this

transformation, and any line perpendicular to it (with gradient -2) is an invariant line.

To show how the equation

$$(A - \lambda I)\begin{bmatrix} x \\ y \end{bmatrix} = \begin{bmatrix} 0 \\ 0 \end{bmatrix}$$

can be used to find the invariate lines, first calculate those λ for which the matrix $(A - \lambda I)$ is singular; i.e. $\det(A - \lambda I) = 0$.

This gives

$$\begin{vmatrix} \frac{3}{5} - \lambda & \frac{4}{5} \\ \frac{4}{5} & -\frac{3}{5} - \lambda \end{vmatrix} = 0$$

$$\Rightarrow \quad \left(\frac{3}{5} - \lambda\right)\left(-\frac{3}{5} - \lambda\right) - \frac{4}{5} \times \frac{4}{5} = 0$$

$$\Rightarrow \quad \lambda^2 - 1 = 0$$

$$\Rightarrow \quad \lambda = \pm 1.$$

Remember that you are looking for solutions (x, y) to the equation

$$\begin{bmatrix} \frac{3}{5} - \lambda & \frac{4}{5} \\ \frac{4}{5} & -\frac{3}{5} - \lambda \end{bmatrix} \begin{bmatrix} x \\ y \end{bmatrix} = \begin{bmatrix} 0 \\ 0 \end{bmatrix}.$$

Substituting back, in turn, these two values of λ:

$$\lambda = 1 \quad \Rightarrow \quad \left. \begin{array}{l} -\dfrac{2}{5}x + \dfrac{4}{5}y = 0 \\ \dfrac{4}{5}x - \dfrac{8}{5}y = 0 \end{array} \right\} \quad \Rightarrow \quad x = 2y,$$

and the solution vectors corresponding to $\lambda = 1$ are of the form

$$\alpha \begin{bmatrix} 2 \\ 1 \end{bmatrix} \text{ for real } \alpha.$$

$$\lambda = -1 \quad \Rightarrow \quad \left. \begin{array}{l} \dfrac{8}{5}x + \dfrac{4}{5}y = 0 \\ \dfrac{4}{5}x + \dfrac{2}{5}y = 0 \end{array} \right\} \quad \Rightarrow \quad y = -2x,$$

and the solution vectors corresponding to $\lambda = -1$ have the form

$$\beta \begin{bmatrix} 1 \\ -2 \end{bmatrix} \text{ for real } \beta.$$

The results, then, for this reflection are that $y = \dfrac{1}{2}x$ is a line of invariant points (signified by $\lambda = 1$), and that $y = -2x$ is an invariant line. (Here the value of λ, namely -1, indicates that the image points of this line are the same distance from $y = \dfrac{1}{2}x$ as their originals, but in the opposite direction). So this method has indeed led to the invariant lines which pass through the origin.

Because the solutions to this type of matrix-vector equation provide some of the characteristics of the associated transformation, the λ's are called **characteristic values**, or **eigenvalues** (from the German word eigenschaft) of the matrix. Their associated solution vectors are called **characteristic vectors**, or **eigenvectors**. Each eigenvalue has a corresponding set of eigenvectors.

Example

Find the eigenvalues and corresponding eigenvectors of the matrix

$$A = \begin{bmatrix} 3 & -1 \\ -1 & 3 \end{bmatrix}.$$

Give a full geometrical description of the plane transformation determined by **A**.

Solution

Eigenvalues are given by $\det(\mathbf{A} - \lambda \mathbf{I}) = 0$. Hence

$$\begin{vmatrix} 3-\lambda & -1 \\ -1 & 3-\lambda \end{vmatrix} = 0$$

$$\Rightarrow \quad (3-\lambda)(3-\lambda) - 1 = 0$$

$$\Rightarrow \quad \lambda^2 - 6\lambda + 8 = 0$$

$$\Rightarrow \quad (\lambda - 2)(\lambda - 4) = 0$$

and $\lambda = 2$ or $\lambda = 4$.

Now $\qquad \lambda = 2 \quad \Rightarrow \quad \left.\begin{array}{r} x - y = 0 \\ -x + y = 0 \end{array}\right\} \quad \Rightarrow \quad y = x$

and $\lambda = 2$ has eigenvectors $\alpha \begin{bmatrix} 1 \\ 1 \end{bmatrix}$.

Also $\qquad \lambda = 4 \quad \Rightarrow \quad \left.\begin{array}{r} -x - y = 0 \\ -x - y = 0 \end{array}\right\} \quad \Rightarrow \quad y = -x$

and $\lambda = 4$ has eigenvectors $\beta \begin{bmatrix} 1 \\ -1 \end{bmatrix}$.

The invariant lines (through the origin) of the transformation are $y = x$ and $y = -x$ (in fact there are no others).

Notice that these lines are perpendicular to each other. For $y = x$, $\lambda = 2$ means that points on this line are moved to points also on the line, twice as far away from the origin and on the same side of O. For $y = -x$, $\lambda = 4$ has a similar significance.

The transformation represented by **A** is seen to be the composition of a stretch parallel to $y = x$, scale factor 2, together with a stretch parallel to $y = -x$, factor 4, in either order.

The composition of two stretches in perpendicular directions is known as a **two-way stretch**.

In general the equation

$$\begin{vmatrix} a-\lambda & b \\ c & d-\lambda \end{vmatrix} = 0$$

is called the **characteristic equation** of the matrix $A = \begin{bmatrix} a & b \\ c & d \end{bmatrix}$. In the 2×2 case the equation is the quadratic

$$\lambda^2 - (a+d)\lambda + (ad - bc) = 0.$$

The sum, $a+d$, of the entries in the leading diagonal of A is known as its **trace**, and so the characteristic equation is

$$\boxed{\lambda^2 - (\text{trace } A)\lambda + \det A = 0}$$

Example

Find the eigenvalues and corresponding eigenvectors of the matrix

$$A = \begin{bmatrix} 2 & 1 \\ -9 & 8 \end{bmatrix}.$$

Determine the coordinates of the invariant point of the transformation given algebraically by

$$x' = 2x + y - 1, \quad y' = -9x + 8y - 3.$$

Deduce the equations of any invariant lines of this transformation.

Solution

The characteristic equation of the matrix

$$A = \begin{bmatrix} 2 & 1 \\ -9 & 8 \end{bmatrix}$$

is

$$\begin{vmatrix} 2-\lambda & 1 \\ -9 & 8-\lambda \end{vmatrix} = 0$$

or

$$\lambda^2 - 10\lambda + 25 = 0.$$
$$\uparrow \qquad \uparrow$$
$$\text{trace } A \quad \det A$$

This has root $\lambda = 5$ (twice) and

$$\lambda = 5 \quad \Rightarrow \quad \left. \begin{array}{l} -3x + y = 0 \\ -9x + 3y = 0 \end{array} \right\} \quad \Rightarrow \quad y = 3x$$

Thus **A** has a single eigenvalue $\lambda = 5$, with eigenvectors $\alpha\begin{bmatrix} 1 \\ 3 \end{bmatrix}$.

For invariant points $x'= x$, $y'= y$ whence $x = 2x + y - 1$,
$y = -9x + 8y - 3$.

Solving simultaneously gives $(x,y) = \left(\tfrac{1}{4}, \tfrac{3}{4}\right)$.

Since the transformation can be written in the form

$$\begin{bmatrix} x' - \tfrac{1}{4} \\ y' - \tfrac{3}{4} \end{bmatrix} = \mathbf{A}\begin{bmatrix} x - \tfrac{1}{4} \\ y - \tfrac{3}{4} \end{bmatrix},$$

there is a single invariant line $\left(y - \tfrac{3}{4}\right) = 3\left(x - \tfrac{1}{4}\right)$. (This arises from the '$y = 3x$' derived from $\lambda = 5$, but the 'y' and the 'x' are translated

by $\begin{bmatrix} \tfrac{1}{4} \\ \tfrac{3}{4} \end{bmatrix}$; in this instance this has given rise to the same line but this

will not, in general, prove to be the case!)

Exercise 9G

1. Show that the transformation represented by the matrix $A = \begin{bmatrix} 2 & -2 \\ -1 & 3 \end{bmatrix}$ has a line of invariant points and an invariant line. Explain the distinction between the two.

2. Find the eigenvalue(s) and eigenvector(s) of the following matrices:

   (a) $A = \begin{bmatrix} 5 & -8 \\ 2 & -3 \end{bmatrix}$;
   (b) $B = \begin{bmatrix} 1 & 1 \\ 0 & 1 \end{bmatrix}$;

   (c) $C = \begin{bmatrix} 1 & 2 \\ 2 & -2 \end{bmatrix}$
   (d) $D = \begin{bmatrix} 2 & 4 \\ 5 & 3 \end{bmatrix}$

3. Find a 2×2 matrix **M** which maps A(0, 2) into A'(1, 3) and leaves B(1 ,1) invariant. Show that this matrix has just one eigenvalue.

4. A linear transformation of the plane is given by
   $$\begin{bmatrix} x' \\ y' \end{bmatrix} = \begin{bmatrix} a & b \\ c & d \end{bmatrix}\begin{bmatrix} x \\ y \end{bmatrix}.$$

   Show that the condition for the transformation to have invariant points (other than the origin) is
   $1 - a - d + ad - bc = 0$.

5. (a) Find the eigenvalues and eigenvectors of the matrix $\begin{bmatrix} 0 & -2 \\ -2 & 0 \end{bmatrix}$.

   (b) A transformation of the plane is given by $x'= 2 - 2y$, $y'= 7 - 2x$. Find the invariant point and give the cartesian equations of the two invariant lines. Hence give a full geometrical description of the transformation.

6. Find the eigenvalues and eigenvectors of the matrices $A = \begin{bmatrix} \tfrac{3}{5} & \tfrac{4}{5} \\ \tfrac{4}{5} & -\tfrac{3}{5} \end{bmatrix}$ and $B = \begin{bmatrix} 3 & -4 \\ 1 & -1 \end{bmatrix}$. Show that the plane transformations represented by **A** and **B** have the same line of invariant points and state its cartesian equation.

7. The eigenvalues of the matrix
   $$T = \begin{bmatrix} a & b \\ c & d \end{bmatrix} \quad (b > 0, c \geq 0)$$

   are equal. Prove that $a = d$ and $c = 0$. If **T** maps the point $(2, -1)$ into the $(1, 2)$, determine the elements of **T**.

9.11 Miscellaneous Exercises

1. By writing the following in standard matrix form describe the transformations of the plane given by

    (a) $x'=3x+4$,
       $y'=3y+2$

    (b) $x'=\frac{3}{5}x+\frac{4}{5}y-\frac{6}{5}$,
       $y'=\frac{4}{5}x-\frac{3}{5}y+\frac{12}{5}$

    (c) $5x'=3x-4y+8$,
       $5y'=4x+3y-6$

    (d) $5x'=13x-4y-4$,
       $5y'=-4x+7y+2$

2. Find the eigenvalues and corresponding eigenvectors of the matrix $\begin{bmatrix} 2 & -1 \\ -4 & 2 \end{bmatrix}$. Deduce the equations of the invariant lines of the transformation defined by

    $x'=2x-y$, $y'=-4x+2y$.

    Explain why one of these lines has an image which is not a line at all. Describe this transformation geometrically.

3. A reflection in the line $y=x-1$ is followed by an anticlockwise rotation of 90° about the point $(-1, 1)$. Express the resultant transformation algebraically.

    Show that this resultant has an invariant line, and give the equation of this line. Describe the resultant transformation in relation to this line.

4. Find the eigenvalues and corresponding eigenvectors of the matrices

    (a) $A = \begin{bmatrix} 2 & -1 \\ 1 & 2 \end{bmatrix}$;

    (b) $B = \begin{bmatrix} 3 & 2 \\ 2 & 6 \end{bmatrix}$.

    In each case deduce the equations of any invariant lines of the transformations which they represent.

    A plane figure F, with area 1 square unit, is transformed by each of these transformations in turn. Write down the area of the image of F in each case.

    Describe geometrically the two transformations.

5. The linear transformation T leaves the line $y = x\tan\frac{\pi}{6}$ invariant and increases perpendicular distances from that line by a factor of 3.

    (a) Determine the 2×2 matrix A representing T.

    (b) Write down the eigenvalues and corresponding eigenvectors of A.

6. A rotation about the point $(-c, 0)$ through an angle θ is followed by a rotation about the point $(c, 0)$ through an angle $-\theta$.

    Show that the resultant of the two rotations is a translation and give the x and y components of this translation in terms of c and θ.

7. A transformation T is defined algebraically by $x'=y-\sqrt{2}$, $y'=x+\sqrt{2}$. Find the invariant points of T and hence give its full geometrical description.

8. A plane transformation T consists of a reflection in the line $y=2x+1$ followed by a rotation through $\frac{\pi}{2}$ anticlockwise about the point $(2,-1)$.

    (a) Express T algebraically.

    (b) Show that T can also be obtained by a translation followed by a reflection in a line through the origin, giving full details of the translation and reflection.

9. A linear transformation T of the plane has one eigenvector $\begin{bmatrix} 1 \\ -\sqrt{3} \end{bmatrix}$ with corresponding eigenvalue 1, and one eigenvector $\begin{bmatrix} \sqrt{3} \\ 1 \end{bmatrix}$ with eigenvalue -4.

    Give a geometric description of T, and find the matrix A representing T.

10. An anticlockwise rotation about $(0,1)$ through an angle θ is followed by a clockwise rotation about the point $(2, 0)$ through an angle θ. Show that the resultant is a translation, stating its vector in terms of θ.

11. Express each of the following transformations of the plane in the form

    $$\begin{bmatrix} x' \\ y' \end{bmatrix} = \begin{bmatrix} a & b \\ c & d \end{bmatrix} \begin{bmatrix} x \\ y \end{bmatrix} + \begin{bmatrix} p \\ q \end{bmatrix},$$

    giving the values of a, b, c, d, p, q in each case:

    (a) T_1: reflection in the line $y=x$.

    (b) T_2: reflection in the line $x+y=3$.

    (c) T_3: rotation through 90° anticlockwise about the point $(1,4)$.

    (d) $T_4 = T_2 T_3 T_1$, that is T_1 followed by T_3 followed by T_2.

    Show that T_4 has a single invariant point and give a simple geometrical description of T_4.

    (Oxford)

12. (a) The transformation T_1 is represented by the

    matrix $A = \begin{bmatrix} -\frac{3}{5} & \frac{4}{5} \\ \frac{4}{5} & \frac{3}{5} \end{bmatrix}$.

    (i) Find the eigenvalues and eigenvectors of **A**.

    (ii) State the equation of the line of invariant points and describe the transformation T_1 geometrically.

    (b) Find the 2×2 matrix **B** which represents the transformation T_2, a rotation about the origin through $\tan^{-1} \frac{3}{4}$ anticlockwise.

    (c) The transformation $T_3 = T_1 T_2 T_1$. Find the 2×2 matrix **C** which represents T_3 and hence describe T_3 geometrically. (Oxford)

13. Explain the difference between an invariant (fixed) line and a line of invariant points. A transformation of the plane is given by the equations $x' = 7 - 2y$, $y' = 5 - 2x$.

    (a) The images of A(0, 2), B(2, 2) and C(0, 4) are A', B', C' respectively. Find the ratio of area A'B'C': area ABC.

    (b) Calculate the coordinates of the invariant point.

    (c) Determine the equations of the invariant lines of the transformation.

    (d) Give a full geometrical description of the transformation. (Oxford)

14. A plane transformation **T** is defined by
    $x' = 7x - 24y + 12$, $y' = -24x - 7y + 56$.

    Show that **T** has just one invariant point P, and find its coordinates.

Prove that **T** is a reflection in a line through P together with an enlargement centre P.

State the scale factor of the enlargement and determine the equation of the line of reflection. (Oxford)

15. The transformation T_1 has a line of fixed points $y = 3x$ and perpendicular distances from this line are multiplied by a factor of 4. T_1 is represented by the 2×2 matrix **A**. Write down the values of the constants λ_1, λ_2 where $A \begin{bmatrix} 1 \\ 3 \end{bmatrix} = \lambda_1 \begin{bmatrix} 1 \\ 3 \end{bmatrix}$ and

$A \begin{bmatrix} -3 \\ 1 \end{bmatrix} = \lambda_2 \begin{bmatrix} -3 \\ 1 \end{bmatrix}$. Hence, or otherwise, show that

$A = \begin{bmatrix} 3.7 & -0.9 \\ -0.9 & 1.3 \end{bmatrix}$.

The transformation T_2 is given by
$x' = 3.7x - 0.9y + 1.8$,
$y' = -0.9x + 1.3y - 0.6$.

Find the line of fixed points of T_2 and describe T_2 geometrically.

Given that T_1^{-1} is the inverse transformation of T_1, express $T_3 = T_1^{-1} T_2$ in the form

$x' = ax + by + c$,

$y' = dx + ey + f$,

and describe T_3 geometrically. (Oxford)

ANSWERS

The answers to the questions set in the Exercises are given below. Answers to questions set in some of the Activities are also given where appropriate.

1 TRIGONOMETRY

Exercise 1A

1. (a) $-2\sin 4x \sin x$　　(b) $2\cos 9x \sin 2x$

   (c) $2\cos\frac{11}{2}x\cos\frac{7}{2}x$　(d) $2\sin 8x \cos 5x$

   (e) $\cos\frac{\pi}{5}\cos\frac{\pi}{3}\cos\frac{2\pi}{5}$　(f) $\sin 50°(2\cos 10°+1)$

   (g) 0

2. $\sqrt{\dfrac{3}{2}}$

3. (a) $\cos 12x + \cos 2x$　(b) $\cos 3x + \cos 2x$

   (c) $\cos 2\theta - \sin 4\theta$

   (d) $\sin 270° + \cos 60° = -0.5$

5. $4\cos 3x \cos 4x \cos 5x$

6. $\sin 4x \sin 8x$

Exercise 1B

	R	α
1.	5	0.9273
2.	5	0.6435
3.	17	0.4900
4.	$2\sqrt{10}$	0.3218
5.	29	0.8098
6.	$\sqrt{197}$	0.0713
7.	$\sqrt{5}$	0.4636
8.	$\sqrt{34}$	0.5404

Exercise 1C

1. $36.87°$, $61.93°$

2. (a) $103.29°, 330.45°$　(b) $49.79°, 197.59°$

3. $2\cos\left(\theta - \dfrac{\pi}{6}\right); \theta = \dfrac{5\pi}{12}, \dfrac{23\pi}{12}$

4. (a) $\pm 23.69°, \pm 104.89°$　(b) $82.5°$

   (c) $86.57°, 326.57°$　(d) $2.04, 5.03$ radians

Exercise 1D

1. (a) $45°, 135°, 90°$　(b) $0°, 60°, 72°, 144°, 180°$

   (c) $0°, 60°, 90°, 180°$

2. $0.714, 3.835$ radians

3. $\sin 3\theta = 3\sin\theta - 4\sin^3\theta$

   (a) $60°, 90°, 120°, 270°, 330°$

   (b) $0°, 98.7°, 180°, 261.3°, 360°$

   (c) $0°, 50.9°, 180°, 309.1°, 360°$

4. $\dfrac{\pi}{24}, \dfrac{5\pi}{24}, \dfrac{13\pi}{24}, \dfrac{17\pi}{24}$

5. $0°, 60°, 72°, 90°, 144°, 180°$

6. $45°, 105°, 135°, 165°, 225°, 285°, 315°, 345°$

7. (a) $\sin\theta = \dfrac{2t}{1+t^2}$　(c) $120°, 240°$

Exercise 1E

1. (a) $x = 180n + (-1)^n 50$

   (b) $\theta = 180n + 75$

   (c) $x = 360n \pm 80.2$

   (d) $\theta = 90n - 5.8$

   (e) $x = 180n - 30.96 + (-1)^n 43.31$ or

   　　$x = 360n + 59.04 \pm 46.69$

   (f) $\theta = 360n + 36.87 \pm 66.42$

   (g) $x = 180n + 45, 90n - 22.5$

   (h) $x = 45n + 15, 45n + 30$

   (i) $x = 45n + 22.5, 60n + (-1)^n 10$

2. (a) $x = n\pi + 0.9553$

   (b) $x = n\pi - \dfrac{\pi}{12}$

Answers

(c) $x = n\pi + (-1)^n 0.3576$

(d) $x = 4n\pi - \dfrac{\pi}{2} \pm \dfrac{2\pi}{3}$

(e) $\theta = n\pi + \dfrac{\pi}{6} + (-1)^n \dfrac{\pi}{4}$

(f) $\theta = 2n\pi \pm \dfrac{\pi}{3} - 1.176$

(g) $x = n\pi, \dfrac{n\pi}{2}$

(h) $x = n\pi + \dfrac{\pi}{2}$

(i) $\theta = 2n\pi \pm \dfrac{2\pi}{3}$

(j) $x = (2n+1)\dfrac{\pi}{10}, n\pi \pm \dfrac{\pi}{6}$

3. $\theta = 2n\pi \pm \dfrac{\pi}{6}, 2n\pi \pm \dfrac{5\pi}{6}$

Exercise 1F

1. 0.1499
2. 0.3898
3. 0.005 215
4. 5.9995
5. $\dfrac{\pi\sqrt{3}}{8}$
6. $\dfrac{\pi}{3}$
7. $\dfrac{\pi}{12\sqrt{6}}$
8. $\dfrac{\pi}{4\sqrt{2}}$
9. $\dfrac{\pi}{3\sqrt{3}}$
10. $\pi - 2$

Exercise 1G

1. 0.1611

3. (a) $\dfrac{\pi}{9}$ (b) $\ln\left(\dfrac{10}{9}\right)$ (c) $\dfrac{1}{4}\ln 3$

4. (b) 0.1943

5. $\sqrt{2}\ln\left(1 + \tan\dfrac{21}{2}\theta\right) + C$

Exercise 1H

1. $\dfrac{2x}{x^2+4} + \dfrac{1}{x^2+4} + \dfrac{2}{2-x}; 1.84$

3. $2\sqrt{3} - \dfrac{\pi}{3}$

4. $A = 1, B = 2, C = 6$

5. (a) $\dfrac{\pi}{3}$ (b) $\dfrac{2\pi}{3\sqrt{3}}$ (c) $\dfrac{\pi}{3\sqrt{3}}$ (d) $\dfrac{\pi}{12}$ (e) π

(f) $\tan^{-1}4 - \tan^{-1}3 \left(= \tan^{-1}\dfrac{1}{13}\right)$

7. $2.025\left(= \dfrac{2\pi}{3} + \ln\left(\dfrac{2+\sqrt{3}}{4}\right)\right)$

8. (a) 4.753 (b) 2.96

9. $A = 1, B = 2, C = -4; 3 + 4\ln 2 - \dfrac{4\pi}{3\sqrt{3}}$

10. (b) 1.087

1.10 Miscellaneous Exercises

1. $\dfrac{\pi}{24}, \dfrac{5\pi}{24}, \dfrac{13\pi}{24}, \dfrac{17\pi}{24}$

2. $\theta = n\pi \pm \dfrac{\pi}{6}$

3. $30°, 60°, 120°, 150°$

4. $x = n\pi \pm \dfrac{\pi}{3}, n\pi \pm \dfrac{\pi}{4}$

5. $60°, 180°$

6. $\alpha = 32.2°; 27.8°$ and $267.8°$

7. (a) $45°, 225°$ (b) $90°, 180°$

8. $x = (2n+1)\dfrac{\pi}{2}, n\pi - \dfrac{\pi}{4}$

10. $\theta = 60n + (-1)^n 10° + 10°$

11. $\dfrac{\pi}{4}$

12. $\dfrac{1-x}{1+x^2} + \dfrac{2}{1+2x}$

13. $f_{max} = 6 + \sqrt{29}$ when $\theta = 201.8°$; $f_{min} = 6 - \sqrt{29}$ when $\theta = 21.8°$

14. $\dfrac{\pi}{4} - \dfrac{1}{2}\ln 2$

15. $\dfrac{2}{2-x} + \dfrac{2x+5}{3+x^2}$

16. $4\cos^2\theta - 1; \theta = 180n, 360n \pm 98.7°$

17. (a) (i) $f_{min} = 2$ when $x = -53.1°$

$f_{max} = 12$ when $x = 126.9°$

(ii) $x = 360n \pm 120° - 53.1°$

(b) $26.6°, 76.7°, 166.7°$

18. $R = 5, \tan\alpha = \dfrac{4}{3}$

(a) (i) $2.1, 6.1$ (ii) $0.9, 2.1, 4.5, 0.3$

(b) $A(0, 1), B(-2.2, 5), C(0.927, \dfrac{5}{6})$

19. $C = 7, D = 2, \alpha = 0.460(\pm 2n\pi)$

20. $\theta = n\pi, n\pi + \dfrac{\pi}{4}, n\pi - 1.249$

21. (b) $\theta = n\pi, (2n+1)\pi, 2n\pi \pm \dfrac{\pi}{3}$

(e) $\dfrac{1}{4} + \dfrac{\sqrt{5}}{4}$ or $a = b = \dfrac{1}{4}$

22. $\theta = (2n+1)\dfrac{\pi}{6}, n\pi \pm \dfrac{\pi}{6}; 19.3°$

23. $A = 2, B = 3, C = -1$

24. $\dfrac{\pi}{8} + \dfrac{1}{2}\ln 2 \approx 1.78$

25. $\cos 2\theta = 2\cos^2\theta - 1$, $\cos 3\theta = 4\cos^3\theta - 3\cos\theta$

26. (a) $\dfrac{\pi}{3} < \theta < \dfrac{\pi}{2}$ and $\dfrac{2\pi}{3} < \theta < \pi$

(b) $\theta = (2n+1)\dfrac{\pi}{2}, 2n\pi \pm \dfrac{\pi}{6}, 2n\pi \pm \dfrac{5\pi}{6}$

27. $5\cos(\theta - 0.6435)$

(a) $B(4\cos\theta, 3\sin\theta)$; Perimeter $= 2f(\theta)$, which has maximum of 10 when $B = (3.2, 1.2)$

2 HYPERBOLIC FUNCTIONS

Exercise 2B

1. (a) $\dfrac{13}{12}$ (b) $\dfrac{5}{13}$ (c) $\dfrac{12}{13}$ (d) $\dfrac{13}{5}$ (e) $\dfrac{65}{72}$

(f) $\dfrac{97}{72}$; $x = \ln\dfrac{3}{2}$

2. (a) $\pm\dfrac{3}{4}$ (b) $\dfrac{17}{8}$ (c) $\pm\dfrac{15}{8}; \dfrac{65}{16}$

4. (a) $0, \ln\dfrac{3}{5}$ (b) $\ln 2$ (c) $\ln\dfrac{5}{3}$

5. $\dfrac{3}{4}, -\dfrac{4}{3}$; $\ln 2, -\ln 3$

6. (a) $\pm\ln 3$ (b) $\ln 2, \ln\left(\dfrac{\sqrt{5}-1}{2}\right)$

7. $R = 7$; $\tanh\alpha = 0.96$; min $= 7$ when $x = \ln 7$

8. $\left(A + B > 0 \text{ and } A^2 - B^2 \le 1\right)$ or $(A + B < 0 \text{ and } A > B)$

9. $c > r$

10. 2.83

Exercise 2C

1. (a) $4\operatorname{sech}^2 4x$ (b) $-2\operatorname{sech} 2x \tanh 2x$

(c) $-5\operatorname{cosech}(5x+3)\coth(5x+3)$

(d) $e^x \cosh(e^x)$ (e) $6\cosh^2 x \sinh 2x$

(f) $\cos x \operatorname{sech}^2(\sin x)$

(g) $5\sinh 5x \sinh 3x + 3\cosh 5x \cosh 3x$

(h) $\dfrac{-2\operatorname{cosech}^2 4x}{\sqrt{(\coth 4x)}}$

2. (a) $\dfrac{1}{4}\cosh 4x$ (b) $\dfrac{x}{2} + \dfrac{1}{12}\sinh 6x$

(c) $\dfrac{x^2}{2}\sinh 2x - \dfrac{x}{2}\cosh 2x + \dfrac{1}{4}\sinh 2x$

(d) $\dfrac{1}{7}\tanh 7x$ (e) $-\dfrac{1}{3}\operatorname{cosech} 3x$

(f) $\ln\cosh x$ (g) $\tanh x - x$

(h) $\dfrac{1}{8}e^{4x} + \dfrac{1}{4}e^{-2x}$

(i) $\dfrac{1}{3}\sinh(x^3 + 4)$

(j) $\dfrac{1}{32}\sinh 4x - \dfrac{1}{4}\sinh 2x + \dfrac{3}{8}x$

(k) $\dfrac{1}{10}\cosh 5x + \dfrac{1}{2}\cosh x$

(l) $2\tan^{-1}(e^x)$

3. $y = 10x - 10\ln 2 + \dfrac{45}{8}$

4. (b) $\left(-\dfrac{1}{2}\ln 7, \dfrac{\sqrt{7}}{3}\right)$; Minimum

(c) $-1 \le \lambda \le 1$

5. $\dfrac{136}{45}$

Exercise 2D

1. (a) $\ln 2$ (b) $\ln\left(2+\sqrt{3}\right)$ (c) $\dfrac{1}{2}\ln 3$

2. $\ln\left(x+\sqrt{\left(x^2+1\right)}\right)$

3. $\ln\left\{\dfrac{1+\sqrt{(1-x)^2}}{x}\right\}$

4. $-\dfrac{3}{4}$

5. $3\dfrac{1}{2}$

Exercise 2E

1. $\dfrac{3}{\sqrt{\left(9x^2+24x+15\right)}}$

2. $\dfrac{1}{2\sqrt{\left(x^2+x\right)}}$

3. $\dfrac{-1}{3x^2+2x}$

4. $2x\sinh^{-1}(2x)+\dfrac{2x^2}{\sqrt{\left(4x^2+1\right)}}$

5. $\dfrac{-1}{x\sqrt{\left(1+x^2\right)}}$

6. $\dfrac{2\sinh 2x}{\sqrt{\left(\cosh^2 2x+1\right)}}$

7. $\dfrac{-1}{x\sqrt{\left(1-x^2\right)}}$

8. $\dfrac{-1}{x\sqrt{\left(1+x^2\right)}}$

Exercise 2F

(Answers are given in a variety of forms on purpose – use a calculator to see whether your answers and these agree.)

1. $\ln\left(2+\sqrt{5}\right)$

2. $\ln\left(2+\sqrt{3}\right)-\ln\left(\dfrac{3+\sqrt{5}}{2}\right)$

3. $\sinh^{-1}1-\sinh^{-1}\dfrac{1}{2}$

4. $\cosh^{-1}4-\cosh^{-1}2$

5. $2\sqrt{2}-2\ln\left(\sqrt{2}-1\right)$

6. $2\sqrt{7}+\dfrac{9}{2}\ln\left(\dfrac{4}{3}-\dfrac{\sqrt{7}}{3}\right)$

7. $\dfrac{3\sqrt{10}}{2}-\sqrt{5}-\dfrac{1}{2}\ln\left(2\sqrt{10}-3\sqrt{5}+5\sqrt{2}-6\right)$

8. $\cosh^{-1}3-\cosh^{-1}2$

9. $4-\sqrt{7}-\ln\left(\dfrac{\sqrt{7}+4}{9}\right)$

10. $\cosh^{-1}5-\cosh^{-1}3$

11. $\dfrac{\sqrt{2}}{4}\left\{2\ln\left(\sqrt{2}+\sqrt{7}\right)-\ln 5\right\}$

12. $\dfrac{3\sqrt{23}}{2}-2\sqrt{2}+\dfrac{2\sqrt{3}}{3}\ln\left\{\dfrac{9+3\sqrt{6}-\sqrt{46}-\sqrt{69}}{2}\right\}$

13. $2\tan^{-1}e$

14. (a) $\ln\left(9+4\sqrt{5}\right)-\ln\left(1+\sqrt{2}\right)+\sqrt{2}-\sqrt{5}$

(b) $2\cosh^{-1}2-\cosh^{-1}-\sqrt{3}=2\ln\left(2+\sqrt{3}\right)-\sqrt{3}$

15. (a) $\ln\left(\dfrac{\sqrt{5}+3}{4}\right)$ (b) $6\sqrt{5}-\dfrac{15}{2}+24\ln 2-8\ln\left(2\sqrt{5}+6\right)$

16. $-\dfrac{1}{2}\ln\left(\sqrt{5}+\sqrt{10}-2\sqrt{2}-2\right)$

17. Right hand branch

2.11 Miscellaneous Exercises

1. $3;\ 1.92;\ e^2-3e^{-2}$

2. $12;$ (a) $2-\ln\dfrac{3}{2}$

3. $x\tanh^{-1}x+\dfrac{1}{2}\ln\left(1-x^2\right)$

4. $\ln 3$

5. (a) $1, 6$ (b) $\ln\left(\dfrac{2}{5}\right)$

7. $\ln\left(\dfrac{1+\sqrt{5}}{2}\right),\ \ln\left(\dfrac{\sqrt{109}-3}{10}\right)$

8. $\dfrac{1}{2}\ln\left(\dfrac{1}{5}\right)$

9. $\dfrac{3}{4}$; $\dfrac{\pi}{32}(15+16\ln 2)$

10. $x=\ln\left(1+\sqrt{2}\right)$ $y=\ln\left(5+\sqrt{24}\right)$

$x=\ln\left(\dfrac{1+\sqrt{37}}{6}\right)$ $y=\ln\left(\dfrac{25+\sqrt{481}}{12}\right)$

11. (a) $\cosh^{-1}3-\cosh^{-1}2$

(b) $2\left(\cosh^{-1}2-\cosh^{-1}3\right)+12\sqrt{2}-4\sqrt{3}$

12. $\tan^{-1}(\tanh x)+$ constant

13. 3.0016

14. (b) $\ln\left(1+\sqrt{2}\right)+1-\sqrt{2}$

15. $\dfrac{e-1}{e+2}$; $y=\dfrac{4}{3}x+\dfrac{1}{2}-\dfrac{4}{3}\left(\dfrac{e-1}{e+1}\right)$; $\dfrac{1}{2}-\dfrac{4}{3}\left(\dfrac{e-1}{e+1}\right)$

16. (a) $\dfrac{\sqrt{3}}{3}\ln\left(4\sqrt{3}+7\right)$ (b) $\dfrac{2\sqrt{3}}{9}\pi$

17. $\dfrac{5}{12}$

18. (a) $R=3$, $\alpha=\ln 3$; Minimum at $\left(\ln 3,\,3\right)$

(b) $\dfrac{1}{2}\ln 2,\,-\dfrac{1}{2}\ln 5$

19. $-\dfrac{1}{2}\ln 5$

21. -0.667

23. $x=\ln\dfrac{1}{2},\ y=\ln\dfrac{3}{2}$

24. (a) $\ln\left(3+2\sqrt{2}\right),\ \ln\left(3-2\sqrt{2}\right),\ \ln\left(2+\sqrt{3}\right),\ \ln\left(2-\sqrt{3}\right)$

(b) $\ln\left(\dfrac{2+\sqrt{3}}{3}\right),\ \ln\left(\dfrac{2-\sqrt{3}}{3}\right)$

25. (a) $\dfrac{\pi}{2}-2\tan^{-1}\left(\dfrac{1}{3}\right)$ (b) $\dfrac{4}{5}\pi$

26. $0,\ \ln\dfrac{5}{3}$

28. $\dfrac{e^5}{10}-\dfrac{e^{-5}}{10}+\dfrac{e^3}{6}-\dfrac{e^{-3}}{6}-e+e^{-1}$

29. $\ln\left\{\dfrac{k\pm\sqrt{k^2-n^2+1}}{(1+n)}\right\}$

3 COMPLEX NUMBERS

Exercise 3A

1. (a) $\pm 3i$ (b) $\pm\dfrac{5}{3}i$ (c) $-1\pm i$

(d) $-\dfrac{1}{2}\pm\dfrac{\sqrt{3}}{2}i$ (e) $-\dfrac{3}{4}\pm\dfrac{\sqrt{7}}{4}i$

2. $x^2-4x+7=0$

3. (a) $5+6i$ (b) $2-2i$ (c) 8 (d) $14i$ (e) $18-i$
   (f) $5+12i$ (g) $4+2i$

4. (a) $-\dfrac{2}{3}$ (b) $\dfrac{3}{2}$

5. (a) $-i$ (b) 1 (c) $-i$ (d) -1 (e) i

6. (a) $-3+4i$ (b) $\dfrac{1}{5}-\dfrac{2}{5}i$ (c) $-\dfrac{3}{25}-\dfrac{4}{25}i$

7. (a) $\dfrac{5}{2}+\dfrac{1}{2}i$ (b) $1-2i$ (c) $-\dfrac{4}{5}+\dfrac{8}{5}i,-\dfrac{4}{5}+\dfrac{8}{5}i$

(d) $\dfrac{2}{13}-\dfrac{3}{13}i$ (e) $-2-3i$ (f) $\dfrac{pr+qs}{r^2+s^2}+\dfrac{(qr-ps)}{r^2+s^2}i$

8. (a) $\dfrac{7}{2}-\dfrac{9}{2}i$ (b) $-\dfrac{14}{25}+\dfrac{2}{25}i$ (c) $-\dfrac{1}{5}i$

9. (a) $\dfrac{4}{5}-\dfrac{7}{5}i$ (b) $-\dfrac{1}{2}+\dfrac{3}{2}i$ (c) $\dfrac{11}{41}+\dfrac{17}{41}i$

10. (a) $x=\dfrac{4}{3},\ y=\dfrac{5}{3}$ (b) $x=4,\ y=-6$

11. (a) $p=-1,\ q=7$ (b) $3i$

12. $\dfrac{7}{2}+\dfrac{1}{2}i$

Exercise 3B

2. (a) $3+4i$ (b) (i) $8+2i$, $1+6i$ (ii) $7+5i,-1-i$

3. (a) $\sqrt{2},-\dfrac{\pi}{4}$ (b) $2,\dfrac{\pi}{3}$ (c) $3\sqrt{2},-\dfrac{\pi}{4}$

(d) $\sqrt{13},0.588$

5. $\sqrt{2},\dfrac{\pi}{4};2,\dfrac{\pi}{6};2\sqrt{2},\dfrac{5\pi}{12};\dfrac{1}{\sqrt{2}},\dfrac{\pi}{12}$

6. (a) $2+2\sqrt{3}i$ (b) $0+5i$ (c) $-3-3i$ (d) $-4+0i$

7. (a) $\left[\sqrt{2},\dfrac{\pi}{4}\right]$ (b) $\left[\sqrt{5},2.678\right]$ (c) $\left[5,\pi\right]$

(d) $\left[4,\dfrac{\pi}{2}\right]$ (e) $[5,0.927]$ (f) $[5,-2.214]$

(g) $[5,-0.927]$ (h) $[5,2.214]$

Exercise 3C

3. (a) $\cos 7\theta+i\sin 7\theta$ (b) $\cos 3\theta+i\sin 3\theta$

Exercise 3D

1. (a) $\pm 2i, \pm 2$ (b) $3i, \pm\dfrac{3\sqrt{3}}{2}-\dfrac{3i}{2}$

   (c) $[1,\pi], \left[1,\dfrac{\pi}{5}\right], \left[1,\dfrac{3\pi}{5}\right], \left[1,-\dfrac{\pi}{5}\right], \left[1,-\dfrac{3\pi}{5}\right]$

2. (a) $2^{\frac{1}{6}}e^{i\frac{\pi}{12}},\ 2^{\frac{1}{6}}e^{i\frac{3\pi}{4}},\ 2^{\frac{1}{6}}e^{-i\frac{7\pi}{12}}$

   (b) $\sqrt{2}\,e^{i\frac{\pi}{4}},\ \sqrt{2}\,e^{i\frac{11\pi}{12}},\ \sqrt{2}\,e^{-i\frac{5\pi}{12}}$

3. $3+0i,\ \dfrac{1}{3}+0i,\ \dfrac{3}{5}-\dfrac{4}{5}i,\ \dfrac{3}{5}+\dfrac{4}{5}i$

4. $-1-\dfrac{i}{3},\ -\dfrac{\sqrt{3}}{6}-1+\dfrac{i}{6},\ \dfrac{\sqrt{3}}{6}-1+\dfrac{i}{6}$

5. $\dfrac{1}{2}+\dfrac{1}{2}i,\ \dfrac{1}{2}-i\left(\dfrac{\sqrt{3}}{2}+1\right),\ \dfrac{1}{2}+i\left(\dfrac{\sqrt{3}}{2}-1\right)$

6. $\dfrac{1}{2}-i\left(\dfrac{3}{2}+\dfrac{3\sqrt{2}}{2}\right), \dfrac{1}{2}+i\left(\dfrac{3}{2}-\dfrac{3\sqrt{2}}{2}\right), \dfrac{1}{2}+i\left(\dfrac{3\sqrt{2}}{2}-\dfrac{3}{2}\right),$

   $\dfrac{1}{2}+i\left(\dfrac{3\sqrt{2}}{2}+\dfrac{3}{2}\right)$

Exercise 3E

1. (a) Circle radius 5 centre $-3+4i$
   (b) Mediator of $-2+0i$ and $5-i$
   (c) Circle radius $\sqrt{13}$ centre $0+3i$
   (d) Isolated points $2+0i$ and $3-i$

2. (a) Circle centre $3+0i$ radius 10;
   $(x-3)^2+y^2=100$

   (b) Circle centre $2\dfrac{1}{2}+0i$ radius $1\dfrac{1}{2}$;
   $(2x-5)^2+4y^2=9$

   (c) Ellipse centre $2\dfrac{1}{2}+0i$ foci at $1+0i,\ 4+0i$
   passing through origin and
   $5+0i;\ 16x^2-80x+25y^2=0$

   (d) Hyperbola centre $4(2x-5)^2-y^2=2$

3. (a) Region in band between concentric circles
   radii 2 and 5, centre $3-i$
   (b) Infinite region bounded by half-lines
   emanating from $0+2i$ making angles $-\dfrac{\pi}{4}$
   and $\dfrac{\pi}{3}$ with real axis

3.13 Miscellaneous Exercises

1. $|z_1|=\sqrt{2}$ $\arg z_1=\dfrac{\pi}{4}$; $|z_2|=2$ $\arg z_2=-\dfrac{\pi}{3}$

   (a) $\left[2\sqrt{2},-\dfrac{\pi}{12}\right]$ (b) $\left[\dfrac{1}{\sqrt{2}},\dfrac{7\pi}{12}\right]$ (c) $\left[\sqrt{2},-\dfrac{7\pi}{12}\right]$

   (d) $\left[2,\dfrac{\pi}{2}\right]$ (e) $[8,-\pi]$ (f) $\left[\dfrac{1}{8},-\dfrac{\pi}{6}\right]$

2. (a) $\left[\dfrac{1}{3},-0.841\right]$ (b) $[9,2.412]$ (c) $[1,-0.730]$

   (d) $[12,-2.301]$ (e) $\left[\dfrac{4}{3},2.301\right]$

3. $\left[2,\dfrac{\pi}{6}\right]$ (a) $8i$ (b) $-128\left(1+\sqrt{3}i\right)$ (c) (i) 6 (ii) 3

4. (a) $16\left(1-\sqrt{3}i\right)$ (b) $2^9\left(1+\sqrt{3}i\right)$ (c) $8(1+i)$

5. $64i$

6. $\dfrac{1}{2}+\dfrac{\sqrt{3}}{2}i,\ i,\ -\dfrac{1}{2}+\dfrac{\sqrt{3}}{2}i$

7. $\omega=-\dfrac{1}{2}+\dfrac{\sqrt{3}}{2}i$

   (a) $1+\omega$ (b) 3 (c) -1 (d) 16ω (e) $9\left(\omega-\omega^2\right)$
   (f) ω^2-1

8. $\pm 111.8°,\ 7.25$

9. $4+6i;\ r=2\sqrt{2},\ \alpha=-\dfrac{3\pi}{4}$
   $A=4,\ B=8,\ C=-4,\ D=8$

10. (a) $1,-\dfrac{\pi}{6}$ (b) 3

11. (b) $138°$ (c) $2-i$

12. (a) $2\sqrt{2}$ (b) $1\pm 2i,\ \dfrac{1}{5}\pm\dfrac{2}{5}i;\ 1.92$

13. (a) $-2-2\sqrt{3}i$ (b) 2   (c) 4

14. $\dfrac{\pi}{16}+\dfrac{7\sqrt{3}}{128}$

15. (a) $1,-1;\ z^2+z-1=0$
    (b) (i) Mediator of $1+0i$ and ω
    (ii) Major arc of circle centre origin radius 1
    from 1 to ω

16. (a) (i) 12 (ii) $-128, -384$
    (b) $3\sqrt{65},\ 8-9i$

4 VECTORS

Exercise 4A

1. $5\mathbf{b}-10\mathbf{a}$, $4\mathbf{a}-2\mathbf{b}$

2. (a) $\overrightarrow{AC}$ (b) $\overrightarrow{BD}$ (c) $\overrightarrow{AD}$

3. $\overrightarrow{DC}=\overrightarrow{EH}=\overrightarrow{FG}=\mathbf{a}$

   $\overrightarrow{BC}=\overrightarrow{GA}=\overrightarrow{FE}=\mathbf{b}$

   $\overrightarrow{DE}=\overrightarrow{CH}=\overrightarrow{BG}=\mathbf{c}$

4. $\mathbf{c}-\mathbf{a}$, $\mathbf{b}-\mathbf{a}$, $\mathbf{b}-\mathbf{c}$

5. $-\mathbf{a}$, $\mathbf{b}-\mathbf{a}$, $2\mathbf{b}$, $2\mathbf{b}-\mathbf{a}$

Exercise 4B

1. (a) (i) $\mathbf{b}-\mathbf{a}$ (ii) $\frac{1}{3}(\mathbf{b}-\mathbf{a})$ (iii) $\mathbf{b}+\mathbf{a}$

   (iv) $\frac{2}{3}\mathbf{b}+\frac{1}{3}\mathbf{a}$ (v) $\frac{4}{3}\mathbf{b}+\frac{2}{3}\mathbf{a}$

2. $\frac{1}{2}(\mathbf{a}+\mathbf{b})$, $\frac{2}{3}(\mathbf{a}+\mathbf{b})$, $\frac{3}{4}$

3. $\mathbf{q}=\frac{1}{3}\mathbf{r}+\frac{4}{3}\mathbf{p}$, $\frac{1}{4}$

4. (a) $\frac{3}{2}\mathbf{b}-\frac{1}{2}\mathbf{a}$ (b) $\frac{3}{4}\mathbf{b}-\frac{1}{4}\mathbf{c}$ (d) $1:1$

5. $1:2$, $6\mathbf{q}-4\mathbf{p}$, $\mathbf{p}-\mathbf{q}$

Exercise 4C

1. (a) $\mathbf{i}+\mathbf{j}+\mathbf{k}$

   (b) $2\mathbf{i}+\mathbf{j}-\mathbf{k}$

   (c) $\mathbf{i}-\mathbf{j}$

2. (a) $(3,-4,1)$ (b) $(1,2,-1)$ (c) $(0,0,-4)$

3. (a) 7 (b) 3 (c) $\sqrt{66}$ (d) $\sqrt{50}$

   $\hat{\mathbf{a}}=\frac{6}{7}\mathbf{i}+\frac{2}{7}\mathbf{j}+\frac{3}{7}\mathbf{k}$

   $\hat{\mathbf{b}}=\frac{2}{3}\mathbf{i}-\frac{1}{3}\mathbf{j}-\frac{2}{3}\mathbf{k}$

4. (a) $3\mathbf{i}+6\mathbf{j}+\mathbf{k}$

   (b) $\mathbf{i}+9\mathbf{j}$

   (c) $\mathbf{i}+9\mathbf{j}$

   (d) $-25\mathbf{i}+33\mathbf{j}-22\mathbf{k}$

Exercise 4D

1. (a) -14 (b) $21°$ (c) $4\mathbf{i}-2\mathbf{j}+3\mathbf{k}$

2. $4\mathbf{i}-2\mathbf{j}+3\mathbf{k}$, $21°$

3. $1:6$

4. 12

5. (a) -3 (b) $\frac{4}{3}$ (c) 10 or $-\frac{2}{3}$

6. $\pm\sqrt{2}$

7. (a) 5 (b) $2\mathbf{i}-5\mathbf{j}-4\mathbf{k}$

8. -1, -1, -1; $\dfrac{4}{3\sqrt{2}}$

4.7 Miscellaneous Exercises

1. $6\mathbf{i}+6\mathbf{j}+0\mathbf{k}$

2. 7

3. $a=-1$, $b=2$

4. $\frac{4}{3}$

5. $\frac{2}{3}\mathbf{i}-\frac{1}{3}\mathbf{j}+\frac{2}{3}\mathbf{k}$

6. $\frac{18}{7}\mathbf{i}-\frac{9}{7}\mathbf{j}+\frac{6}{7}\mathbf{k}$

8. (a) $\mathbf{p}-\mathbf{q}$, $\mathbf{q}-3\mathbf{p}$

   (b) $\frac{1}{2}\mathbf{q}-\frac{3}{2}\mathbf{p}$

   (c) $\left(k-\frac{3}{2}\right)\mathbf{p}+\left(\frac{1}{2}-k\right)\mathbf{q}$

   (d) $\frac{3}{2}$

10. 10

12. (a) $5\mathbf{i}+9\mathbf{j}+\mathbf{k}$

    (b) $3\mathbf{i}+\mathbf{j}+5\mathbf{k}$

13. $6\mathbf{i}+2\mathbf{j}$, $0\mathbf{i}+6\mathbf{j}$

14. (a) 0, -4

    (b) $72.5°$

15. (a) $50°$

    (b) $\frac{4}{3}\mathbf{i}+\frac{7}{3}\mathbf{j}+\frac{14}{3}\mathbf{k}$

16. $-\frac{4}{17}$, 8.26

5 VECTOR GEOMETRY

There are many equivalent correct answers in this chapter.

Exercise 5A

1. $\mathbf{r}=-2\mathbf{i}+\mathbf{j}+4\mathbf{k}+\lambda(3\mathbf{i}+6\mathbf{j}+2\mathbf{k})$

   $\dfrac{x+2}{3}\;\dfrac{x+2}{3}=\dfrac{y-1}{6}=\dfrac{z-4}{2}$

2. (a) $\mathbf{r}=\mathbf{i}-2\mathbf{j}+\mathbf{k}+\lambda(-2\mathbf{i}+2\mathbf{j}-4\mathbf{k})$

   (b) $\mathbf{r}=8\mathbf{i}+\mathbf{j}+4\mathbf{k}+\lambda(4\mathbf{i}+\mathbf{j}+\mathbf{k})$

   (c) $\mathbf{r}=3\mathbf{i}+\mathbf{j}-2\mathbf{k}+\lambda(-2\mathbf{i}+2\mathbf{j}-4\mathbf{k})$

3. (a) $\mathbf{i}+\mathbf{j}+\mathbf{k}$ (c) No

Exercise 5B

1. $\mathbf{r}=(2,-1,0)+\lambda(-3,4,4)+\mu(1,1,2)$

2. $4x+10y-72=-2$

3. Equivalent equations

4. $\mathbf{r}.(\mathbf{i}+2\mathbf{j}-3\mathbf{k})=0$

7. $\mathbf{r}=4\mathbf{i}+2\mathbf{j}+3\mathbf{k}$

8. $y+3z=14$

5.4 Miscellaneous Exercises

1. (a) $2\mathbf{i}-4\mathbf{j}-2\mathbf{k}$

   (d) $56°$

2. (a) $-3\mathbf{j}-4\mathbf{k}$

   (b) $\mathbf{r}.(-3\mathbf{j}-4\mathbf{k})=0$

   (c) $\dfrac{1}{\sqrt{26}}$

3. (a) $\mathbf{i}+2\mathbf{j}+3\mathbf{k}$

   (b) $40°$

4. (a) $\mathbf{r}=3\mathbf{i}-\mathbf{j}+2\mathbf{k}+5(-\mathbf{i}+\mathbf{j}+3\mathbf{k})$

   (b) $6\mathbf{i}-4\mathbf{i}-7\mathbf{k}$

   (e) $3\sqrt{2}$

5. (b) $9\sqrt{3}$

   (c) $10\mathbf{i}+10\mathbf{j}+12\mathbf{k}$ or $-2\mathbf{i}+10\mathbf{j}$

6. $-7\mathbf{i}-14\mathbf{j}+14\mathbf{k}$; $\mathbf{r}.\mathbf{n}=21$; 1; $18.4°$

7. (a) $6\mathbf{i}+6\mathbf{j}+3\mathbf{k}$; $\mathbf{r}.(2\mathbf{i}+2\mathbf{j}+\mathbf{k})=11$

   (b) $\sin^{-1}\left(\frac{7}{9}\right)$

8. $6\mathbf{i}+6\mathbf{j}+18\mathbf{k}$; $\mathbf{r}.(2\mathbf{i}-\mathbf{j}+6\mathbf{k})=25$; 2; $\dfrac{5\sqrt{41}}{2}$

9. $\frac{1}{2}\mathbf{j}+\frac{1}{2}\mathbf{k}$; $\mathbf{r}.(\mathbf{j}+\mathbf{k})=1$

   $5\mathbf{i}-2\mathbf{j}+3\mathbf{k}$; $\mathbf{r}.(\mathbf{i}+7\mathbf{j}+5\mathbf{k})=6$; $11.5°$

10. (a) 20, $\frac{20}{21}$

    (b) $\mathbf{r}=6\mathbf{i}+3\mathbf{j}+2\mathbf{k}+t(-4\mathbf{i}-\mathbf{j}-\mathbf{k})$

    $-\frac{14}{11}\mathbf{i}+\frac{13}{11}\mathbf{j}+\frac{2}{11}\mathbf{k}$

11. $3y+4z=20$, $x+2y+2z=12$,

    $p=2$, $q=5$,

    $\mathbf{r}=2\mathbf{i}+5\mathbf{k}+\lambda(-2\mathbf{i}+4\mathbf{j}-3\mathbf{k})$,

    3 or $\frac{48}{11}$

12. (a) $PC^2=11\lambda^2+22\lambda+17$

    (b) $\mathbf{i}-4\mathbf{j}+7\mathbf{k}$, $\mathbf{r}.(\mathbf{i}-4\mathbf{j}+7\mathbf{k})=21$

    (c) $x+2y+z=9$

    (d) 11

13. (a) $\mathbf{d}=5\mathbf{i}+16\mathbf{j}$

    (b) 147, $32.6°$

    (c) 94

    (d) $3\mathbf{i}+8\mathbf{j}-\mathbf{k}$

14. (a) 7, 6, $\frac{20}{21}$

    (b) $2\mathbf{i}+\frac{24}{5}\mathbf{j}+\frac{12}{5}\mathbf{k}$

    (c) $-\frac{9}{4}$

6   SEQUENCES AND SERIES

Exercise 6A

1. 387 000

2. $n=33$, $d=3\frac{1}{2}$; 1450

3. (a) 71

4. $x=2$, $-\frac{32}{3}$

5. 100

6. $\frac{1}{2}(\sqrt{5}-1)$

7. n^2+2n-3; $a=5$, $d=2$. 99

9. $A=1$

10. $S_k=k(2k+1)(3k+1)$

11. $\dfrac{n}{2}(6n^2+15n+11)$

12. $U_r=6r+2$. $(n+1)(9n+2)$

Exercise 6C

2. $\dfrac{\frac{1}{2}}{r}-\dfrac{\frac{1}{2}}{r+2}$

3. $r.r!$

4. 1

5. $\dfrac{2r+1}{r^2(r+1)^2}$

6. $\dfrac{5}{2}-\dfrac{2n+5}{(n+1)(n+2)}$

7. $\dfrac{1}{2n}$

10. $\dfrac{\frac{1}{2}}{r}-\dfrac{1}{r+1}+\dfrac{\frac{1}{2}}{r+2}$

Exercise 6D

1. 0.98

2. (a) $q=-\frac{1}{8}$ (b) $-\frac{1}{3}$

3. (a) $\frac{1}{2}$ (b) $\frac{1}{4}$ (c) $\frac{15}{16}$ (d) 0 (e) 2

(f) 0 (g) $\frac{3}{4}$

4. 2

5. $\frac{n}{3}(n+1)(n+2)$; $\frac{8}{9}$

6. (a) 32 (b) $x > \frac{1}{2}\ln 3$

Exercise 6E

1. (a) $1+x-x^2+\frac{5}{3}x^2-\ldots$, $|x|<\frac{1}{3}$

(b) $\frac{1}{2}-\frac{x}{4}+\frac{x^2}{8}-\frac{x^2}{16}+\ldots$, $|x|<2$

(c) $1+\frac{x}{4}-\frac{x^2}{32}+\frac{x^2}{128}-\ldots$, $|x|<2$

(d) $\frac{1}{25}+\frac{6x}{125}+\frac{27x^2}{625}+\frac{108x^3}{3125}+\ldots$, $|x|<\frac{5}{3}$

(e) $1+2x+2x^2+2x^3+\ldots$, $|x|<1$

(f) $1-x-\frac{x^2}{2}+\frac{x^3}{2}+\ldots$, $|x|<1$

2. (a) $1+11x+64x^2+\ldots$

(b) $2-\frac{3}{4}x^2-\frac{1}{4}x^3+\ldots$

3. $3-5x+7x^2-15x^3+\ldots$, $|x|<\frac{1}{2}$

4. $4+\frac{y}{8}-\frac{y^2}{512}$

5. $1+4x-\frac{7}{2}x^2+5x^3+\ldots$; $\frac{1}{\sqrt{3}}\approx 0.577(36)$

6. $x+7x^2+33x^3+\ldots$, $|x|<\frac{1}{3}$

7. $1-x^2+\frac{1}{2}x^4+\ldots$

8. $1+\frac{1}{2}x+\frac{3}{8}x^2+\frac{5}{16}x^3+\ldots$; $\sqrt{10}\approx 3.1621875$

9. $k=\frac{3}{256}$

Exercise 6F

1. (a) $1-2x+2x^2-\frac{4}{3}x^3+\ldots$

(b) $\frac{x}{2}-\frac{x^2}{8}+\frac{x^3}{24}-\frac{x^4}{64}+\ldots$

(c) $3x-\frac{9x^3}{2}+\frac{81x^5}{40}-\frac{243x^7}{560}+\ldots$

(d) $1-\frac{x^2}{8}+\frac{x^4}{384}-\frac{x^6}{46080}+\ldots$

(e) $2x+\frac{2}{3}x^3+\frac{2}{5}x^5+\frac{2}{7}x^7+\ldots$

(f) $-1+2x+8x^2-\frac{4}{3}x^3+\ldots$

(g) $\frac{1}{2}-\frac{3}{4}x+\frac{5}{8}x^2-\frac{19}{48}x^3+\ldots$

(h) $-2+5x-\frac{9}{2}x^2+\frac{17}{6}x^3+\ldots$

2. (a) $x+\frac{x^3}{6}+\ldots$

(b) $1-\frac{1}{4}x^2+\ldots$

(c) $\tan^{-1}\left(\frac{3}{4}\right)+\frac{4}{5}x-\frac{6}{25}x^2-\frac{2}{15}x^3+\ldots$

(d) $2+2x\ln 2+2x^2(\ln 2)^2+\frac{2}{3}x^3(\ln 2)^3+\ldots$

3. $A=3$, $B=-8$

4. $A=-\frac{1}{2}$, $B=\frac{7}{24}$

5. $\frac{d^3y}{dx^3}=2\frac{dy}{dx}(1+3y^2)$; $\tan x = x+\frac{x^3}{3}+\ldots$

6. $-\ln(1-x)$; $2-2\ln 2$

7. $f''(0)=6$, $f'''(0)=108$

$2-4x+3x^2+18x^3+\ldots$

8. $A=\frac{7}{6}$, $B=\frac{323}{72}$

9. $1+2x+2x^2+\frac{4}{3}x^3+\ldots$; $\frac{1}{3}x^3$;

0.287

10. 0.0406

11. 1, $\frac{1}{2}$, $\frac{1}{4}$, $\frac{5}{8}$; $1+\frac{x}{2}+\frac{x^2}{8}+\frac{5x^3}{48}\ldots$

0.102 54

12. $\frac{dy}{dx}=\frac{\cos x}{1+\sin x}$; $x-\frac{x^2}{2}+\frac{x^3}{6}-\frac{x^4}{12}\ldots$;

$k=\frac{1}{6}$

Exercise 6G

1. (a) $\frac{3^n}{n!}$ (b) $\frac{(-1)^{n+1}4^n}{n}$ (c) $\frac{(-1)^n 4^n}{(2n)!}$

(d) $\frac{(-1)^{n+1}}{2(2n)!}$ (b) $\frac{(-1)^n e}{n!}$ (f) $\frac{1}{2^{2n+1}(2n+1)!}$

2. $\frac{\frac{1}{3}}{2-x}+\frac{\frac{1}{3}}{1+x}$

3. $A=3$, $B=-2$, $C=-1$; $x+7x^2+33x^3$

$-\frac{1}{3}<x<\frac{1}{3}$; $3^{n+1}-(3+n)2^n$

5. $(-1)^n 4$

6. $\frac{1}{3}(n+1)(n+2)(5n+6)2^{n-2}$

8. (a) $-8x-7x^2-\frac{62}{3}x^3+\ldots$; (b) $-\frac{1}{3}\le x\le\frac{1}{3}$

(c) $-\dfrac{2}{n}\left(3^n+(-1)^n2^{n-1}\right)$

6.10 Miscellaneous Exercises

1. 26 years

2. $\dfrac{\frac{1}{2}}{2r-1}-\dfrac{\frac{1}{2}}{r}+\dfrac{\frac{1}{2}}{2r+1};\quad \ln2-\frac{1}{2}$

3. $1-\dfrac{x}{6}+\dfrac{x^2}{24}\;\ldots;\quad |x|<3$

4. 2

6. (a) 1.998 (b) $\dfrac{\pi}{6}$

7 (b) $1-\dfrac{1}{(n+2)};\quad 1$

8. $\ln2,0,1,0,-2;\quad y=\ln2+\dfrac{x^2}{2}-\dfrac{x^4}{12}\ldots$

9. $0<a<2;$ (a) 4.91 (c) 22

10. $\dfrac{n}{3}\left(7n^3-1\right)$

11. (a) $\ln2$ (b) $2e^{\frac{1}{2}}-3$

12. $\frac{8}{3}+\frac{7}{6}x-\frac{11}{36}x^2-\frac{7}{12}x^3;\quad 3.1238$

14. (b) $\dfrac{3}{(1+x)}+\dfrac{1}{(1-2x)}+\dfrac{2}{(1-2x)^2}$

(c) $6+7x+31x^2+69x^3+\ldots$

16. 1.443

17. (b) 64

18. (a) $2\ln2$

(b) $1+2x+3x^2+4x^3+\ldots;\quad (n+1)x^n;\quad 4$

19. $x-\dfrac{x^2}{2}+\dfrac{2x^3}{3}-\ldots$

20. (b) $\dfrac{4^{n+1}(n-1)}{3(n+2)}+\dfrac{2}{3}$

21. (a) $\dfrac{n}{3}\left(4n^2+6n-1\right)$ (c) $\frac{1}{2}$

(d) 0 (n odd), -2^n (n even); $|x|<\frac{1}{2}$

7 PROPERTIES OF CURVES

Exercise 7A

1. $\left(\dfrac{1}{3},-\dfrac{416}{27}\right)$

2. Minimum at $(0,0)$, Maximum at $(-2,-4)$

3. $\left(\ln\left[1+\sqrt{2}\right],\dfrac{1}{\sqrt{2}}\right)$ and $\left(\ln\left[\sqrt{2}-1\right],\dfrac{1}{\sqrt{2}}\right)$

4. (a) $(0,10),(-1,0),(2,0),(5,0)$

(b) $(2,0)$

5. Minimum at $(0,0)$, Maximum at $\left(\dfrac{2}{3},\dfrac{4}{9}e^2\right)$

6. $\left(-1,-\dfrac{1}{e}\right);\;\left\{y:y\ge-\dfrac{1}{e}\right\}$

7. $\dfrac{dy}{dx}=\dfrac{2-x}{\left(x^2+2\right)^{\frac{3}{2}}};\;\left(2,\dfrac{1}{\sqrt{6}}\right)$ Maximum

8. $\left(\dfrac{1}{2}\ln\left(\dfrac{2}{3}\right),\sqrt{24}\right)$ Minimum

Exercise 7B

1. (a) $\left(0,-\dfrac{3}{2}\right),(-3,0),(1,0),x=-2,y=x$

(b) $(0,1),(3,0),\;x=-3,x=1,y=0$

(c) $\left(-4^{\frac{1}{3}},0\right),\;y=x,x=0$

(d) $(0,0),\;y=1$

2. $A=1,B=2,C=-1\quad x=2,y=x+2$

3. (a) $(0,2),(-2,0)$ (b) $\left(-5,-\dfrac{1}{12}\right)$

(c) $x=1,\;y=0$

4. (a) $\dfrac{dy}{dx}=\dfrac{x^2+4x+2a(a+1)}{(x+2)^2}$

(b) $x=-2,\;y=x+a-2$

5. $(0,0),(-1,-0)\;\left(3+2\sqrt{3},\dfrac{1}{2}\left[12+7\sqrt{3}\right]\right),$

$\left(3-2\sqrt{3},\dfrac{1}{2}\left[12-7\sqrt{3}\right]\right);\;x=3,y=x+4$

6. $a=1,b=1$

7. (a) $(0,0)$ (b) $x=1,x=-1$

Exercise 7C

2. $\dfrac{1-\sqrt{109}}{2}\le y\le\dfrac{1+\sqrt{109}}{2}$

3. $4-2\sqrt{10}<k<4+2\sqrt{10}$

4. (a) $y\le2,y\ge6$ (b) $y\le\dfrac{1}{6},y\ge\dfrac{1}{2}$

5. (a) $(0,-3),\left(\dfrac{3}{4},0\right)$ (b) $(-2,1)$ and $\left(-\dfrac{1}{2},-4\right)$

6. $\dfrac{1}{2}\le y\le 13\dfrac{1}{2}$ $\left(-4,\dfrac{1}{2}\right)$ and $\left(\dfrac{6}{5},13\dfrac{1}{2}\right)$

7. $(2,0)$ and $(-2,2)$

Exercise 7D

1. (a), (b), (c), (e), (i) are even (d), (f), (g), (h) are odd

2. $\left(1,\dfrac{1}{2}\right);\left(\sqrt{3},\dfrac{\sqrt{3}}{4}\right);(0,0)$

Exercise 7E

6. $\left(\pm1,\dfrac{1}{2}\right)$

8. $\left(\dfrac{4}{5},\pm\dfrac{16\sqrt{5}}{125}\right)$

10. $y=\pm x\sqrt{3}$

11. (a) $y=1,\ x=-5$ (b) $\left(0,\dfrac{2}{5}\right)$ and $(-2,0)$

12. $\left(\dfrac{4}{3},\dfrac{256}{27}\right)$ $k>\dfrac{16}{3\sqrt{3}}$

Exercise 7F

1. $27x^2=4y^3$

2. $x^3+y^3=xy$

3. $y^2=\dfrac{1-x^2}{x^2}$

4. $x^2(1+y^2)=1$

5. $27(x-2)^2=(y+3)(y-6)^2$

6. $\dfrac{4}{x}=\dfrac{y}{3}+\dfrac{3}{y}$

7. $x(2-x)^2=8y^2$

8. $(x^2+y^2)^3=a^2x^2y^2$

9. $\dfrac{x^2}{a^2}-\dfrac{y^2}{b^2}=1$

10. $(x^2+y^2-9)^2=4(x+3)^2+4y^2$

Exercise 7G

2. (a) $\dfrac{dy}{dx}=\dfrac{1}{\sqrt{t}},\ \dfrac{d^2y}{dx^2}=-\dfrac{1}{6t^2}$

(b) $\dfrac{dy}{dx}=\dfrac{t(2-t^3)}{1-2t^3},\ \dfrac{d^2y}{dx^2}=-\dfrac{2(1+t^3)^4}{(1-2t^3)^3}$

(c) $\dfrac{dy}{dx}=\dfrac{1}{t},\ \dfrac{d^2y}{dx^2}=-\dfrac{\sqrt{1+t^2}}{t^3}$

(d) $\dfrac{dy}{dx}=\coth\theta,\ \dfrac{d^2y}{dx^2}=-\dfrac{b}{a^2}\operatorname{cosec}^3\theta$

4. (a) $(-2,3),5$ (b) $(-1,3),6$

Exercise 7H

1. $4y-3x+2=0$

2. $5y+2x=17$

3. $2y+x=2$

5. $Q\left(\dfrac{12}{5},\dfrac{4}{5}\right),\ R\left(-\dfrac{12}{5},\dfrac{36}{5}\right)$

7. $\left(\dfrac{21}{4},\dfrac{3}{2}\right)$

8. $4y\sin t+x\cos t=4$

9. $12x=y^2,\ R\left(3[2+p^2+pq+q^2],-3pq[p+q]\right)$

10. $y=m(x-1),\ m=\pm2$

7.11 Miscellaneous Exercises

1. (a) $(x-2)^3=(y+1)^2$

(b) $\left(\dfrac{a}{x}\right)^{\frac{2}{3}}+\left(\dfrac{y}{a}\right)^{\frac{2}{3}}=1$

(c) $y=\dfrac{2abx}{x^2-a^2}$

2. $R=3,\ \alpha=\ln3$

3. $\pm\sqrt{3},\ -1\pm\sqrt{2}$

4. $-\dfrac{1}{4}$

5. (a) $(1,0),1$

(b) $\left(\dfrac{1}{\sqrt{e}},\dfrac{-1}{2e}\right),2$

6. (b) $x=-1$

7. $-\sec^2\theta$

8. 3

9. (a) $k \leq 1, k \geq \dfrac{7}{4}$

   (b) (i) $x = \pm 2, y = 2$

   (ii) $(-1, 1)$ and $\left(-4, \dfrac{7}{4}\right)$

11. $A = 2, B = 5, C = 6; x = 1, y = 2x + 5;$

   $\left(1 + \sqrt{3}, 7 + 4\sqrt{3}\right)$ and $\left(1 - \sqrt{3}, 7 - 4\sqrt{3}\right)$

12. (a) $\dfrac{\pi}{6}, \dfrac{5\pi}{6}$ (b) $-\sqrt{3} \leq y \leq \sqrt{3}$

   (c) $y = \dfrac{1}{3}\left(x - \dfrac{\pi}{2}\right)$

13. $x = -2, y = 3$

14. (a) $x = -1, y = x; (0, -2), (1, 0)$ and $(-2, 0)$

15. (a) $x = -1, y = -3$ (b) $(1, 0), (-3, -8)$

16. $3y = x + \dfrac{21}{4}$

17. $2y \pm x = 0; (4t, 2t)$ and $\left(\dfrac{4}{t}, -\dfrac{2}{t}\right)$

18. $\left(14, -\dfrac{49}{6}\right); \quad x^2 + 2xy = 4y$

19. (c) $(-a, 0)$

20. $\dfrac{-3}{2}\sin t; \dfrac{7a}{8}$

21. (a) $\dfrac{1}{4} < k < 1, \left\{y : y \leq \dfrac{1}{4}, y \geq 1\right\}$

   (b) $(0, 1)$ and $\left(3, \dfrac{1}{4}\right)$

   (c) $x = 1, x = -3, y = 0$

22. (b) $\left(\dfrac{1}{3}, \dfrac{2}{9}\right)$ and $(3, 2)$ (c) $x = \dfrac{5}{3}$

23. (a) $\left(-\dfrac{2b}{a}, -\dfrac{a^2}{4b}\right)$

24. (a) $b = 2, c = 0, h = 0, k = 1$

   (b) $A = 1, B = 5, C = 1$

25. $y + \operatorname{cosech} t = t \operatorname{cosech} t$

26. $y - 2x + 4 = 0; N(4, 4)$

27. $R\left(apq, a[p + q]\right); \quad x + \dfrac{4a^3}{y^2} + 2a = 0$

28. $\left(\dfrac{a}{2\cos\theta}, \dfrac{b}{2\sin\theta}\right); \dfrac{a^2}{x^2} + \dfrac{b^2}{y^2} = 4$

29. $pqy + x = c(p + q); \quad 4xy = 3c^2$

8 FURTHER CALCULUS

Exercise 8A

1. 2

2. 9

3. $\dfrac{32}{15}$

4. $\dfrac{2}{(\pi - 2)}$

5. $-\dfrac{3}{5}$

6. $-\dfrac{1}{2}$

8. $1, \dfrac{1}{8}$

Exercise 8B

1. Both equal 52. Graph is a straight line.

2. (1) (a) (i) 19.306   (ii) 15.057
       (b) (i) 15.370   (ii) 13.640
   (2) (a) (i) −3.1875   (ii) −3.234
       (b) (i) −3.25   (ii) −3.25
   (3) (a) (i) 3.5246   (ii) 3.5400
       (b) (i) 3.5443   (ii) 3.545
   (4) (a) (i) 0.527 55   (ii) 0.524 63
       (b) (i) 0.5238   (ii) 0.523 65

3. (1) $13\dfrac{1}{3}$ (2) −3.25   (3) 3.545   (4) 0.523 60

Exercise 8C

1. $\dfrac{31\pi}{5}$

2. $\dfrac{179\pi}{6}$

3. $\pi\left(\sqrt{3} - \dfrac{\pi}{3}\right)$

4. $(6, 8)$ and $(-6, 8)$ Area $= 16 + 100\tan^{-1}\dfrac{3}{4} \approx 80.35$

   Volume $= \dfrac{544\pi}{3}$

5. (a) $\dfrac{20}{3}$ (b) $\pi\left(\dfrac{27}{2} + 2\ln 2\right)$

8. (a) $\dfrac{5}{12}$ (b) (i) $\dfrac{5}{14}\pi$ (ii) $\dfrac{2}{5}\pi$

Exercise 8D

1. $\dfrac{\pi}{6}$

2. $8\left(1-\cos\dfrac{\pi}{8}\right)$

3. Consider arc from $t=0$ to $t=\dfrac{\pi}{2}$ and multiply by 4.

4. $\ln\left(\dfrac{\sqrt{3}}{\sqrt{2}-1}\right)$

6. $2\tan^{-1}e^2+2\tan^{-1}e-\pi$

7. $\dfrac{a}{2}\left\{3\pi\sqrt{(9\pi^2+1)}+\ln\left(3\pi+\sqrt{(9\pi^2+1)}\right)\right\}$

8. 8

Exercise 8E

1. $\dfrac{6\pi}{5}$

2. (a) $\dfrac{3\sqrt{17}}{2}\pi$ (b) $\pi\left(2+\dfrac{e^4}{4}-\dfrac{e^4}{4}\right)$

    (c) $\pi\left(3\sqrt{10}-\sqrt{2}\right)-\pi\ln\left(\sqrt{10}-3\sqrt{2}+2\sqrt{5}-3\right)$

3. $\dfrac{2\pi}{5}$

4. $\dfrac{384\pi}{5}\left(\sqrt{2}+1\right)$

Exercise 8F

1. $\dfrac{3}{16}\pi,\ \dfrac{16}{35}$

2. $\dfrac{\pi^4}{16}-3\pi^2+24,\ \dfrac{\pi^5-80\pi^3+1920\pi-3840}{32}$

3. $\dfrac{1}{65}\left(22e^\pi+6\right)$

5. $\dfrac{\pi}{2}$

6. $\dfrac{5}{4},\ \dfrac{3}{4},\ I_n=\dfrac{1}{n}\cdot\dfrac{3}{4}\left(\dfrac{5}{4}\right)^{n-1}+\left(\dfrac{n-1}{n}\right)I_{n-2},\ \dfrac{57}{64},$

$\dfrac{3}{8}\ln2+\dfrac{735}{1024}$

8.8 Miscellaneous Exercises

1. $16\sqrt{2}-8$

2. $\dfrac{1}{2}a\sinh\left(\dfrac{k}{a}\right)$

3. $\dfrac{6x-y}{x-2y}$

4. $\dfrac{1}{2}\ln3;\ 0.17$

5. (a) 0.181

6. $\dfrac{5}{7}$

7. $(0,0),\ (-2,-4)$ Minimum at $(0,0)$,
    Maximum at $(-2,-4)$; 5.622; $\ln5\approx1.62$

8. $5\ln5-4;\ 4.9$

9. $1.434;\ 0.717$

10. $\dfrac{1}{x^2}(1-\ln x);\ x<e,\ x>e;\ \dfrac{1}{2}(\ln5)^2;\ 1.4$

11. 59.9

12. $\dfrac{1}{2}\ln13;\ 1.277\,82;\ 2.56$

13. $\dfrac{\pi}{4}-\dfrac{2}{3};\ \dfrac{1}{2}\ln2-\dfrac{1}{4}$

14. $\left(\sqrt{3}-\dfrac{\sqrt{6}}{4}\right)a$

16. $\dfrac{3}{4}$

17. (a) $\left(\dfrac{4}{5},\ \pm\dfrac{16}{25\sqrt{5}}\right)$

    (b) $\dfrac{32}{105}$

18. $I_n=\dfrac{x^4}{4}(\ln x)^n-\dfrac{n}{4}I_{n-1};$

$\dfrac{x^4}{4}(\ln x)^3-\dfrac{3x^4}{16}(\ln x)^2+\dfrac{3x^4(\ln x)}{32}-\dfrac{3x^4}{128}+\text{constant}$

20. $\pi+2\sqrt{2}$

21. $15+\ln2;\ 384\pi$

22. $\dfrac{38}{15},\ \dfrac{1}{8}\left(3\ln\left(1+\sqrt{2}\right)-\sqrt{2}\right)$

9 MATRICES AND TRANSFORMATIONS

Exercise 9A

1. (a) $x=-2\ x=-2,\ y=15$
    (b) $x=3,\ y=-7$
    (c) $x=4,\ y=-2$

(d) Infinitely many solutions, all lying on the line
$3x - y = 4$

(e) No solutions; the equations are inconsistent.

2. $\mathbf{A}^2 = \begin{bmatrix} -1 & -2 \\ 4 & -1 \end{bmatrix}$, $\mathbf{A}^3 = \begin{bmatrix} -5 & -1 \\ 2 & -5 \end{bmatrix}$

$\mathbf{A}^0 = \begin{bmatrix} 1 & 0 \\ 0 & 1 \end{bmatrix}$

3. Either $(b = c)$ or $(b = -c$ and $a = d)$

4. (a) $h = 5$ (b) $a = \alpha, b = -6\alpha$

5. (a) $\begin{bmatrix} 6 & 0 \\ 0 & 6 \end{bmatrix}$ (b) e.g. $\begin{bmatrix} 1 & 1 \\ 1 & 1 \end{bmatrix} \begin{bmatrix} 1 & -1 \\ -1 & 1 \end{bmatrix}$

Exercise 9B

1. (a) -3 (b) 0 (c) $x^2 + 3x + 2$

2. $\mathbf{A}^{-1} = \frac{1}{4} \begin{bmatrix} 6 & -19 \\ -2 & 7 \end{bmatrix}$, $\mathbf{B}^{-1}$ does not exist,

$\mathbf{C}^{-1} = \frac{1}{(3a + 4)} \begin{bmatrix} 3 & 4 \\ -1 & a \end{bmatrix}$

3. $-6, 1$

4. $x = \frac{19}{11}, y = \frac{6}{11}$

8. $\mathbf{AB} = \begin{bmatrix} -9 & 4 \\ -2 & 1 \end{bmatrix}$; $(\mathbf{AB})^{-1} = \begin{bmatrix} -1 & 4 \\ -2 & 9 \end{bmatrix}$

9. (i) Rows of A interchanged
   (ii) Row 2 added to Row 1
   (iii) Row 1 subtracted from Row 2
   (iv) Row 1 scaled by a factor of k
   (v) $m \times$ Row 2 added to Row 1

10. (b) $\lambda^2 - \lambda(a + d) + ad - bc = 0$

Exercise 9C

1. (a) $(-1, 1)$ (b) $(0, 1)$

   (c) The line $y = \frac{7}{15}x$

   (d) The line $y = 1$

   (e) The line $x + 2y = 3$

   (f) $(1, 2)$

   (g) No invariant points

2. $y = x$ and $y = -x$

3. $(1, 2)$, $y = x + 1$ and $y = 3 - x$

4. $y = x - 2$ and $y = 1 - \frac{1}{2}x$

5. $y = 2x$. Projection onto the line $y = 2x$

Exercise 9D

1. (a) Anticlockwise rotation about 0 through

   $\theta = 26.6°$ $\left(\cos^{-1}\left(\frac{2}{\sqrt{5}} \right) \right)$

   (b) Relection in the line $y = x \tan \theta$ where

   $\theta = 13.3°$ $\left(\tan^{-1}(\sqrt{5} - 2) \right)$

   (c) Reflection in the line $y = x \tan \theta$ where

   $\theta \approx 48.2°$ $\left(\tan^{-1} \frac{\sqrt{5}}{2} \right)$

   (d) Clockwise rotation about 0 through
   $\cos^{-1} 0.6$ $(\approx 53.13°)$

   (e) Reflection in the line $y = x \tan \theta$ where

   $\theta \approx 126.9°$ $\left(\tan^{-1}\left(-\frac{4}{3} \right) \right)$

2. (a) $\begin{bmatrix} -\frac{1}{2} & \frac{\sqrt{3}}{2} \\ \frac{\sqrt{3}}{2} & \frac{1}{2} \end{bmatrix}$ (b) $\begin{bmatrix} -\frac{1}{\sqrt{2}} & -\frac{1}{\sqrt{2}} \\ \frac{1}{\sqrt{2}} & -\frac{1}{\sqrt{2}} \end{bmatrix}$

   (c) $\begin{bmatrix} \frac{1}{3} & \frac{2\sqrt{2}}{3} \\ \frac{-2\sqrt{2}}{3} & \frac{1}{3} \end{bmatrix}$ (d) $\begin{bmatrix} -\frac{4}{5} & -\frac{3}{5} \\ -\frac{3}{5} & \frac{4}{5} \end{bmatrix}$

Exercise 9E

1. (a) $\begin{bmatrix} x' - a \\ y' \end{bmatrix} = \begin{bmatrix} k & 0 \\ 0 & k \end{bmatrix} \begin{bmatrix} x - a \\ y \end{bmatrix}$

   (b) $\begin{bmatrix} x - 1 \\ y \end{bmatrix} = \begin{bmatrix} \frac{1}{\sqrt{2}} & -\frac{1}{\sqrt{2}} \\ \frac{1}{\sqrt{2}} & \frac{1}{\sqrt{2}} \end{bmatrix} \begin{bmatrix} x - 1 \\ y \end{bmatrix}$

2. A: Reflection in $y = x(\sqrt{2} - 1)$

   B: Rotation through 45° anticlockwise about 0

   $\mathbf{AB} = \begin{bmatrix} 1 & 0 \\ 0 & -1 \end{bmatrix}$ a reflection in the x-axis

   $\mathbf{BA} = \begin{bmatrix} 0 & 1 \\ 1 & 0 \end{bmatrix}$, a reflection in the line $y = x$

3. (a) Reflection in the line $y = 1$

   (b) $x' = \frac{1}{\sqrt{2}}x + \frac{1}{\sqrt{2}}y$; $y' = -\frac{1}{\sqrt{2}}x + \frac{1}{\sqrt{2}}y$

4. (a) Rotation through θ anticlockwise about (2, 1), where $\theta \approx 233.13°$

   (b) Reflection in the line $x + 2y = 3$

   (c) Stretch perpendicular to $x + 2y = 3$, s.f. 5

5. (a) $x' = -y,\ y' = x$ (b) $x' = y + 2,\ y' = x - 2$

   (c) $x' = 1 - y,\ y' = x - 3$

   (d) $x' = \dfrac{1}{2}x - \dfrac{\sqrt{3}}{2}y + \dfrac{3}{2} + \sqrt{3}$,

   $y' = \dfrac{\sqrt{3}}{2}x + \dfrac{1}{2}y + 1 - \dfrac{3\sqrt{3}}{2}$

6. $\begin{bmatrix} k\cos^2\theta + \sin^2\theta & -(k-1)\sin\theta\cos\theta \\ -(k-1)\sin\theta\cos\theta & k\sin^2\theta + \cos^2\theta \end{bmatrix}$

Exercise 9F

1. (a) $\begin{bmatrix} -\frac{1}{2} & \frac{\sqrt{3}}{2} \\ \frac{\sqrt{3}}{2} & \frac{1}{2} \end{bmatrix}$ (b) $\begin{bmatrix} 0 & -1 \\ 1 & 0 \end{bmatrix}$

   (c) $\begin{bmatrix} -\frac{1}{2} & -\frac{\sqrt{3}}{2} \\ -\frac{\sqrt{3}}{2} & \frac{1}{2} \end{bmatrix}$

   (i) Reflection in the line $y = x\tan 105°$

   (ii) Rotation of 30° anticlockwise about 0

2. $\mathbf{T_1}$ is a rotation of 90° anticlockwise about (3, 2)

   $\mathbf{T_2}: x' = y - 2,\ y' = x + 2$

   $\mathbf{T_3}: x' = y - 5,\ y' = 5 - x$, which is a rotation of 90° clockwise about (0, 5)

3. Rotation clockwise about 0 through an angle $2(\theta - \phi)$, or equivalent

4. $\mathbf{U}: x' = -y - 1,\ y' = x - 1$

   $\mathbf{V}: x' = x - 2,\ y' = y - 2$

   (0, −1) is the invariant point of $\mathbf{U}$. $\mathbf{V}$ is a translation of $\begin{bmatrix} -2 \\ -2 \end{bmatrix}$

5. $\mathbf{T_3}: x' = 4 - 2x,\ y' = 2y$

   Enlargement centre $\left(\dfrac{4}{3}, 0\right)$ and s.f. 2

Exercise 9G

1. $y = \dfrac{1}{2}x$ is the line of invariant points, $y = -x$ is an invariant line

2. (a) $\lambda = 1$ has eigenvectors $\alpha\begin{bmatrix} 2 \\ 1 \end{bmatrix}$

(b) $\lambda = 1$ has eigenvectors $\alpha\begin{bmatrix} 1 \\ 0 \end{bmatrix}$

(c) $\lambda = 2$ has eigenvectors $\alpha\begin{bmatrix} 2 \\ 1 \end{bmatrix}$, and

   $\lambda = -3$ has eigenvectors $\beta\begin{bmatrix} 1 \\ -2 \end{bmatrix}$

(d) $\lambda = -2$ has eigenvectors $\alpha\begin{bmatrix} 1 \\ -1 \end{bmatrix}$ and

   $\lambda = 7$ has eigenvectors $\beta\begin{bmatrix} 4 \\ 5 \end{bmatrix}$

3. $\mathbf{M} = \begin{bmatrix} \frac{1}{2} & \frac{1}{2} \\ -\frac{1}{2} & \frac{3}{2} \end{bmatrix}$

5. (a) $\lambda = 2$ has eigenvectors $\alpha\begin{bmatrix} 1 \\ -1 \end{bmatrix}$

   $\lambda = -2$ has eigenvectors $\beta\begin{bmatrix} 1 \\ 1 \end{bmatrix}$

   (b) $(4, -1)$; $x + y = 3$, $y = x - 5$

   An enlargement s.f. 2, centre (4−1), together with a reflection in $x + y = 3$

6. $\mathbf{A}$ has eigenvalues 1, with eigenvectors $\alpha\begin{bmatrix} 2 \\ 1 \end{bmatrix}$, and

   -1, with eigenvectors $\beta\begin{bmatrix} 1 \\ -2 \end{bmatrix}$.

   $\mathbf{B}$ has eigenvalue 1, with eigenvectors $\gamma\begin{bmatrix} 2 \\ 1 \end{bmatrix}$;

   $y = \dfrac{1}{2}x$.

7. $\mathbf{T} = \begin{bmatrix} 2 & 5 \\ 0 & 2 \end{bmatrix}$

9.11 Miscellaneous Exercises

1. (a) Enlargement centre $(-2, -1)$ s.f. 3

   (b) Reflection in $y = \dfrac{1}{2}x + 3$

   (c) Rotation through $\cos^{-1}\left(\dfrac{3}{5}\right)$ anticlockwise about (2, 1)

   (d) Stretch perpendicular to $y = 2x - 1$ with s.f. 3

2. $\lambda = 0$ has eigenvectors $\alpha\begin{bmatrix} 1 \\ 2 \end{bmatrix}$ and

$\lambda = 4$ has eigenvectors $\beta\begin{bmatrix} 1 \\ -2 \end{bmatrix}$. Fixed lines $y = 2x$

and $y = -2x$. All points on $y = 2x$ are mapped onto the origin. Projection onto the line $y = -2x$

3. $x' = 1 - x$, $y' = y + 3$. Reflection in $x = \dfrac{1}{2}$ together

with a translation of $\begin{bmatrix} 0 \\ 3 \end{bmatrix}$

4. (a) $\lambda = 2 + i$ has eigenvectors $\alpha\begin{bmatrix} i \\ 1 \end{bmatrix}$ and

$\lambda = 2 - i$ has eigenvectors $\beta\begin{bmatrix} 1 \\ i \end{bmatrix}$.

No invariant lines.

(b) $\lambda = 2$ has eigenvectors $\alpha\begin{bmatrix} 2 \\ -1 \end{bmatrix}$ and

$\lambda = 7$ has eigenvectors $\beta\begin{bmatrix} 1 \\ 2 \end{bmatrix}$;

$y = 2x$ and $y = -\dfrac{1}{2}x$

Areas of $\mathbf{F}$ are $\det \mathbf{A} = 5$ and $\det \mathbf{B} = 14$ respectively.

(a) Rotation anticlockwise about 0 through

$\cos^{-1}\left(\dfrac{2}{\sqrt{5}}\right)$ together with an enlargement

centre 0 s.f. $\sqrt{5}$

(b) Two-way stretch; one stretch parallel to

$y = -\dfrac{1}{2}x$ with s.f. 2 and the second parallel

to $y = 2x$ with s.f. 7

5 (a) $\begin{bmatrix} \dfrac{3}{2} & -\dfrac{\sqrt{3}}{2} \\ -\dfrac{\sqrt{3}}{2} & \dfrac{5}{2} \end{bmatrix}$

(b) $\lambda = 1$ has eigenvectors $\alpha\begin{bmatrix} \sqrt{3} \\ 1 \end{bmatrix}$ and

$\lambda = 3$ has eigenvectors $\beta\begin{bmatrix} 1 \\ -\sqrt{3} \end{bmatrix}$

6. Translation of $\begin{bmatrix} 2c(1 - \cos\theta) \\ 2c\sin\theta\cos\theta \end{bmatrix}$

7. Invariant points all lie on $y = x + \sqrt{2}$; T is a reflection in this line.

8. (a) $x' = -\dfrac{4}{5}x - \dfrac{3}{4}y + \dfrac{3}{5}$,

$y' = -\dfrac{3}{5}x - \dfrac{4}{5}y - \dfrac{19}{5}$

(b) Translation of $\begin{bmatrix} -\dfrac{9}{5} \\ \dfrac{17}{5} \end{bmatrix}$ followed by the

reflection in the line $y = -3x$.

9. Stretch perpendicular to $y = -x\sqrt{3}$ with s.f. -4 or reflection in $y = -x\sqrt{3}$ together with stretch s.f. 4 perpendicular to $y = -x\sqrt{3}$.

$\mathbf{A} = \dfrac{1}{4}\begin{bmatrix} -11 & -5\sqrt{3} \\ -5\sqrt{3} & -1 \end{bmatrix}$

10. $\begin{bmatrix} 2 + \sin\theta - 2\cos\theta \\ \cos\theta + 2\sin\theta - 1 \end{bmatrix}$

11 (a) $\begin{bmatrix} x' \\ y' \end{bmatrix} = \begin{bmatrix} 0 & 1 \\ 1 & 0 \end{bmatrix}\begin{bmatrix} x \\ y \end{bmatrix}$

(b) $\begin{bmatrix} x' \\ y' \end{bmatrix} = \begin{bmatrix} 0 & -1 \\ -1 & 0 \end{bmatrix}\begin{bmatrix} x \\ y \end{bmatrix} + \begin{bmatrix} 3 \\ 3 \end{bmatrix}$

(c) $\begin{bmatrix} x' \\ y' \end{bmatrix} = \begin{bmatrix} 0 & -1 \\ 1 & 0 \end{bmatrix}\begin{bmatrix} x \\ y \end{bmatrix} + \begin{bmatrix} 5 \\ 3 \end{bmatrix}$

(d) $\begin{bmatrix} x' \\ y' \end{bmatrix} = \begin{bmatrix} 0 & -1 \\ 1 & 0 \end{bmatrix}\begin{bmatrix} x \\ y \end{bmatrix} + \begin{bmatrix} 0 \\ -2 \end{bmatrix}$

T_4 is a rotation 90° anticlockwise about $(1, -1)$

12. (a) (i) $\lambda = 1$ has eigenvectors $\alpha\begin{bmatrix} 1 \\ 2 \end{bmatrix}$ and

$\lambda = -1$ has eigenvectors $\beta\begin{bmatrix} 1 \\ -2 \end{bmatrix}$

(ii) T_1 is a reflection in $y = 2x$

(b) $\mathbf{B} = \begin{bmatrix} \dfrac{4}{5} & -\dfrac{3}{5} \\ \dfrac{3}{5} & \dfrac{4}{5} \end{bmatrix}$

(c) $\mathbf{C} = \begin{bmatrix} \dfrac{4}{5} & \dfrac{3}{5} \\ -\dfrac{3}{5} & \dfrac{4}{5} \end{bmatrix}$ and T_3 is a rotation clockwise

about O through $\tan^{-1}\left(\dfrac{3}{4}\right)$.

13. (a) 1:4 (b) (1, 3) (c) $y = x + 2$ and $x + y = 4$

(d) Enlargement centre (1, 3) s.f. 2 together with a reflection in $y + x = 4$

14. (2, 1). Enlargement s.f. 25, reflection in $3x + 4y = 10$

15. $\lambda_1 = 1$, $\lambda_2 = 4$. Fixed line $y = 3x + 2$.

Stretch perpendicular to $y = 3x + 2$ with s.f. 4.

$T_1^{-1}: x' = x + 0.45$, $y' = y - 0.15$ being a translation

of $\begin{bmatrix} 0.45 \\ -0.15 \end{bmatrix}$

INDEX